quiz 3-6

Vector
Analysis

Books by LOUIS BRAND

Published by John Wiley & Sons, Inc.

VECTOR ANALYSIS, 282 pages.

ADVANCED CALCULUS, 574 pages.

VECTOR AND TENSOR ANALYSIS, 439 pages.

VECTORIAL MECHANICS, 556 pages.

Vector

Analysis

LOUIS BRAND, E.E., Ph.D., Sc.D.

M. D. Anderson Professor of Mathematics

University of Houston

New York · John Wiley & Sons, Inc.

London

Library of Congress Catalog Card Number: 57–5905

PRINTED IN THE UNITED STATES OF AMERICA

I dedicate this book to my former teacher and dean,
HERMAN SCHNEIDER
in tribute to the originator of cooperative education at its fiftieth anni-
versary, 1906–1956:

"JOINING THEORY AND PRACTICE
LINKING EDUCATION AND INDUSTRY
THROUGH KNOWLEDGE AND EXPERIENCE."

*(Inscription at west end of the Herman Schneider Quadrangle,
University of Cincinnati.)*

Preface

A vectorial treatment of differential geometry, mechanics, hydro-dynamics, and electrodynamics is now practically standard procedure. The use of vectors not only simplifies and condenses the exposition but also makes mathematical and physical concepts more tangible and easy to grasp. The day is not far distant when vector algebra will be introduced in analytic geometry, thus giving the student the double advantage of an early introduction to the subject and a welcome relief from a multiplicity of formulas to be memorized. The dot and cross product of Gibbs, so intimately involved in all questions of perpen-dicularity and parallelism, enable one to write the equations of lines and planes at will and to solve all distance problems in the most nat-ural manner. Even the simple distributive law, $\lambda(\mathbf{u} + \mathbf{v}) = \lambda\mathbf{u} + \lambda\mathbf{v}$, gives one the power to use the properties of similar triangles without figures and virtually in the dark. And then that tremendous step from two to three dimensions—which usually occurs so late in the course that the student misses it altogether—need never be taken at all. For we *start* in three dimensions, the world we actually live in, and this on the fine axiom of J. Willard Gibbs: *The whole is simpler than its parts.*

Vector analysis has also breached the walls of the calculus and now puts in an appearance in every modern textbook in that subject. The gradient, divergence, and rotation, in their capacity of invariants, form the natural language of spatial science. Avoidance of them is futile, and using long scalar notations every time they occur is wasteful of

vii

time and effort. I believe that the introduction of divergence and rotation from the beginning as invariants of a dyadic (the gradient of a vector) is not only the proper procedure but is actually the simplest in the long run. Although it requires a slight knowledge of dyadics, or tensors of valence two, the time is well spent; for the world is full of important tensors that the earnest student might just as well encounter head on. In this book the use of dyadics is held to a drastic minimum; and hence rigid dynamics (with its inertia dyadic) and the theory of elasticity (with its stress and strain tensors) have been regretfully omitted. Besides, this book was designed as a short course to give a beginning student the tools of vector algebra and calculus and a brief glimpse beyond into their manifold applications. Thus the equation for the angular rate of change of a radial unit vector is actually the key to the eccentricities of gyroscopic behavior. But in this book we have stopped short of gyroscopes as being beyond its proper scope. After all, a short book in vector analysis cannot pretend to be in addition a treatise on mathematical physics. But the applications have been developed to that extent so that the uses of the potential function, both scalar and vector, are fully illustrated. Moreover the basic postulates of the sciences dealt with have been brought to the foreground to put their logical structure in sharp relief.

Since the concept of a vector has been greatly generalized in geometry and mathematical physics, the final chapter gives a brief introduction to abstract vector spaces, together with the ideas of linear dependence, basis, and dimension. As this chapter is necessarily abstract, an especial effort was made to keep the exposition as simple and clear as possible.

In my more comprehensive book on *Vector and Tensor Analysis*, I quoted the eloquent words of Bertrand Russell on mathematics as a science and as an art. They deserve to be quoted again:

> The true spirit of delight, the exaltation, the sense of being more than man, which is the touchstone of the highest excellence, is to be found in mathematics as surely as in poetry. What is best in mathematics deserves not merely to be learned as a task, but also to be assimilated as a part of daily thought, and brought again and again before the mind with ever-renewed encouragement. Real life is, to most men, a long second-best, a perpetual compromise between the real and the possible; but the world of pure reason knows no compromise, no practical limitations, no barrier to the creative activity embodying in splendid edifices the passionate aspiration after the perfect from which all great work springs.

As very full cross references are given in this book, an article as well as a page number is given at the top of each page. Equations are numbered serially (1), (2), $\cdots$ in each article. A reference to an equation in another article is made by giving article and number to the left and right of a point; thus (8.3) means equation (3) of § 8. Figures are given the number of the article in which they appear followed by a, b, c, $\cdots$; thus Fig. 2c is the third figure of § 2. In footnotes, references to my books, *Vectorial Mechanics*, *Vector and Tensor Analysis*, *Advanced Calculus*, are simply made by title.

Bold-face type is used in the text to denote vectors or dyadics. The magnitude of a vector $\mathbf{v}$ is denoted by $|\mathbf{v}|$ or, on occasion, by v. A displacement (or "arrow" vector) from A to B is written $\overrightarrow{AB}$. Superimposed arrows may also be used to denote vectors in manuscript.

Finally, I wish to express my grateful appreciation for the contribution of the Taft fund toward typing the manuscript, and to extend thanks to my colleagues Professors Jaeger and Restemeyer for their advice and suggestions. I am also indebted to Mrs. Anne Hagedorn for her efficient and painstaking help in the preparation of the manuscript.

LOUIS BRAND

University of Cincinnati
January 1957

Contents

Contents

Contents

Chapter 7. FLUID MECHANICS

Chapter 8. ELECTRODYNAMICS

Chapter 9. VECTOR SPACES

APPENDIX

Science and the applications of science are united together as the tree and its fruit.

PASTEUR

Chapter 1

Vector Algebra

1. Vectors. *A vector is a directed line segment.* A vector from the point A to the point B is denoted by $\overrightarrow{AB}$. The vector $\overrightarrow{AB}$ has the *length* AB and the *direction* from A to B. Besides *proper vectors*, which have a definite length and direction, we shall introduce the *zero vector* $\overrightarrow{AA}$ which has zero length but no definite direction.

A *scalar* is a number whose value is the same in all systems of reference. Thus the length of a vector is a scalar; but the direction cosines of a vector are not scalars as their values depend on the choice of coordinate axes.

In addition to the foregoing notation, in which we specify a vector by giving its end points, we shall also use single letters in boldface type (as **u**, **v**, **w**) to denote vectors. The zero vector is then written **0** in bold type. The length of the vector **u** is denoted by $|\mathbf{u}|$; and $|\mathbf{0}| = 0$. A vector of length 1 is called a *unit vector*. In manuscript, a vector may be denoted by a single letter with an arrow above it.

We shall now construct an algebra of vectors by defining equality, addition, and multiplication of vectors by real numbers or *scalars*.

Two vectors are said to be equal when they have the same length and direction. Thus a vector $\mathbf{u} = \overrightarrow{AB}$ is equal to all vectors obtained from $\overrightarrow{AB}$ by a parallel displacement or *translation*. The initial point of **u** may be chosen at pleasure, say P; then $\mathbf{u} = \overrightarrow{PQ}$ when the arrow $\overrightarrow{PQ}$ has the same length as $\overrightarrow{AB}$ and is parallel to $\overrightarrow{AB}$ in the same sense. In

1

Fig. 2*b* for example, the vectors forming the opposite sides of a parallelogram are equal and may be represented by the same letter; thus

$$\overrightarrow{AB} = \overrightarrow{DC} = \mathbf{u}, \qquad \overrightarrow{AD} = \overrightarrow{BC} = \mathbf{v}.$$

Vectors that conform to the above definition of equality are said to be *free*. But in some applications other definitions are advisable. Thus the forces acting on a rigid body may be regarded as vectors which are restricted to lie on a given line, their *line of action*. Such force vectors are not free; for they may only be shifted along a fixed line since other translations alter their dynamic effect. We shall call a vector confined to a definite line of action a *line vector*. Two line vectors are equal when and only when they have the same length and the same direction and lie on the same line.

Vectors that have a fixed position in space are called *bound vectors*. Thus the forces acting on a deformable body may be regarded as bound vectors, for any translation of such a force alters its effect on the body. Two bound vectors are equal when they have the same length, direction, and position in space.

In this chapter all vectors are regarded as *free*; and we begin our vector algebra by defining the addition of free vectors and their multiplication by numbers.

2. Addition of Vectors. A rectilinear displacement, or *translation*, from A to B may be represented as a vector $\overrightarrow{AB}$. If a particle is given two displacements, one from A to B, and a second from B to C, the result is the same as if the particle were given a single displacement from A to C. This suggests the relation

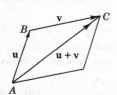

$$(1) \qquad \overrightarrow{AB} + \overrightarrow{BC} = \overrightarrow{AC}.$$

We shall regard this equation as the *definition* of vector addition; thus the sum of two vectors $\mathbf{u}$, $\mathbf{v}$, (Fig. 2*a*) is defined by the

Fig. 2*a*. Triangle construction.

TRIANGLE CONSTRUCTION. *Draw* $\mathbf{v}$ *from the end of* $\mathbf{u}$; *then the vector directed from the beginning of* $\mathbf{u}$ *to the end of* $\mathbf{v}$ *is the sum of* $\mathbf{u}$ *and* $\mathbf{v}$ *and is written* $\mathbf{u} + \mathbf{v}$.

Since any side of a triangle is less than the sum of the other two sides,

$$(2) \qquad |\mathbf{u} + \mathbf{v}| \leqq |\mathbf{u}| + |\mathbf{v}|,$$

the equal sign holding only when $\mathbf{u}$ and $\mathbf{v}$ have the same direction.

Vector addition is commutative:

(3) $$\mathbf{u} + \mathbf{v} = \mathbf{v} + \mathbf{u}.$$

This is apparent from Fig. 2*b*; for

$$\mathbf{u} + \mathbf{v} = \overrightarrow{AB} + \overrightarrow{BC} = \overrightarrow{AC}, \qquad \mathbf{v} + \mathbf{u} = \overrightarrow{AD} + \overrightarrow{DC} = \overrightarrow{AC}.$$

Vector addition is associative:

(4) $$(\mathbf{u} + \mathbf{v}) + \mathbf{w} = \mathbf{u} + (\mathbf{v} + \mathbf{w}).$$

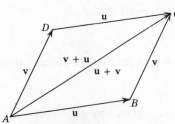

Fig. 2*b*. Commutative law.   Fig. 2*c*. Associative law

This is apparent from Fig. 2*c*; for

$$(\mathbf{u} + \mathbf{v}) + \mathbf{w} = (\overrightarrow{AB} + \overrightarrow{BC}) + \overrightarrow{CD} = \overrightarrow{AC} + \overrightarrow{CD} = \overrightarrow{AD},$$

$$\mathbf{u} + (\mathbf{v} + \mathbf{w}) = \overrightarrow{AB} + (\overrightarrow{BC} + \overrightarrow{CD}) = \overrightarrow{AB} + \overrightarrow{BD} = \overrightarrow{AD}.$$

Since both sums in (4) are the same, they are simply written $\mathbf{u} + \mathbf{v} + \mathbf{w}$.

From the commutative and associative laws we readily deduce the following

THEOREM. *The sum of any number of vectors is independent of the order in which they are added and of their grouping to form partial sums.*

To construct the sum of any number of vectors, form a broken line whose directed segments represent those vectors taken in any order whatever; then the vector directed from the beginning to the end of the broken line will be the required sum. If A, B, $C, \cdots, G, H$ are the successive vertices of the broken line (Fig. 2*d*), then

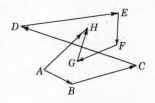

Fig. 2*d*. Vector sum.

(5) $$\overrightarrow{AB} + \overrightarrow{BC} + \cdots + \overrightarrow{GH} = \overrightarrow{AH}.$$

If in constructing a vector sum the end point of the last vector coincides

with the origin of the first, we say that the sum of the vectors is *zero*. Thus, if H coincides with A in (5), we write

$$(6) \qquad \vec{AB} + \vec{BC} + \cdots + \vec{GA} = \vec{AA} = \mathbf{0}.$$

If $\vec{AB} = \mathbf{u}$, we have

$$\vec{AA} + \vec{AB} = \vec{AB}, \qquad \vec{AB} + \vec{BB} = \vec{AB};$$

$$(7) \qquad \mathbf{0} \ + \ \mathbf{u} = \mathbf{u}, \qquad\quad \mathbf{u} \ + \ \mathbf{0} = \mathbf{u}.$$

3. Subtraction of Vectors. The sum of two vectors is zero when and only when they have the same length and opposite directions:

$$\vec{AB} + \vec{BA} = \mathbf{0}.$$

If $\vec{AB} = \mathbf{u}$, it is natural to write $\vec{BA} = -\mathbf{u}$ in order that the characteristic equation for negatives

$$(1) \qquad \mathbf{u} + (-\mathbf{u}) = \mathbf{0}$$

will hold for vectors as well as for numbers.   Hence by definition:

The negative of a vector is a vector of the same length but opposite direction.

Note also that $-(-\mathbf{u}) = \mathbf{u}$ holds for vectors as well as for numbers.

The difference $\mathbf{u} - \mathbf{v}$ of two vectors is defined by the equation

$$(2) \qquad (\mathbf{u} - \mathbf{v}) + \mathbf{v} = \mathbf{u}.$$

On adding $-\mathbf{v}$ to both sides, and using (1), we have

$$(3) \qquad \mathbf{u} - \mathbf{v} = \mathbf{u} + (-\mathbf{v});$$

subtracting a vector is the same as adding its negative.   The construction of $\mathbf{u} - \mathbf{v}$ satisfying (2) is shown in Fig. 3a.

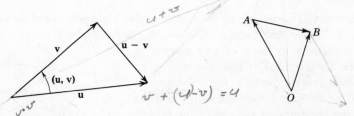

Fig. 3a. Vector subtraction.   Fig. 3b. Difference of position
                                                    vectors.

With respect to an origin O any point P in space is determined by its *position vector* $\vec{OP}$. Any vector $\vec{AB}$ may be expressed as the difference of position vectors to its end points (Fig. 3b.): thus

$$\vec{AB} = \vec{AO} + \vec{OB} = \vec{OB} + (-\vec{OA}),$$

and, from (3),

(4) $$\overrightarrow{AB} = \overrightarrow{OB} - \overrightarrow{OA}.$$

4. Multiplication of Vectors by Numbers. The vector $\mathbf{u} + \mathbf{u}$ is naturally denoted by $2\mathbf{u}$; similarly, we write $-\mathbf{u} + (-\mathbf{u}) = -2\mathbf{u}$. Thus $2\mathbf{u}$ and $-2\mathbf{u}$ denote vectors twice as long as $\mathbf{u}$; $2\mathbf{u}$ has the same direction as $\mathbf{u}$, $-2\mathbf{u}$ the opposite direction. This notation is generalized as follows:

The product of a vector $\mathbf{u}$ by a number λ (written $\lambda\mathbf{u}$ or $\mathbf{u}\lambda$) is defined as a vector $|\lambda|$ times as long as $\mathbf{u}$ and having the same direction as $\mathbf{u}$, or the opposite, according as λ is positive or negative.

In accordance with this definition

(1) $\qquad (-\alpha)\mathbf{u} = \alpha(-\mathbf{u}) = -\alpha\mathbf{u}, \qquad (-\alpha)(-\mathbf{u}) = \alpha\mathbf{u};$
and

(2) $\qquad \alpha\mathbf{u} = \mathbf{u}\alpha, \qquad (\alpha\beta)\mathbf{u} = \alpha(\beta\mathbf{u}), \qquad (\alpha + \beta)\mathbf{u} = \alpha\mathbf{u} + \beta\mathbf{u}.$

Moreover since the corresponding sides of similar triangles are proportional,

(3) $$\alpha(\mathbf{u} + \mathbf{v}) = \alpha\mathbf{u} + \alpha\mathbf{v}.$$

This is clear from Fig. 4*a*, in which $\alpha > 0$. The distributive law (3) is a potent tool in obtaining geometric information by algebraic means.

The developments thus far show that:

As far as addition, subtraction, and multiplication by numbers are concerned, vectors obey the laws of ordinary algebra.

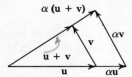
Fig. 4*a*. Distributive law.

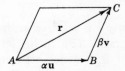
Fig. 4*b*. Basis in a plane.

If $\mathbf{u}$ and $\mathbf{v}$ are parallel vectors, they have the same or opposite directions and $\mathbf{v}$ is a numerical multiple of $\mathbf{u}$:

$$\mathbf{v} = \alpha\mathbf{u}.$$

If $\mathbf{u}$, $\mathbf{v}$, $\mathbf{r}$ are coplanar vectors ($\mathbf{u}$ and $\mathbf{v}$ not parallel), we can write

(4) $$\mathbf{r} = \alpha\mathbf{u} + \beta\mathbf{v}.$$

For, if we construct a parallelogram on $\mathbf{r}$ as diagonal with sides parallel to $\mathbf{u}$ and $\mathbf{v}$, we have (Fig. 4*b*)

(5) $$\mathbf{r} = \overrightarrow{AC} = \overrightarrow{AB} + \overrightarrow{BC} = \alpha\mathbf{u} + \beta\mathbf{v}.$$

If **u**, **v**, **w**, **r** are vectors in space (**u**, **v**, **w** not coplanar), we can write

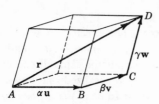

Fig. 4c. Basis in space.

(6) $$\mathbf{r} = \alpha\mathbf{u} + \beta\mathbf{v} + \gamma\mathbf{w}.$$

For, if we construct a parallelepiped on **r** as diagonal with sides parallel to **u**, **v**, **w**, we have (Fig. 4c)

$$\mathbf{r} = \overrightarrow{AD} = \overrightarrow{AB} + \overrightarrow{BC} + \overrightarrow{CD}$$
$$= \alpha\mathbf{u} + \beta\mathbf{v} + \gamma\mathbf{w}.$$

PROBLEMS

1. Show that $\overrightarrow{AB} + \overrightarrow{AC} = 2\,\overrightarrow{AM}$, where M is the mid-point of BC.

2. Show that $\overrightarrow{AB} + \overrightarrow{CD} = 2\,\overrightarrow{MN}$, where M and N are the mid-points of AC and BD.

3. $\overrightarrow{AB}$ and $\overrightarrow{CD}$ are *line vectors* (§1) acting along two intersecting lines. Show that $\overrightarrow{AC} + \overrightarrow{DB}$ is the same for all positions of $\overrightarrow{AB}$ and $\overrightarrow{CD}$.

4. If A, B, C, D are any four points, prove that

$$\overrightarrow{AB} + \overrightarrow{AD} + \overrightarrow{CB} + \overrightarrow{CD} = 4\,\overrightarrow{PQ},$$

where P and Q are the mid-points of AC and BD.

5. Point of Division. If A, B, C are points of a straight line, C is said to divide the segment AB in the ratio λ if

(1) $$\overrightarrow{AC} = \lambda\,\overrightarrow{CB}.$$

Evidently λ is positive or negative according as C lies within or without the segment AB; to the left of A, λ varies between 0 and -1, to the right of B, λ varies between $-\infty$ and -1. As C describes the entire line in the sense AB, λ varies as follows:

$$-1 < \lambda < 0 \quad (A) \qquad 0 < \lambda < \infty \quad (B) \qquad -\infty < \lambda < -1.$$

Thus $\lambda = 0$, $\lambda = \pm\infty$, $\lambda = -1$ when C is at A, at B, or at the infinitely distant "point" of the line.

To find the position vector of C relative to an origin O (Fig. 5a), write (1) in the form

$$\overrightarrow{OC} - \overrightarrow{OA} = \lambda(\overrightarrow{OB} - \overrightarrow{OC});$$

then

(2) $$\overrightarrow{OC} = \frac{\overrightarrow{OA} + \lambda\,\overrightarrow{OB}}{1 + \lambda};$$

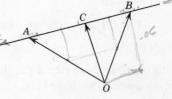

Fig. 5a. Point of division.

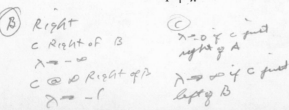

$$c = \frac{a + \beta/\alpha\, b}{1 + \beta/\alpha} = \frac{\alpha a + \beta b}{\alpha + \beta}$$

We shall denote the position vectors of A, B, C by $\mathbf{a}$, $\mathbf{b}$, $\mathbf{c}$; then, if $\lambda = \beta/\alpha$, (2) becomes

(3)
$$\mathbf{c} = \frac{\alpha \mathbf{a} + \beta \mathbf{b}}{\alpha + \beta} \,.$$

$\alpha c + \beta c = \alpha a + \beta b$

$\alpha a + \beta b - (\alpha + \beta) c = 0$

if $\gamma = -(\alpha + \beta)$

— chen

This equation states that C divides AB in the ratio β/α. Thus the midpoint of AB ($\alpha = \beta = 1$) has the position vector $\frac{1}{2}(\mathbf{a} + \mathbf{b})$.

From (3) we now deduce

THEOREM 1. *Three distinct points A, B, C will lie on a line when and only when there exist three nonzero numbers α, β, γ, such that*

(4)
$$\alpha \mathbf{a} + \beta \mathbf{b} + \gamma \mathbf{c} = 0, \qquad \alpha + \beta + \gamma = 0.$$

Proof. If A, B, C are collinear, C divides AB in some ratio β/α which is not 0, ∞, or -1; hence α, β, and $\alpha + \beta$ are not zero. Thus (3) holds good; and on putting $\gamma = -(\alpha + \beta)$ we obtain (4). Conversely, equations (4) give (3) on dividing

$$\alpha \mathbf{a} + \beta \mathbf{b} = -\gamma \mathbf{c} \quad \text{by} \quad \alpha + \beta = -\gamma;$$

hence C lies on the line AB.

The symmetrical relations (4) disclose how each point divides the segment formed by the other two. Thus (4) states that A, B, C divide BC, CA, AB, respectively, in the ratios γ/β, α/γ, β/α, whose product is 1.

THEOREM 2. *Four points A, B, C, D, no three of which are collinear, will lie in a plane when and only when there exist four nonzero numbers α, β, γ, δ, such that*

(5)
$$\alpha \mathbf{a} + \beta \mathbf{b} + \gamma \mathbf{c} + \delta \mathbf{d} = 0, \qquad \alpha + \beta + \gamma + \delta = 0.$$

Proof. If A, B, C, D are coplanar, either AB is parallel to CD, or AB cuts CD in a point P (not A, B, C, or D). In the respective cases, we have

AB Parallel to CD   *AB cuts CD in a pt P*

$$\mathbf{b} - \mathbf{a} = k(\mathbf{d} - \mathbf{c}), \qquad \frac{\mathbf{a} + \lambda \mathbf{b}}{1 + \lambda} = \frac{\mathbf{c} + \lambda' \mathbf{d}}{1 + \lambda'} = \mathbf{p},$$

where λ, λ' are neither 0 nor -1. In both cases $\mathbf{a}$, $\mathbf{b}$, $\mathbf{c}$, $\mathbf{d}$ are connected by a linear relation of the form (5).

Conversely let us assume that equations (5) hold good. If $\alpha + \beta = 0$ (and hence $\gamma + \delta = 0$), we have

$$\alpha(\mathbf{a} - \mathbf{b}) + \gamma(\mathbf{c} - \mathbf{d}) = 0, \qquad \alpha \overrightarrow{BA} = -\gamma \overrightarrow{DC},$$

and the lines AB and CD are parallel. If $\alpha + \beta \neq 0$ (and hence $\gamma + \delta \neq 0$),

$$(6) \qquad \frac{\alpha \mathbf{a} + \beta \mathbf{b}}{\alpha + \beta} = \frac{\gamma \mathbf{c} + \delta \mathbf{d}}{\gamma + \delta} = \mathbf{p},$$

where P is a point common to the lines AB, CD; for (3) shows that P divides AB and CD in the ratios β/α, δ/γ. In both cases A, B, C, D are coplanar.

Note that (5) is packed with information. If $\beta + \gamma \neq 0$,

$$(7) \qquad \frac{\beta \mathbf{b} + \gamma \mathbf{c}}{\beta + \gamma} = \frac{\alpha \mathbf{a} + \delta \mathbf{d}}{\alpha + \delta} = \mathbf{q},$$

and, if $\gamma + \alpha \neq 0$,

$$(8) \qquad \frac{\gamma \mathbf{c} + \alpha \mathbf{a}}{\gamma + \alpha} = \frac{\beta \mathbf{b} + \delta \mathbf{d}}{\beta + \delta} = \mathbf{r}.$$

The complete quadrangle $ABCD$ (Fig. 5b) has four *vertices*, and six *sides*, the lines which join them; and the three pairs of opposite sides meet in the *diagonal points* P, Q, R given by (6), (7), (8). These equations state how each diagonal point divides the sides on which it lies.

If QR produced cuts AB at S, the points S and P divide AB internally and externally in the numerically equal ratios $\pm\beta/\alpha$. Such points are called *harmonic conjugates* relative to AB (see Ex.1). To show this we eliminate $\mathbf{d}$ from

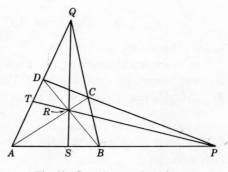

Fig. 5b. Complete quadrangle.

$$\alpha \mathbf{a} + \delta \mathbf{d} = (\alpha + \delta)\mathbf{q}, \qquad \beta \mathbf{b} + \delta \mathbf{d} = (\beta + \delta)\mathbf{r},$$

by subtraction. We thus obtain

$$\alpha \mathbf{a} - \beta \mathbf{b} = (\alpha + \delta)\mathbf{q} - (\beta + \delta)\mathbf{r},$$

$$\frac{\alpha \mathbf{a} - \beta \mathbf{b}}{\alpha - \beta} = \frac{(\alpha + \delta)\mathbf{q} - (\beta + \delta)\mathbf{r}}{\alpha - \beta} = \mathbf{s}.$$

This states that S divides AB in the ratio $-\beta/\alpha$.

If PR produced cuts AD at T, T and Q divide AD internally and externally in numerical equal ratios $\pm\delta/\alpha$. Thus T and Q are harmonic conjugates relative to AD.

Example 1. Two points C, D divide the segment AB internally and externally in numerically equal ratios $\pm\lambda$ are said to be *harmonic conjugates* relative to A, B. Then the points A, B are also harmonic conjugates relative to C, D; for, if we solve

$$c = \frac{a + \lambda b}{1 + \lambda}, \qquad d = \frac{a - \lambda b}{1 - \lambda}$$

for $\mathbf{a}$ and $\mathbf{b}$, we find that A, B divide the segment CD in the ratios $\pm(1 - \lambda)/(1 + \lambda)$.

When C is any point on the line AB, the following construction will locate its harmonic conjugate D relative to AB. Take a point P not on the line AB, and draw PA, PB, PC (Fig. 5c). Choose Q at pleasure on PC, draw the lines AQ and BQ, and let them cut PB at X, PA at Y. Then XY produced will cut AB at D. This follows from the properties of the complete quadrangle $ABXY$ deduced above.

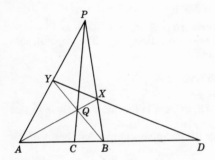

Fig. 5c. Construction of harmonic
conjugates.

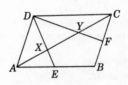

Fig. 5d. Trisection of
diagonal.

Example 2. In the parallelogram $ABCD$, E and F are the middle points of the sides AB, BC (Fig. 5d). How do the lines DE and DF divide the diagonal AC?

The hypotheses of our problem are expressed by the equations:

$$\mathbf{d} - \mathbf{a} = \mathbf{c} - \mathbf{b}, \qquad 2\mathbf{e} = \mathbf{a} + \mathbf{b}, \qquad 2\mathbf{f} = \mathbf{b} + \mathbf{c}.$$

To find the point X when DE cuts AC, eliminate $\mathbf{b}$ from the first and second equations. Thus

$$\mathbf{d} - \mathbf{a} + 2\mathbf{e} = \mathbf{a} + \mathbf{c}, \qquad \frac{\mathbf{d} + 2\mathbf{e}}{3} = \frac{2\mathbf{a} + \mathbf{c}}{3} = \mathbf{x};$$

for the first member represents a point on DE, the second member a point on AC, and, since the points are the same, the point is at the intersection X of these lines. Comparison with (3) now shows that X divides DE in the ratio 2/1, AC in the ratio 1/2.

To find the point Y where DF cuts AC, eliminate $\mathbf{b}$ from the first and third equations. Thus

$$\mathbf{d} - \mathbf{a} + 2\mathbf{f} = 2\mathbf{c}, \qquad \frac{\mathbf{d} + 2\mathbf{f}}{3} = \frac{\mathbf{a} + 2\mathbf{c}}{3} = \mathbf{y}.$$

Hence Y divides DF in the ratio 2/1, AC in the ratio 2/1.

Example 3. The Trapezoid. If $ABCD$ is a trapezoid with AB parallel to DC (Fig. 5e), then

$$\overrightarrow{AB} = \lambda\, \overrightarrow{DC} \quad\text{or}\quad \mathbf{b} - \mathbf{a} = \lambda(\mathbf{c} - \mathbf{d}),$$

and hence

$$\mathbf{b} + \lambda\mathbf{d} = \mathbf{a} + \lambda\mathbf{c}, \qquad \mathbf{b} - \lambda\mathbf{c} = \mathbf{a} - \lambda\mathbf{d}.$$

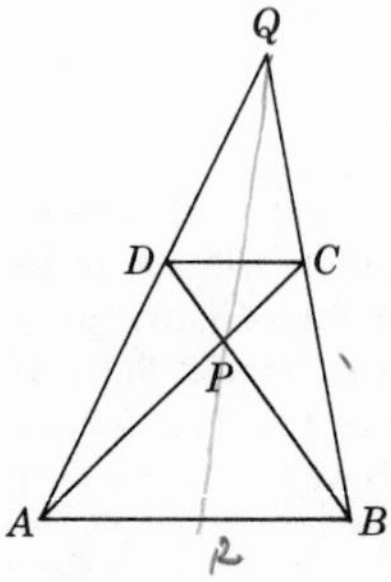

These equations may be written

$$\frac{\mathbf{b} + \lambda\mathbf{d}}{1 + \lambda} = \frac{\mathbf{a} + \lambda\mathbf{c}}{1 + \lambda} = \mathbf{p}, \qquad \frac{\mathbf{b} - \lambda\mathbf{c}}{1 - \lambda} = \frac{\mathbf{a} - \lambda\mathbf{d}}{1 - \lambda} = \mathbf{q},$$

where P is the point where the diagonals BD, AC meet, and Q is the point where the sides BC, AD meet. Evidently P divides the diagonals in the same ratio λ, and Q divides the sides (externally) in the ratio $-\lambda$. Since

$$(1 + \lambda)\mathbf{p} + (1 - \lambda)\mathbf{q} = \mathbf{a} + \mathbf{b},$$

Fig. 5e. Trapezoid.

PQ produced will bisect AB at R; for $\mathbf{r} = \tfrac{1}{2}(\mathbf{a} + \mathbf{b})$.

In particular, if $\lambda = 1$, the trapezoid becomes a parallelogram. The diagonals then bisect each other at P, while Q recedes to infinity.

PROBLEMS

1. From (2.2) prove that $|\mathbf{a} - \mathbf{b}| \geq \big|\,|\mathbf{a}| - |\mathbf{b}|\,\big|$.

2. If P lies on the line ABC and divides AB, BC, CA in the ratios λ, μ, ν, show that $\lambda\mu\nu = -1$.

3. If ABC is any triangle and L, M, N are the mid-points of its sides, show that, for any choice of O,

$$\overrightarrow{OA} + \overrightarrow{OB} + \overrightarrow{OC} = \overrightarrow{OL} + \overrightarrow{OM} + \overrightarrow{ON}.$$

4. If $\overrightarrow{OA'} = 3\,\overrightarrow{OA}$, $\overrightarrow{OB'} = 2\,\overrightarrow{OB}$, in what ratio does the point P in which AB and $A'B'$ intersect divide these segments?

5. If $ABCD$ is a quadrilateral (plane or skew), show that the mid-points of its sides are the vertices of a parallelogram whose center is $(\mathbf{a} + \mathbf{b} + \mathbf{c} + \mathbf{d})/4$.

6. In the triangle ABC (Fig. 5f) prove that the segments AD, BE cannot bisect each other.

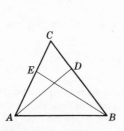

Fig. 5f. Nonbisecting segments.

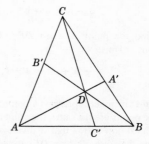

Fig. 5g. Theorem of Ceva.

7. In a plane quadrilateral $ABCD$ the point Q in which the diagonals AC, BD intersect divides these segments in the ratios $4/3$ and $2/3$, respectively. In what ratio does the point P, in which the sides AB, CD intersect, divide these segments?

8. Theorem of Ceva. The point D lies in the plane of the triangle ABC (Fig. 5g); then (Theorem 2)

$$\alpha\mathbf{a} + \beta\mathbf{b} + \gamma\mathbf{c} + \delta\mathbf{d} = 0, \qquad \alpha + \beta + \gamma + \delta = 0.$$

If AD, BD, CD meet the opposite sides in A', B', C', respectively, prove that A', B', C' divide BC, CA, AB in the ratios $\gamma/\beta, \alpha/\gamma, \beta/\alpha$ whose product is 1.

9. In Prob. 8, prove that A', B', C' divide DA, DB, DC in the ratios $\alpha/\delta, \beta/\delta, \gamma/\delta$ whose sum is -1.

10. Justify *ab initio* the construction for harmonic conjugates given in Ex. 1, Fig. 5c.

11. The complete quadrangle $ABCD$ (Fig. 5b) has the diagonals AC, BD, PQ. Prove that their mid-points $\frac{1}{2}(\mathbf{a} + \mathbf{c}), \frac{1}{2}(\mathbf{b} + \mathbf{d}), \frac{1}{2}(\mathbf{p} + \mathbf{q})$ are collinear (*Newton line*).
[From (6), (7), and (8),

$$(\alpha + \beta)\mathbf{p} = \alpha\mathbf{a} + \beta\mathbf{b}, \qquad (\beta + \gamma)\mathbf{q} = \beta\mathbf{b} + \gamma\mathbf{c}, \qquad (\gamma + \alpha)\mathbf{r} = \gamma\mathbf{c} + \alpha\mathbf{a};$$

hence show that

$$(\alpha + \beta)(\beta + \gamma)(\mathbf{p} + \mathbf{q}) = \alpha\gamma(\mathbf{a} + \mathbf{c}) - \beta\delta(\mathbf{b} + \mathbf{d}).]$$

12. Desargues' Theorem. Let ABC and $A'B'C'$ be two triangles, in the same or different planes; then, if the lines AA', BB', CC' meet at S, the three pairs of corresponding sides $(BC, B'C'), (CA, C'A'), (AB, A'B')$, intersect in collinear points P, Q, R (Fig. 5h).

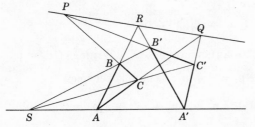 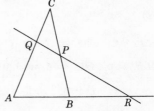

Fig. 5h. Desargues' theorem.   Fig. 5i. Theorem of Menelaus.

[In view of (5.4) we may write

$$\alpha\mathbf{a} + \alpha'\mathbf{a}' = \beta\mathbf{b} + \beta'\mathbf{b}' = \gamma\mathbf{c} + \gamma'\mathbf{c}' = \mathbf{s},$$

$$\alpha + \alpha' = \beta + \beta' \quad = \gamma + \gamma' \quad = 1.$$

Find $\mathbf{p}, \mathbf{q}, \mathbf{r}$, and show that

$$(\beta - \gamma)\mathbf{p} + (\gamma - \alpha)\mathbf{q} + (\alpha - \beta)\mathbf{r} = 0.]$$

13. Theorem of Menelaus. A line cuts the sides BC, CA, AB of the triangle ABC in the points P, Q, R. If P divides BC in the ratio γ/β, and Q divides CA in the ratio α/γ, prove that R divides AB in the ratio $-\beta/\alpha$. The product of the division ratios is thus -1 (Fig. 5i).

14. Prove the converse of the theorem of Menelaus: If P, Q, R divide BC, CA, AB in the ratios $\gamma/\beta, \alpha/\gamma, -\beta/\alpha$ whose product is -1, the points P, Q, R are collinear.

15. Pascal's Theorem. The points A, B, C and A', B', C', respectively, lie on two lines that intersect at O. If BC' and CB', CA' and AC', AB' and BA' cut in the points P, Q, R, show that P, Q, R are collinear.

[If $\mathbf{a} = \alpha\mathbf{e}$, $\mathbf{a}' = \alpha'\mathbf{e}'$, etc., where $\mathbf{e}$, $\mathbf{e}'$ are unit vectors along the lines, show that

$$\alpha\alpha'(\gamma\gamma' - \beta\beta')\mathbf{p} + \beta\beta'(\alpha\alpha' - \gamma\gamma')\mathbf{q} + \gamma\gamma'(\beta\beta' - \alpha\alpha')\mathbf{r} = \mathbf{0}.]$$

16. $ABCD$ are the vertices of a parallelogram traversed counterclockwise. Take points P and Q on the sides AB and CD, respectively. If PD meets QA in R, PC meets QB in S, prove that the line RS passes through T, the intersection of the diagonals.

6. Linear Relations Independent of the Origin. We have seen that the position vectors of collinear or coplanar points satisfy a linear equation in which the sum of the scalar coefficients is zero. The significance of such relations is given by the

THEOREM. *A linear relation of the form*

(1) $$\lambda_1\mathbf{p}_1 + \lambda_2\mathbf{p}_2 + \cdots + \lambda_n\mathbf{p}_n = \mathbf{0},$$

connecting the position vectors of the points P_1, P_2, $\cdots$, P_n, *will be independent of the position of the origin* O *when and only when the sum of the scalar coefficients is zero:*

(2) $$\lambda_1 + \lambda_2 + \cdots + \lambda_n = 0.$$

Proof. Change from O to a new origin O'. Writing $\overrightarrow{OP_i} = \mathbf{p}_i$, $\overrightarrow{O'P_i} = \mathbf{p}_i'$, $\overrightarrow{OO'} = \mathbf{d}$, we have $\mathbf{p}_i = \mathbf{d} + \mathbf{p}_i'$; hence (1) becomes

$$(\lambda_1 + \lambda_2 + \cdots + \lambda_n)\mathbf{d} + \lambda_1\mathbf{p}_1' + \lambda_2\mathbf{p}_2' + \cdots + \lambda_n\mathbf{p}_n' = \mathbf{0}.$$

This equation will have the same form as (1) when and only when (2) is satisfied.

For two, three, and four points, such linear relations have a simple geometric meaning: namely, the points are coincident, collinear, or coplanar, respectively. The question now arises: What geometric property relates five or more points whose position vectors satisfy a linear relation independent of the origin?

7. Centroid. If a point P is associated with a real number m, we speak of P as a *weighted point* and denote it by the symbol mP. The points, for example, may represent particles of matter, and the numbers, their masses or electric charges. In the latter case, the numbers may be positive or negative. We shall now define a point P^* called the *centroid* of a set of weighted points.

The centroid *of n weighted points* $m_i P_i$ $(i = 1, 2, \cdots, n)$ *for which* $\sum m_i \neq 0$ *is defined as the point P* for which*

$$\sum m_i \, \overrightarrow{P^*P_i} = \mathbf{0}. \tag{1}$$

The case $\sum m_i = 0$ must be excluded; for then (1) would hold for any choice of P^* (§6).

We first show that, when $\sum m_i \neq 0$, there is one and only one point P^* that satisfies (1). For, with an arbitrary origin O, (1) can be written

$$\sum m_i \, (\overrightarrow{OP_i} - \overrightarrow{OP^*}) = \mathbf{0} \tag{3.4},$$

and hence

$$(\sum m_i) \, \overrightarrow{OP^*} = \sum m_i \, \overrightarrow{OP_i}. \tag{2}$$

This relation, independent of the origin O, fixes the position of P^* relative to O. Thus P^* is *unique*, and its position vector relative to any origin is

$$\mathbf{p}^* = \frac{\sum m_i \mathbf{p}_i}{\sum m_i} \, . \tag{3}$$

In particular, if $O = P^*$, (3) reduces to (1). Thus relative to any origin, *the centroid of a set of weighted points has a position vector that equals the weighted average of the given set of position vectors.*

The centroid of the points $m_i P_i$ is not altered when the numbers m_i are replaced by another set cm_i proportional to them; for in (3) the constant c may be canceled from numerator and denominator. In particular, if the numbers m_i are all equal, we may replace all m_i by 1. The centroid of n equally weighted points is called their *mean center* and is given by

$$\mathbf{p}^* = \frac{\sum \mathbf{p}_i}{n} \, . \tag{4}$$

If the set of points $m_i P_i$ has a subset whose weighted centroid is $m'P'$, we may write (3) in the form

$$\mathbf{p}^* = \frac{\sum' m_i \mathbf{p}_i + \sum'' m_i \mathbf{p}_i}{\sum' m_i + \sum'' m_i} = \frac{m' \mathbf{p}' + \sum'' m_i \mathbf{p}_i}{m' + \sum'' m_i},$$

where $\sum'$, $\sum''$ denote summations over the subset and the remaining points, respectively. This equation shows that P^* is also the centroid of the point $m'P'$, and the points $m_i P_i$ not included in the subset. Thus, in finding centroids, *any subset of points may be replaced by its weighted centroid.*

Example 1. The centroid of two points αA, βB is given by

$$\mathbf{p}^* = \frac{\alpha\mathbf{a} + \beta\mathbf{b}}{\alpha + \beta}, \qquad \alpha + \beta \neq 0; \qquad 2p^* = a + 6$$

hence P^* divides AB in the inverse ratio β/α of their weights. In particular, if $\alpha = \beta$, P^* is the mid-point of AB. *The mean center of two points lies midway between them.*

Example 2. The mean center P^* of three points A, B, C is given by

$$3\mathbf{p}^* = \mathbf{a} + \mathbf{b} + \mathbf{c}.$$

Let L, M, N denote the mid-points of BC, CA, AB (Fig. 7a); then

$$3\mathbf{p}^* = \mathbf{a} + 2\mathbf{l} = \mathbf{b} + 2\mathbf{m} = \mathbf{c} + 2\mathbf{n};$$

hence the segments AL, BM, CN are all divided by P^* in the ratio $2/1$. If A, B, C are not collinear, they are the vertices of a triangle with AL, BM, CN as medians. *The medians of a triangle meet at the mean center of its vertices and are all divided there in the ratio of $2/1$.*

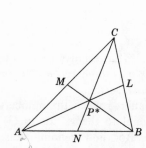

Fig. 7a. Mean center of three points.

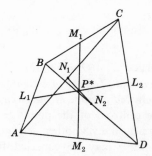

Fig. 7b. Mean center of four points.

Example 3. The mean center P^* of four points A, B, C, D is given by

$$4\mathbf{p}^* = \mathbf{a} + \mathbf{b} + \mathbf{c} + \mathbf{d}.$$

Let L_1, L_2; M_1, M_2; N_1, N_2 be the mid-points of AB, CD; BC, DA; AC, BD, respectively (Fig. 7b). Then

$$4\mathbf{p}^* = 2\mathbf{l}_1 + 2\mathbf{l}_2 = 2\mathbf{m}_1 + 2\mathbf{m}_2 = 2\mathbf{n}_1 + 2\mathbf{n}_2;$$

hence the segments L_1L_2, M_1M_2, N_1N_2 are all divided in the ratio $1/1$ (bisected) by P^*. *The bisectors of the opposite sides of the quadrangle $ABCD$ (plane or skew) meet in the mean center of its vertices and are all bisected there.*

Example 4. If the points A', B', C' divide the sides BC, CA, AB of the triangle ABC in the ratios γ/β, α/γ, β/α whose product is 1, the lines AA', BB', CC' meet in a point, the centroid P^* of αA, βB, γC.

Since A' is the centroid of βB and γC (Ex. 1),

$$(\alpha + \beta + \gamma)\mathbf{p}^* = \alpha\mathbf{a} + \beta\mathbf{b} + \gamma\mathbf{c} = \alpha\mathbf{a} + (\beta + \gamma)\mathbf{a}'.$$

Hence P^* lies on AA' and, similarly, on BB' and CC'. We have thus proved the converse of the theorem of Ceva (Prob. 5.8).

We can now answer the question raised at the end of §6. *A set of n weighted points $m_i P_i$ $(m_i \neq 0)$ which satisfy a linear relation*

$$(5) \qquad \sum m_i \mathbf{p}_i = \mathbf{0}, \qquad \sum m_i = 0,$$

independent of the origin, has the intrinsic property that any point of the set is the centroid of the remaining weighted points.

Proof. On dividing

$$-m_1 \mathbf{p}_1 = m_2 \mathbf{p}_2 + m_3 \mathbf{p}_3 + \cdots + m_n \mathbf{p}_n$$

by

$$-m_1 = m_2 + m_3 + \cdots + m_n,$$

we obtain

$$\mathbf{p}_1 = \frac{m_2 \mathbf{p}_2 + m_3 \mathbf{p}_3 + \cdots + m_n \mathbf{p}_n}{m_2 + m_3 + \cdots + m_n}.$$

Thus P_1 is the centroid of $m_2 P_2, \cdots, m_n P_n$.

A set of n points having this property is readily constructed. Take any set of $n - 1$ weighted points $m_i P_i$, and adjoin to the set their centroid P_n with the weight

$$m_n = -(m_1 + m_2 + \cdots + m_{n-1}) \neq 0.$$

Then, since

$$-m_n \mathbf{p}_n = m_1 \mathbf{p}_1 + m_2 \mathbf{p}_2 + \cdots + m_{n-1} \mathbf{p}_{n-1},$$

the set of n weighted points $m_i P_i$ satisfies (5). We shall call such sets of points *self-centroidal*.

Theorem 5.1 shows that nonzero weights may be assigned to any three collinear points A, B, C so that they form a self-centroidal set:

$$(6) \qquad \alpha \mathbf{a} + \beta \mathbf{b} + \gamma \mathbf{c} = \mathbf{0}, \qquad \alpha + \beta + \gamma = 0,$$

Theorem 5.2 shows that nonzero weights may be assigned to any four coplanar points A, B, C, D, no three of which are collinear, so that they form a self-centroidal set:

$$(7) \qquad \alpha \mathbf{a} + \beta \mathbf{b} + \gamma \mathbf{c} + \delta \mathbf{d} = \mathbf{0}, \qquad \alpha + \beta + \gamma + \delta = 0.$$

In both cases the *ratios* of the weights are determined.

As a natural extension of these results we have the

THEOREM. *If A, B, C, D, E are five points, no four of which are coplanar, nonzero weights may be assigned to them so that they form a self-centroidal set:*

$$(8) \quad \alpha \mathbf{a} + \beta \mathbf{b} + \gamma \mathbf{c} + \delta \mathbf{d} + \varepsilon \mathbf{e} = \mathbf{0}, \qquad \alpha + \beta + \gamma + \delta + \varepsilon = 0.$$

The ratios *of weights are uniquely determined by the relative positions of the points.*

Proof. We note first that, if any weight is zero, four points are coplanar contrary to hypothesis. Since

$$\overrightarrow{EA} = \mathbf{a} - \mathbf{e}, \qquad \overrightarrow{EB} = \mathbf{b} - \mathbf{e}, \qquad \overrightarrow{EC} = \mathbf{c} - \mathbf{e}, \qquad \overrightarrow{ED} = \mathbf{d} - \mathbf{e}$$

are not coplanar, we have a linear relation between these vectors (§4), say

$$\alpha(\mathbf{a} - \mathbf{e}) + \beta(\mathbf{b} - \mathbf{e}) + \gamma(\mathbf{c} - \mathbf{e}) + \delta(\mathbf{d} - \mathbf{e}) = \mathbf{0}.$$

With $\varepsilon = -(\alpha + \beta + \gamma + \delta)$, this is a relation of the form (8).

Now let α', β', γ', δ', ε' be a second set of weights, for which

(9) $\alpha'\mathbf{a} + \beta'\mathbf{b} + \gamma'\mathbf{c} + \delta'\mathbf{d} + \varepsilon'\mathbf{e} = \mathbf{0}, \qquad \alpha' + \beta' + \gamma' + \delta' + \varepsilon' = 0.$

Multiply (8) by ε', (9) by ε, and subtract. Then

$$(\alpha\varepsilon' - \alpha'\varepsilon)\mathbf{a} + \cdots + (\delta\varepsilon' - \delta'\varepsilon)\mathbf{d} = \mathbf{0},$$

$$(\alpha\varepsilon' - \alpha'\varepsilon) + \cdots + (\delta\varepsilon' - \delta'\varepsilon) = 0;$$

thus A, B, C, D will be coplanar unless all the coefficients are zero. Since A, B, C, D are *not* coplanar by hypothesis, we must have

$$\alpha/\alpha' = \beta/\beta' = \gamma/\gamma' = \delta/\delta' = \varepsilon/\varepsilon'.$$

PROBLEMS

1. Prove that the sum of n vectors

$$\sum_{i=1}^{n} \overrightarrow{A_iB_i} = n\,\overrightarrow{A^*B^*}$$

where A^* and B^* are the mean centers of the points A_i and B_i, respectively.

2. Let A, B, C, D be the vertices of a tetrahedron and P^* their mean center. If A', B', C', D' are the mean centers of the triads BCD, CDA, DAB, ABC, show that P^* divides each of the segments AA', BB', CC', DD' in the ratio of $3/1$.

3. Lines drawn through a point E and the vertices A, B, C, D of a tetrahedron cut the planes of the opposite faces in A', B', C', D'. Show that the sum of the ratios in which these points divide EA, EB, EC, ED is -1. [Use (8).]

4. Carnot's Transversal Theorem. A line cuts the sides of a plane polygon $P_1P_2\cdots P_n$ in n distinct points R_1, R_2, $\cdots$, R_n. Show that the product of the ratios in which R_1 divides P_1P_2, R_2 divides P_2P_3, $\cdots$, R_n divides P_nP_1, is $(-1)^n$.

[Write
$$(x_1 - x_2)\mathbf{r}_1 = x_1\mathbf{p}_1 - x_2\mathbf{p}_2,$$
$$(x_2 - x_3)\mathbf{r}_2 = x_2\mathbf{p}_2 - x_3\mathbf{p}_3,$$
$$\cdots\cdots\cdots\cdots\cdots\cdots\cdots\cdots\cdots$$
$$(x_n - x_{n+1})\mathbf{r}_n = x_n\mathbf{p}_n - x_{n+1}\mathbf{p}_1.$$

The sum of the weighted points on the left is $(x_1 - x_{n+1})\mathbf{p}_1$. If $x_1 - x_{n+1} \neq 0$, P_1 will be their centroid; since this is impossible (why?), $x_{n+1} = x_1$.]

5. A plane cuts the sides of a skew polygon $P_1 P_2 \cdots P_n$ in n distinct points $R_1, R_2, \cdots, R_n$. Show that the product of the division ratios of Prob. 4 is $(-1)^n$.

8. Rectangular Components.   Let **i**, **j**, **k** denote a *dextral* set of mutually perpendicular unit vectors; then the thumb, index, and middle fingers of the *right hand* can be extended in the directions of **i**, **j**, **k**.†   Let **i**, **j**, **k**, drawn from a common origin O, give the positive directions along the system of rectangular axes $Oxyz$.

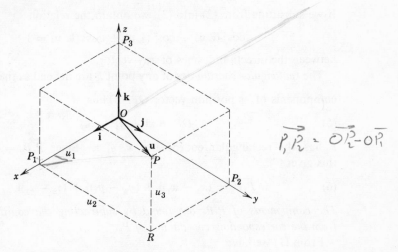

Fig. 8. Rectangular components of a vector.

Any vector **u** may now be expressed in the form

(1) $$\mathbf{u} = u_1 \mathbf{i} + u_2 \mathbf{j} + u_3 \mathbf{k}.$$

Draw $\overrightarrow{OP} = \mathbf{u}$ from the origin, and let $\overrightarrow{OP_1}$, $\overrightarrow{OP_2}$, $\overrightarrow{OP_3}$ be the orthogonal projections of $\overrightarrow{OP}$ on the axes.   Then (Fig. 8)

$$\overrightarrow{OP} = \overrightarrow{OP_1} + \overrightarrow{P_1 R} + \overrightarrow{RP} = \overrightarrow{OP_1} + \overrightarrow{OP_2} + \overrightarrow{OP_3},$$

or, since $\overrightarrow{OP_1}$, $\overrightarrow{OP_2}$, $\overrightarrow{OP_3}$ are numerical multiples of **i**, **j**, **k**, we obtain $u = \overrightarrow{OP}$ in the form (1). The numbers u_1, u_2, u_3, are called the *rectangular components* of **u**.   Evidently u_1 is the length OP_1 taken positive or negative according as $\overrightarrow{OP_1}$ has the direction of **i** of $-$**i**; and, from the right triangle $OP_1 P$, $u_1 = |\mathbf{u}| \cos (\mathbf{i}, \mathbf{u})$ where $(\mathbf{i}, \mathbf{u})$ is the angle between **i** and **u**.   Thus

† A right-handed screw, revolved in a nut from **i** to **j**, will move in the direction **k**.

the rectangular coordinates of a vector are the products of its length by its direction cosines:

(2) $u_1 = |\mathbf{u}| \cos (\mathbf{i}, \mathbf{u})$, $u_2 = |\mathbf{u}| \cos (\mathbf{j}, \mathbf{u})$, $u_3 = |\mathbf{u}| \cos (\mathbf{k}, \mathbf{u})$.

From the Pythogorean theorem,

$$(OP)^2 = (OR)^2 + (RP)^2 = (OP_1)^2 + (OP_2)^2 + (OP_3)^2,$$

(3) $|\mathbf{u}|^2 = u_1{}^2 + u_2{}^2 + u_3{}^2.$

If we substitute from (2) into (3), we obtain the relation

(4) $\cos^2 (\mathbf{i}, \mathbf{u}) + \cos^2 (\mathbf{j}, \mathbf{u}) + \cos^2 (\mathbf{k}, \mathbf{u}) = 1$

between the direction cosines of any vector.

The *rectangular coordinates* of any point P are defined as the rectangular components of its position vector $\overrightarrow{OP}$. Thus, if

(5) $\overrightarrow{OP} = x\mathbf{i} + y\mathbf{j} + z\mathbf{k},$

P has the rectangular coordinates x, y, z. Since $\overrightarrow{P_1P_2} = \overrightarrow{OP_2} - \overrightarrow{OP_1}$, this gives

(6) $\overrightarrow{P_1P_2} = (x_2 - x_1)\mathbf{i} + (y_2 - y_1)\mathbf{j} + (z_2 - z_1)\mathbf{k}.$

The components of $\overrightarrow{P_1P_2}$ are found by subtracting the coordinates of P_1 from the corresponding coordinates of P_2.

From (1) we have

(7) $\lambda\mathbf{u} = \lambda u_1\mathbf{i} + \lambda u_2\mathbf{j} + \lambda u_3\mathbf{k},$

(8) $\mathbf{u} + \mathbf{v} = (u_1 + v_1)\mathbf{i} + (u_2 + v_2)\mathbf{j} + (u_3 + v_3)\mathbf{k}.$

We shall sometimes specify vectors by writing their components in brackets: $\mathbf{u} = [u_1, u_2, u_3]$. In this notation, (7) and (8) become

$$\lambda\mathbf{u} = [\lambda u_1, \lambda u_2, \lambda u_3],$$

$$\mathbf{u} + \mathbf{v} = [u_1 + v_1, u_2 + v_2, u_3 + v_3];$$

and, in particular,

$$-\mathbf{u} = [-u_1, -u_2, -u_3],$$

$$\mathbf{u} - \mathbf{v} = [u_1 - v_1, u_2 - v_2, u_3 - v_3].$$

If $\mathbf{u}$ is a vector in the xy-plane and θ is the angle $(\mathbf{i}, \mathbf{u})$, then

$$(\mathbf{j}, \mathbf{u}) = (\mathbf{j}, \mathbf{i}) + (\mathbf{i}, \mathbf{u}) = \theta - \frac{\pi}{2}, \qquad (\mathbf{k}, \mathbf{u}) = \frac{\pi}{2} \,;$$

hence the direction cosines of u are

$$\cos \theta, \qquad \cos \left(\theta - \frac{\pi}{2}\right) = \sin \theta, \qquad \cos \frac{\pi}{2} = 0 \cdot$$

Thus **u** has the components:

$$u_1 = |\mathbf{u}| \cos \theta, \qquad u_2 = |\mathbf{u}| \sin \theta, \qquad u_3 = 0,$$

and

(9) $$\mathbf{u} = |\mathbf{u}|(\mathbf{i} \cos \theta + \mathbf{j} \sin \theta).$$

Example. Addition Theorems for the Sine and Cosine. Let **a** and **b** be two unit vectors such that the angles $(\mathbf{i}, \mathbf{a}) = \alpha$, $(\mathbf{i}, \mathbf{b}) = \alpha + \beta$; then

$$\mathbf{a} = \mathbf{i} \cos \alpha + \mathbf{j} \sin \alpha,$$

(i) $$\mathbf{b} = \mathbf{i} \cos (\alpha + \beta) + \mathbf{j} \sin (\alpha + \beta).$$

If **b** is referred to rectangular axes along

$$\mathbf{i}_1 = \mathbf{a}, \qquad \mathbf{j}_1 = \mathbf{i} \cos (\alpha + \tfrac{1}{2}\pi) + \mathbf{j} \sin (\alpha + \tfrac{1}{2}\pi),$$

we have also

(ii) $$\mathbf{b} = \mathbf{i}_1 \cos \beta + \mathbf{j}_1 \sin \beta,$$

$$= (\mathbf{i} \cos \alpha + \mathbf{j} \sin \alpha) \cos \beta + \{\mathbf{i} \cos (\alpha + \tfrac{1}{2}\pi) + \mathbf{j} \sin (\alpha + \tfrac{1}{2}\pi)\} \sin \beta$$

On equating the components of **b** in (i) and (ii), we obtain

(iii) $$\cos (\alpha + \beta) = \cos \alpha \cos \beta + \cos (\alpha + \tfrac{1}{2}\pi) \sin \beta,$$

(iv) $$\sin (\alpha + \beta) = \sin \alpha \cos \beta + \sin (\alpha + \tfrac{1}{2}\pi) \sin \beta.$$

In particular, when $\alpha = \tfrac{1}{2}\pi$, we have

$$\cos (\beta + \tfrac{1}{2}\pi) = -\sin \beta, \qquad \sin (\beta + \tfrac{1}{2}\pi) = \cos \beta,$$

since $\cos \pi = -1$, $\sin \pi = 0$; therefore

$$\cos (\alpha + \beta) = \cos \alpha \cos \beta - \sin \alpha \sin \beta,$$

$$\sin (\alpha + \beta) = \sin \alpha \cos \beta + \cos \alpha \sin \beta.$$

These addition theorems, deduced without benefit of a figure, hold for all values of α and β, positive or negative.

9. Products of Two Vectors. Hitherto we have considered only the products of vectors by numbers. Next we shall define two operations between vectors, which are known as "products," because they have some properties in common with the products of numbers. These products of vectors, however, will also prove to have properties in striking disagreement with those of numbers.

Since one of these products is a scalar and the other a vector, they are called the *scalar product* and *vector product*, respectively. The definitions of these new products may seem rather arbitrary to one unfamiliar with the history of vector algebra. We present this algebra in the form and notation due to the American mathematical physicist, J. Willard Gibbs (1839–1903).†   It is an offshoot of the *algebra of quaternions*, adapted to the uses of geometry and physics.   See Brand's *Vector and Tensor Analysis*, Chapter X, for a brief account of quaternion algebra and its applications; in §184 it is shown how the scalar and vector products originated.

10. Scalar Product.   *The scalar product of two vectors* **u** *and* **v**, *written* **u · v**, *is defined as the product of their lengths and the cosine of their included angle:*

(1) $$\mathbf{u} \cdot \mathbf{v} = |\mathbf{u}|\,|\mathbf{v}| \cos(\mathbf{u}, \mathbf{v}).$$

Here $(\mathbf{u}, \mathbf{v})$ denotes the smallest angle, taken positive, between **u** and **v**. The scalar product is therefore a *number* which for *proper* (nonzero) vectors is positive, zero, or negative, according as the angle $(\mathbf{u}, \mathbf{v})$ is acute, right, or obtuse.   Hence, for *proper* vectors,

(2) $$\mathbf{u} \cdot \mathbf{v} = 0 \quad \text{implies} \quad \mathbf{u} \perp \mathbf{v}.$$

When **u** and **v** are parallel,

$$\mathbf{u} \cdot \mathbf{v} = |\mathbf{u}|\,|\mathbf{v}|, \quad \text{or} \quad -|\mathbf{u}|\,|\mathbf{v}|,$$

according as the vectors have the same or opposite directions. The "square" of **u** is $\mathbf{u} \cdot \mathbf{u} = |\mathbf{u}|^2$.

From (1) we see that

$$(-\mathbf{u}) \cdot \mathbf{v} = \mathbf{u} \cdot (-\mathbf{v}) = -\mathbf{u} \cdot \mathbf{v}, \qquad (-\mathbf{u}) \cdot (-\mathbf{v}) = \mathbf{u} \cdot \mathbf{v},$$

(3) $$(\alpha\mathbf{u}) \cdot (\beta\mathbf{v}) = \alpha\beta\mathbf{u} \cdot \mathbf{v}.$$

The last result is obvious when α and β are positive numbers; the other cases then follow from the equations preceding.

The definition (1) shows that *scalar multiplication is commutative:*

(4) $$\mathbf{u} \cdot \mathbf{v} = \mathbf{v} \cdot \mathbf{u}.$$

As $(\mathbf{u} \cdot \mathbf{v}) \cdot \mathbf{w}$ is not defined (the dot is only used between *vectors*), the associative law need not be considered. We observe, however, that in general $(\mathbf{u} \cdot \mathbf{v})\mathbf{w} \neq \mathbf{u}(\mathbf{v} \cdot \mathbf{w})$.

Scalar multiplication is distributive with respect to addition:

(5) $$\mathbf{w} \cdot (\mathbf{u} + \mathbf{v}) = \mathbf{w} \cdot \mathbf{u} + \mathbf{w} \cdot \mathbf{v}.$$

† Professor of mathematical physics at Yale University. His pamphlet on the *Elements of Vector Analysis* was privately printed in 1881. A more complete treatise on *Vector Analysis*, Yale University Press, 1901, based on Gibb's lectures, was written by Professor E. B. Wilson.

Proof. If *l* is a directed line whose sense is given by the *unit* vector **e**, the orthogonal projection of a vector **u** upon *l* (proj$_l$ **u**) is a numerical multiple of **e**. This number is called the *component* of **u** upon *l* (comp$_l$ **u**); its defining equation is therefore

(6)   **e** comp$_l$ **u** = proj$_l$ **u**.

We compute comp$_l$ **u** as in §8: namely

(7)   comp$_l$ **u** = |**u**| cos (**e**, **u**);

or, since |**e**| = 1,

(8)   comp$_l$ **u** = **e** · **u**.

Moreover, since (Fig. 10*a*)

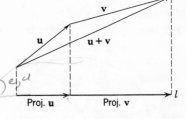

Fig. 10*a*. Projection is distributive.

(9)   proj$_l$ (**u** + **v**) = proj$_l$ **u** + proj$_l$ **v**,

(6) shows that also

(10)   comp$_l$ (**u** + **v**) = comp$_l$ **u** + comp$_l$ **v**.

Now, if we write **w** = |**w**| **e**,

$$\mathbf{w} \cdot (\mathbf{u} + \mathbf{v}) = |\mathbf{w}|\, \mathbf{e} \cdot (\mathbf{u} + \mathbf{v}) \qquad (3)$$
$$= |\mathbf{w}|\, \text{comp}_w (\mathbf{u} + \mathbf{v}) \qquad (8)$$
$$= |\mathbf{w}|\, (\text{comp}_w \mathbf{u} + \text{comp}_w \mathbf{v}) \qquad (10)$$
$$= |\mathbf{w}|\, (\mathbf{e} \cdot \mathbf{u} + \mathbf{e} \cdot \mathbf{v}) \qquad (8)$$
$$= \mathbf{w} \cdot \mathbf{u} + \mathbf{w} \cdot \mathbf{v}. \qquad (3).$$

By repeated applications of (5), we may expand the scalar product of two vector sums, just as in ordinary algebra. For example

$$(\mathbf{a} + \mathbf{b}) \cdot (\mathbf{c} + \mathbf{d}) = \mathbf{a} \cdot \mathbf{c} + \mathbf{a} \cdot \mathbf{d} + \mathbf{b} \cdot \mathbf{c} + \mathbf{b} \cdot \mathbf{d}.$$

If **c** ≠ **0** in the equation,

(11)   **a** · **c** = **b** · **c**   or   (**a** − **b**) · **c** = 0,

we can conclude *either* that **a** − **b** = **0** *or* that **a** − **b** is perpendicular to **c**. Thus we cannot "cancel" **c** in (11) to obtain **a** = **b** unless we know that **a** − **b** and **c** are not perpendicular.

Since **i**, **j**, **k** are mutually perpendicular unit vectors,

(12) $\left(\mathbf{i} \cdot \mathbf{i}\right) = \left(\mathbf{j} \cdot \mathbf{j}\right) = \left(\mathbf{k} \cdot \mathbf{k}\right) = 1$, $\mathbf{i} \cdot \mathbf{j} = \mathbf{j} \cdot \mathbf{k} = \mathbf{k} \cdot \mathbf{i} = 0$.

Hence, if we expand the product,

we obtain $$\mathbf{u} \cdot \mathbf{v} = (u_1\mathbf{i} + u_2\mathbf{j} + u_3\mathbf{k}) \cdot (v_1\mathbf{i} + v_2\mathbf{j} + v_3\mathbf{k}),$$

(13) $$\mathbf{u} \cdot \mathbf{v} = u_1v_1 + u_2v_2 + u_3v_3.$$

The scalar product of two vectors is equal to the sum of the products of their corresponding rectangular components.

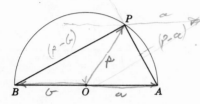

Fig. 10*b*. Right angle inscribed in semicircle.

Fig. 10*c*. Plane triangle.

Example 1.   The angle $(\mathbf{u}, \mathbf{v})$ between two vectors $\mathbf{u}, \mathbf{v}$ may be found from (1):

(14) $$\cos (\mathbf{u}, \mathbf{v}) = \frac{\mathbf{u} \cdot \mathbf{v}}{|\mathbf{u}|\,|\mathbf{v}|}.$$

In space, angles are regarded as positive; and $(\mathbf{u}, \mathbf{v})$ denotes the smallest angle θ in the interval $0 \leq \theta \leq 180°$.

Thus, when $\mathbf{u} = [1, 2, -2]$, $\mathbf{v} = [2, 2, 1]$,

$$|\mathbf{u}| = |\mathbf{v}| = \sqrt{1 + 4 + 4} = 3, \qquad \mathbf{u} \cdot \mathbf{v} = 2 + 4 - 2 = 4,$$
$$\cos (\mathbf{u}, \mathbf{v}) = 4/9 = 0\cdot 4444, \qquad (\mathbf{u}, \mathbf{v}) = 63°37'.$$

Example 2.   If $\mathbf{u} + \mathbf{v} + \mathbf{w} = 0$ and $|\mathbf{u}| = 3$, $|\mathbf{v}| = 5$, $|\mathbf{w}| = 7$, find the angle $(\mathbf{u}, \mathbf{v})$.

Since $\mathbf{u} + \mathbf{v} = -\mathbf{w}$,

$$\mathbf{w} \cdot \mathbf{w} = \mathbf{u} \cdot \mathbf{u} + 2\mathbf{u} \cdot \mathbf{v} + \mathbf{v} \cdot \mathbf{v};$$

hence $$\mathbf{u} \cdot \mathbf{v} = \tfrac{1}{2}(49 - 9 - 25) = 15/2$$

$$\cos (\mathbf{u}, \mathbf{v}) = \frac{15/2}{15} = \frac{1}{2}, \qquad (\mathbf{u}, \mathbf{v}) = 60°.$$

Example 3.   *An angle inscribed in a semicircle is a right angle.*

Proof.   Let P be any point on the semicircle with center at O and AOB as diameter (Fig. 10*b*).   Then

$$\overrightarrow{AP} \cdot \overrightarrow{BP} = (\mathbf{p} - \mathbf{a}) \cdot (\mathbf{p} - \mathbf{b}) = (\mathbf{p} - \mathbf{a}) \cdot (\mathbf{p} + \mathbf{a}) = \mathbf{p} \cdot \mathbf{p} - \mathbf{a} \cdot \mathbf{a} = 0;$$

hence AP and BP are perpendicular.

Example 4.   The Cosine Law.   In the triangle ABC, let A, B, C denote the interior angles and a, b, c the sides opposite them (Fig. 10*c*).   Then, from $\mathbf{a} + \mathbf{b} + \mathbf{c} = 0$, we have

$$\mathbf{a} \cdot \mathbf{a} = (\mathbf{b} + \mathbf{c}) \cdot (\mathbf{b} + \mathbf{c}) = \mathbf{b} \cdot \mathbf{b} + \mathbf{c} \cdot \mathbf{c} + 2\mathbf{b} \cdot \mathbf{c},$$

or $$a^2 = b^2 + c^2 - 2bc \cos A,$$

for the angle $(\mathbf{b}, \mathbf{c}) = \pi - A$.   This is the *cosine law* for plane triangles.

Example 5. The identity

$$(\mathbf{a} - \mathbf{b}) \cdot (\mathbf{h} - \mathbf{c}) + (\mathbf{b} - \mathbf{c}) \cdot (\mathbf{h} - \mathbf{a}) + (\mathbf{c} - \mathbf{a}) \cdot (\mathbf{h} - \mathbf{b}) = 0$$

shows that the altitudes of a triangle ABC meet in a point H, the *orthocenter* of the triangle (Fig. 10d); for, if two terms of this equation are zero, the third is likewise.

Similarly, the identity

$$(\mathbf{a} - \mathbf{b}) \cdot \left(\mathbf{k} - \frac{\mathbf{a} + \mathbf{b}}{2}\right) + (\mathbf{b} - \mathbf{c}) \cdot \left(\mathbf{k} - \frac{\mathbf{b} + \mathbf{c}}{2}\right) + (\mathbf{c} - \mathbf{a}) \cdot \left(\mathbf{k} - \frac{\mathbf{c} + \mathbf{a}}{2}\right) = 0$$

shows that the perpendicular bisectors of the triangle ABC meet in a point K, the *circumcenter* of the triangle.

For the orthocenter H and circumcenter K the individual terms of the foregoing equations vanish; for example,

$$(\mathbf{a} - \mathbf{b}) \cdot (\mathbf{h} - \mathbf{c}) = 0,$$
$$(\mathbf{a} - \mathbf{b}) \cdot (2\mathbf{k} - \mathbf{a} - \mathbf{b}) = 0.$$

On adding these, we obtain

$$(\mathbf{a} - \mathbf{b}) \cdot (\mathbf{h} + 2\mathbf{k} - \mathbf{a} - \mathbf{b} - \mathbf{c}) = 0,$$

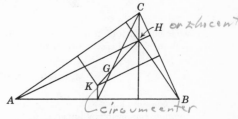

Fig. 10d. Euler line of a triangle.

or, on writing $\mathbf{g} = \frac{1}{3}(\mathbf{a} + \mathbf{b} + \mathbf{c})$ for the position vector of the mean center G of the triangle ABC,

$$(\mathbf{a} - \mathbf{b}) \cdot (\mathbf{h} + 2\mathbf{k} - 3\mathbf{g}) = 0.$$

Since this equation also holds when $\mathbf{a} - \mathbf{b}$ is replaced by $\mathbf{b} - \mathbf{c}$ and $\mathbf{c} - \mathbf{a}$, we conclude that

$$\mathbf{h} + 2\mathbf{k} - 3\mathbf{g} = 0;$$

for, if $\mathbf{h} + 2\mathbf{k} - 3\mathbf{g} \neq 0$, the vector would be perpendicular to the three sides of ABC. Therefore, *the mean center of a triangle lies on the line joining the orthocenter to the circumcenter and divides it in the ratio of* $2/1$. This line is called the *Euler line* of the triangle.

Example 6. Theorems of Lagrange. If P^* is the centroid of n weighted points $m_i P_i$ for which $\Sigma m_i = M$, we have the theorems:

(15) $$\Sigma \, m_i (OP_i)^2 = M(OP^*)^2 + \Sigma \, m_i (P^*P_i)^2,$$
(16) $$\Sigma \, m_i m_j (P_i P_j)^2 = M\Sigma \, m_i (P^*P_i)^2,$$

where the left-hand sum is taken over all $\frac{1}{2}n(n - 1)$ combinations of $i, j \, (i \neq j)$.

Proof of (15). Since $\overrightarrow{OP_i} = \overrightarrow{OP^*} + \overrightarrow{P^*P_i}$,

$$(OP_i)^2 = \overrightarrow{OP_i} \cdot \overrightarrow{OP_i} = (OP^*)^2 + (P^*P_i)^2 + 2\,\overrightarrow{OP^*} \cdot \overrightarrow{P^*P_i}.$$

see p. 13 bop

Multiply this equation by m_i, and sum over the n points. Then, on the right the first sum is $M(OP^*)^2$, the second is $\Sigma \, m_i (P^*P_i)^2$, and the third is zero since $\Sigma \, m_i \, \overrightarrow{P^*P_i} = 0$ by (7.1).

Proof of (16). Since $\overrightarrow{P_i P_j} = \overrightarrow{P^*P_j} - \overrightarrow{P^*P_i}$,

$$(P_i P_j)^2 = \overrightarrow{P_i P_j} \cdot \overrightarrow{P_i P_j} = (P^*P_j)^2 + (P^*P_i)^2 - 2(\overrightarrow{P^*P_j}) \cdot (\overrightarrow{P^*P_i}),$$

Multiply this equation by $m_i m_j$, and sum from $i, j = 1$ to n; then, on the left,

$$\sum_{j=1}^{n} \sum_{i=1}^{n} m_i m_j (P_i P_j)^2 = 2 \sum_{(ij)} m_i m_j (P_i P_j)^2,$$

where the last sum if extended over all distinct combinations (ij) in which $i \neq j$ (when $i = j$, $P_i P_j = 0$). On the right, the first and second sums are equal and together contribute

$$2 \sum_{j=1}^{n} m_j \sum_{i=1}^{n} m_i (P^* P_i)^2 = 2M \sum m_i (P^* P_i)^2,$$

while both factors in the third sum vanish by (7.1). On dividing by 2 we obtain (16).

In the special case when all weights $m_i = 1$, $M = n$. Hence, on dividing (15) by n, we get

(15)′   Mean $(OP_i)^2 = (OP^*)^2 +$ Mean $(P^* P_i)^2$.

This equation holds as $n \to \infty$ and may be applied to continuous point aggregates if we compute the means by integration.

In (16) there are $\frac{1}{2} n(n-1)$ terms in the left-hand sum, and n terms in the right-hand sum; hence

(16)′   Mean $(P_i P_j)^2 = \dfrac{2n}{n-1}$ Mean $(P^* P_i)^2$.

On passing to the limit $n \to \infty$, $2n/(n-1) \to 2$ and we obtain the interesting formula

(17)   Mean $(PP')^2 = 2$ Mean $(P^* P)^2$ $(n = \infty)$.

This may be applied to continuous point aggregates if we compute the means as integrals. For example, for the points forming a sphere of radius a about O, $P^* P = r$ and

$$\text{Mean } (P^* P)^2 = \frac{1}{V} \int_0^a r^2 \, dV \qquad (dV = 4\pi r^2 \, dr)$$

$$= \frac{3}{4\pi a^3} \int_0^a 4\pi r^4 \, dr = \frac{3}{5} a^2,$$

$$\text{Mean } (PP')^2 = \frac{6}{5} a^2.$$

11. Vector Product. *The vector product of two vectors* **u** *and* **v**, *written* **u** × **v**, *is defined as the vector,*

(1) $\mathbf{u} \times \mathbf{v} = |\mathbf{u}| \, |\mathbf{v}| \sin (\mathbf{u}, \mathbf{v}) \, \mathbf{e}, \quad = -\mathbf{v} \times \mathbf{u}$

where **e** *is a unit vector perpendicular to both* **u** *and* **v** *and forming with them a dextral set* **u**, **v**, **e**. *If* **u** *and* **v** *are not parallel, a right-handed screw revolved from* **u** *toward* **v** *will advance in its nut toward* **u** × **v**.

When **u** and **v** are parallel, **e** is not defined; but in this case sin $(\mathbf{u}, \mathbf{v}) = 0$ and $\mathbf{u} \times \mathbf{v} = \mathbf{0}$. Moreover, if **u** and **v** are not zero, $\mathbf{u} \times \mathbf{v} = \mathbf{0}$ only when sin $(\mathbf{u}, \mathbf{v}) = 0$. Hence, for proper vectors,

(2) $$\mathbf{u} \times \mathbf{v} = \mathbf{0} \quad \text{implies} \quad \mathbf{u} \parallel \mathbf{v}.$$

In particular, $\mathbf{u} \times \mathbf{u} = \mathbf{0}$.

From (1) we see that

$$(-\mathbf{u}) \times \mathbf{v} = \mathbf{u} \times (-\mathbf{v}) = -\mathbf{u} \times \mathbf{v}, \qquad (-\mathbf{u}) \times (-\mathbf{v}) = \mathbf{u} \times \mathbf{v},$$

(3) $$(\alpha\mathbf{u}) \times (\beta\mathbf{v}) = \alpha\beta \, \mathbf{u} \times \mathbf{v}.$$

The last result is obvious when α and β are positive numbers; the other cases then follow from the equations preceding.

If **u** and **v** are interchanged in (1), the scalar factors are not altered, but **e** is reversed; hence

(4) $$\mathbf{v} \times \mathbf{u} = -\mathbf{u} \times \mathbf{v}.$$

Vector multiplication is anticommutative.

Draw **u** and **v** from the point A, and let p be a plane perpendicular to **u** at A (Fig, 11a). Then $\mathbf{u} \times \mathbf{v}$ may be formed by a sequence of three operations:

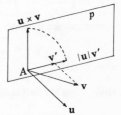

Fig. 11a. Vector product.

    (P)   Project **v** on p, and obtain $\mathbf{v}'$;

    (M)   Multiply $\mathbf{v}'$ by $|\mathbf{u}|$, and obtain $|\mathbf{u}|\mathbf{v}'$;

    (R)   Revolve $|\mathbf{u}|\mathbf{v}'$ about **u** through $+90°$.

The resulting vector agrees with $\mathbf{u} \times \mathbf{v}$ in magnitude; for $|\mathbf{v}'| = |\mathbf{v}|$ sin $(\mathbf{u}, \mathbf{v})$, and also in direction (upward in the figure). We indicate this method of forming $\mathbf{u} \times \mathbf{v}$ by the notation

(5) $$\mathbf{u} \times \mathbf{v} = \text{RMP}\mathbf{v}.$$

This means that **v** is *projected*, and the projection *multiplied*, and finally *revolved* as previously described. Now each of these operators is *distributive*: operating on the sum of two vectors is the same as operating on the vectors separately and adding the results; hence

$$\text{RMP}(\mathbf{v} + \mathbf{w}) = \text{RM}(\text{P}\mathbf{v} + \text{P}\mathbf{w}) = \text{R}(\text{MP}\mathbf{v} + \text{MP}\mathbf{w}) = \text{RMP}\mathbf{v} + \text{RMP}\mathbf{w}.$$

Thus, from (5),

(6) $$\mathbf{u} \times (\mathbf{v} + \mathbf{w}) = \mathbf{u} \times \mathbf{v} + \mathbf{u} \times \mathbf{w}, \qquad (\mathbf{v} + \mathbf{w}) \times \mathbf{u} = \mathbf{v} \times \mathbf{u} + \mathbf{w} \times \mathbf{u}.$$

Vector multiplication is distributive with respect to addition.

By repeated applications of (6) we may expand the vector product of two vector sums just as in ordinary algebra, *provided that the order of the factors is not altered.* For example,

$$(\mathbf{a} + \mathbf{b}) \times (\mathbf{c} + \mathbf{d}) = \mathbf{a} \times \mathbf{c} + \mathbf{a} \times \mathbf{d} + \mathbf{b} \times \mathbf{c} + \mathbf{b} \times \mathbf{d}.$$

If $\mathbf{c} \neq \mathbf{0}$ in the equation

$$\mathbf{a} \times \mathbf{c} = \mathbf{b} \times \mathbf{c} \qquad \text{or} \qquad (\mathbf{a} - \mathbf{b}) \times \mathbf{c} = \mathbf{0},$$

we can conclude *either* that $\mathbf{a} - \mathbf{b} = \mathbf{0}$ *or* that $\mathbf{a} - \mathbf{b}$ and $\mathbf{c}$ are parallel. We cannot "cancel" $\mathbf{c}$ to obtain $\mathbf{a} = \mathbf{b}$ unless $\mathbf{a} - \mathbf{b}$ and $\mathbf{c}$ are not parallel.

Vector multiplication is not associative; for we shall see in §12 that, in general, $(\mathbf{u} \times \mathbf{v}) \times \mathbf{w} \neq \mathbf{u} \times (\mathbf{v} \times \mathbf{w})$.

Since the unit vectors $\mathbf{i}$, $\mathbf{j}$, $\mathbf{k}$ form a *dextral* orthogonal set, we have the cyclic relations

(7) $\mathbf{i} \times \mathbf{j} = \mathbf{k}, \qquad \mathbf{j} \times \mathbf{k} = \mathbf{i}, \qquad \mathbf{k} \times \mathbf{i} = \mathbf{j}; \qquad \mathbf{i} \times \mathbf{i} = \mathbf{j} \times \mathbf{j} = \mathbf{k} \times \mathbf{k} = \mathbf{0}.$

Hence, if we expand the product,

$$\mathbf{u} \times \mathbf{v} = (u_1\mathbf{i} + u_2\mathbf{j} + u_3\mathbf{k}) \times (v_1\mathbf{i} + v_2\mathbf{j} + v_3\mathbf{k}),$$

we obtain

(8) $\mathbf{u} \times \mathbf{v} = (u_2 v_3 - u_3 v_2)\mathbf{i} + (u_3 v_1 - u_1 v_3)\mathbf{j} + (u_1 v_2 - u_2 v_1)\mathbf{k}.$

The components of $\mathbf{u} \times \mathbf{v}$ are the determinants formed by columns 2 and 3, 3 and 1 (not 1 and 3), 1 and 2 of the array $\begin{pmatrix} u_1 & u_2 & u_3 \\ v_1 & v_2 & v_3 \end{pmatrix}$; hence we may write

(9) $$\mathbf{u} \times \mathbf{v} = \begin{vmatrix} \mathbf{i} & \mathbf{j} & \mathbf{k} \\ u_1 & u_2 & u_3 \\ v_1 & v_2 & v_3 \end{vmatrix}.$$

For example, if $\mathbf{u} = [2, -3, 5]$, $\mathbf{v} = [-1, 4, 2]$, we compute the components of $\mathbf{u} \times \mathbf{v}$ from the array

$$\begin{pmatrix} 2 & -3 & 5 \\ -1 & 4 & 2 \end{pmatrix};$$

$$\begin{vmatrix} -3 & 5 \\ 4 & 2 \end{vmatrix} = -26, \qquad \begin{vmatrix} 5 & 2 \\ 2 & -1 \end{vmatrix} = -9, \qquad \begin{vmatrix} 2 & -3 \\ -1 & 4 \end{vmatrix} = 5.$$

Thus $\mathbf{u} \times \mathbf{v} = [-26, -9, 5]$.   As a check, we verify that $\mathbf{u} \times \mathbf{v}$ is perpendicular to both $\mathbf{u}$ and $\mathbf{v}$: $-52 + 27 + 25 = 0$, $26 - 36 + 10 = 0$.

A plane area A, whose boundary is traced in a definite sense, corresponds to a *vector area* $A\mathbf{e}$ normal to the plane; here $\mathbf{e}$ is the unit vector in the direction a right-handed screw would move if turned in the given sense. We may now interpret $\mathbf{u} \times \mathbf{v}$ as a vector area; for the area of the parallelogram whose sides are $\mathbf{u}$, $\mathbf{v}$ is $A = |\mathbf{u}|\,|\mathbf{v}|\,\sin(\mathbf{u}, \mathbf{v})$, and its sense of circuit, shown by the arrows in Fig. 11b, corresponds to the direction of $\mathbf{u} \times \mathbf{v}$ or $\mathbf{e}$. Thus, from (1),

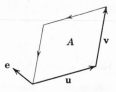

Fig. 11b. Vector area.

(10) $\mathbf{u} \times \mathbf{v} = $ vector area of the oriented parallelogram $\mathbf{u}$, $\mathbf{v}$.

Example 1. Distance of a Point from a Plane. If a plane is given by three of its points A, B, C, we can find the shortest distance d of a point R to the plane directly. *The equation of the plane is not needed.*

First, find a vector normal to the plane, say $\overrightarrow{AB} \times \overrightarrow{AC}$, and let $\mathbf{n}$ be a *unit* vector in its direction. Then, if $\mathbf{u}$ is any vector from R to the plane (as $\overrightarrow{RA}$), d is numerically equal to the component of u on the normal:

$$d = |\text{comp}_n\,\mathbf{u}| = |\mathbf{n} \cdot \mathbf{u}|.$$

The computation is checked by making another choice for $\mathbf{u}$, say $\overrightarrow{RB}$ or $\overrightarrow{RC}$.

Thus, if the plane is given by

$$A(2, 4, 1), \qquad B(-1, 0, 1), \qquad C(-1, 4, 2),$$

we find that

$$\overrightarrow{AB} \times \overrightarrow{AC} = [-3, -4, 0] \times [-3, 0, 1] = [-4, 3, -12].$$

$$\mathbf{n} = [-4, 3, -12]/13.$$

The distance of the point $R(1, -2, 1)$ from plane is now

$$|\mathbf{n} \cdot \overrightarrow{RA}| = \frac{[-4, 3, -12] \cdot [1, 6, 0]}{13} = \frac{14}{13}.$$

To check, compute $\mathbf{n} \cdot \overrightarrow{RB}$.

Example 2. Distance of a Point from a Line. If the line is given by two of its points A, B, we can find the shortest distance d of a point R to the line directly. *The equations of the line are not needed.*

First find from $\overrightarrow{AB}$ a *unit* vector $\mathbf{e}$ along the line. Then, if $\mathbf{u}$ is any vector from R to the line (as $\overrightarrow{RA}$),

$$d = |\mathbf{u}|\,\sin(\mathbf{u}, \mathbf{e}) = |\mathbf{u} \times \mathbf{e}|.$$

The computation is checked by making another choice for $\mathbf{u}$, say $\overrightarrow{RB}$.

Thus, if the line is given by $A(2, 3, 0)$, $B(-1, 2, 4)$,

$$\overrightarrow{AB} = [-3, -1, 4], \qquad \mathbf{e} = [-3, -1, 4]/\sqrt{26}.$$

To find the distance of the point $R(3, 1, -1)$ from the line, compute we

$$\overrightarrow{RA} \times \mathbf{e} = \frac{[-1, 2, 1] \times [-3, -1, 4]}{\sqrt{26}} = \frac{[9, 1, 7]}{\sqrt{26}},$$

$$|\overrightarrow{RA} \times \mathbf{e}| = \sqrt{\frac{81 + 1 + 49}{26}} = \sqrt{\frac{131}{26}} = 2.245.$$

To check, compute $|\overrightarrow{RB} \times \mathbf{e}|$.

Example 3. Distance between Two Lines. If two nonparallel lines are given by the points A, B and C, D, we can find the shortest distance d between them directly.

First find a vector $\overrightarrow{AB} \times \overrightarrow{CD}$ which is perpendicular to both lines, and let $\mathbf{n}$ be a *unit* vector in its direction. Then, if $\mathbf{u}$ is any vector from one line to the other (as $\overrightarrow{AC}$), d is numerically equal to the component of $\mathbf{u}$ on the common perpendicular:

$$d = |\text{comp}_n \mathbf{u}| = |\mathbf{n} \cdot \mathbf{u}|.$$

Thus let the lines AB, CD be given by the points

$$A(1, -2, -1), \qquad B(4, 0, -3); \qquad C(1, 2, -1), \qquad D(2, -4, -5).$$

We have
$$\overrightarrow{AB} \times \overrightarrow{CD} = [3, 2, -2] \times [1, -6, -4] = 10[-2, 1, -2],$$

$$\mathbf{n} = [-2, 1, -2]/3.$$

The shortest distance d between the lines is now

$$|\mathbf{n} \cdot \overrightarrow{AC}| = \frac{[-2, 1, -2] \cdot [0, 4, 0]}{3} = \frac{4}{3}.$$

To check, compute $\mathbf{n} \cdot \overrightarrow{BD}$.

Example 4. In the triangle ABC (Fig. 11c) the position vectors of A, B, C are $\mathbf{a}$, $\mathbf{b}$, $\mathbf{c}$ and the sides are $a = |\mathbf{c} - \mathbf{b}|$, $b = |\mathbf{a} - \mathbf{c}|$, $c = |\mathbf{b} - \mathbf{a}|$; hence

$$(\mathbf{b} - \mathbf{a}) \times (\mathbf{c} - \mathbf{a}) = bc \sin A\,\mathbf{n}.$$

where $\mathbf{n}$ is a unit normal to the plane ABC. But from the distributive law

(11) $bc \sin A\,\mathbf{n} = \mathbf{a} \times \mathbf{b} + \mathbf{b} \times \mathbf{c} + \mathbf{c} \times \mathbf{a}.$

From (11) we can make a series of deductions.

(i)   The vector $\mathbf{a} \times \mathbf{b} + \mathbf{b} \times \mathbf{c} + \mathbf{c} \times \mathbf{a}$ is normal to the plane ABC.

(ii)   The area of the triangle ABC is
$$\tfrac{1}{2}bc \sin A = \tfrac{1}{2}|\mathbf{a} \times \mathbf{b} + \mathbf{b} \times \mathbf{c} + \mathbf{c} \times \mathbf{a}|.$$

(iii) On dividing (11) by abc we find that $\sin A/a$ equals an expression unaltered by cyclical permutation of its letters; hence

$$\frac{\sin A}{a} = \frac{\sin B}{b} = \frac{\sin C}{c}$$

This is the *sine law* for plane triangles.

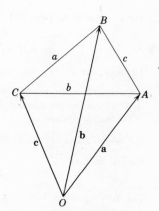

Fig. 11c. Triangle defined by position vectors.

Example 5. The equations

(12) $$\mathbf{r} \cdot \mathbf{a} = \alpha, \qquad \mathbf{r} \times \mathbf{b} = \mathbf{c} \qquad (\mathbf{a} \cdot \mathbf{b} \neq 0),$$

in which $\mathbf{a}$, $\mathbf{b}$, $\mathbf{c}$, α are given, have the unique solution

(13) $$\mathbf{r} = \frac{\mathbf{a} \times \mathbf{c} + \alpha \mathbf{b}}{\mathbf{a} \cdot \mathbf{b}}.$$

From $\mathbf{a} \times (\mathbf{r} \times \mathbf{b}) = \mathbf{a} \times \mathbf{c}$ we have, from (12.1)

$$(\mathbf{a} \cdot \mathbf{b})\mathbf{r} - (\mathbf{a} \cdot \mathbf{r})\mathbf{b} = \mathbf{a} \times \mathbf{c}.$$

Hence the solution, if one exists, is given by (13). Direct substitution of (13) in (12) verifies the solution.

PROBLEMS

1. Find the angle between the vectors:

(a) $[1, 1, 0]$, $[1, 0, 1]$;

(b) $[2, -1, 3]$, $[-1, 4, 2]$;

(c) $[1, 1, 0]$, $[-1, -1, 0]$;

(d) $[1, 1, 1]$, $[1, 1, -1]$;

(e) $[a, b, c]$, $[b, c, a]$, $[c, a, b]$.

2. Show that $\mathbf{a} = [2, 3, -1]$, $\mathbf{b} = [1, 1, 5]$, $\mathbf{c} = [16, -11, -1]$ form a dextral set of mutually orthogonal vectors.

3. Find the perpendicular distance from $P(1, -2, 1)$ to the plane ABC, given the points

$$A(2, 4, 1), \qquad B(-1, 0, 1), \qquad C(-1, 4, 2).$$

4. Find the shortest distance between the lines AB, CD, given the points

$$A(1, 2, 3), \qquad B(-1, 0, 2); \qquad C(0, 1, 7), \qquad D(2, 0, 5).$$

5. Prove that the sum of the squares of the diagonals of a parallelogram is equal to the sum of the squares of its sides.

6. If the vectors $\overrightarrow{OA}$, $\overrightarrow{OB}$, $\overrightarrow{OC}$ are equal in length and coplanar, prove that

$$\overrightarrow{OA} + \overrightarrow{OB} + \overrightarrow{OC} = \overrightarrow{OH},$$

where H is orthocenter of the triangle ABC (the point in which its altitudes intersect).
[Dot-multiply $\mathbf{a} + \mathbf{b} + \mathbf{c} = \mathbf{h}$ by $\mathbf{a} - \mathbf{b}$, $\mathbf{b} - \mathbf{c}$, $\mathbf{c} - \mathbf{a}$ in turn.]

7. Prove *Schwarz's inequality*:

$$(a_1 b_1 + a_2 b_2 + a_3 b_3)^2 \leq (a_1^2 + a_2^2 + a_3^2)(b_1^2 + b_2^2 + b_3^2)$$

the equal sign holding only when $a_1/b_1 = a_2/b_2 = a_3/b_3$.

8. If A, B, C, D are any four points in space, show that

$$\overrightarrow{AB} \times \overrightarrow{CD} + \overrightarrow{BC} \times \overrightarrow{AD} + \overrightarrow{CA} \times \overrightarrow{BD}$$

is independent of D.

9. In the triangle ABC (opposite sides a, b, c), the point R divides BC in the ratio $\lambda/1$. Prove that

$$(AR)^2 = \frac{c^2 + \lambda b^2}{1 + \lambda} - \frac{\lambda a^2}{(1 + \lambda)^2}.$$

10. A face of a polyhedron of area A is said to have the vector area $A\mathbf{n}$, where $\mathbf{n}$ is an outward unit normal to the face. Show that the four faces of a tetrahedron $ABCD$ have vector areas whose sum is zero.

[If the circuit ABC is counterclockwise viewed from without, the face ABC has the vector area $\frac{1}{2}(\mathbf{a}\times\mathbf{b}+\mathbf{b}\times\mathbf{c}+\mathbf{c}\times\mathbf{a})$.]

11. If A, B, C, D are the vertices of a square in circuital order, prove that

$$(OA)^2 + (OC)^2 = (OB)^2 + (OD)^2 \qquad \text{for any } O. \qquad [\text{Use } (10.15').]$$

12. If P and P' are points on the surface of a sphere of radius a, prove that

$$\text{Mean } (PP')^2 = 2a^2.$$

13. If r is the radius of a sphere circumscribed about a regular tetrahedron of side a, prove that $r^2 = 3a^2/8$. [Use $(10.16')$.]

14. If P^* and Q^* are the mean centers of p points P_i and q points Q_j, respectively, prove that

$$\text{Mean } (P_iQ_j)^2 = \text{Mean } (P^*P_i)^2 + \text{Mean } (Q^*Q_j)^2 + (P^*Q^*)^2.$$

15. The points A', B', C' divide the sides BC, CA, AB of the triangle ABC in the ratio $1/2$. The pairs of lines (AA', BB'), (BB', CC'), (CC', AA') intersect at P, Q, R, respectively. Show that the area of the triangle PQR is $1/7$ the area of ABC.

$$[\text{Vector area } PQR = \tfrac{1}{2}(\mathbf{p}\times\mathbf{q} + \mathbf{q}\times\mathbf{r} + \mathbf{r}\times\mathbf{p}).]$$

16. Prove that

$$|\mathbf{a}|^2 + |\mathbf{b}|^2 + |\mathbf{c}|^2 + |\mathbf{a}+\mathbf{b}+\mathbf{c}|^2 = |\mathbf{b}+\mathbf{c}|^2 + |\mathbf{c}+\mathbf{a}|^2 + |\mathbf{a}+\mathbf{b}|^2.$$

17. Prove that

$$|\mathbf{a}| + |\mathbf{b}| + |\mathbf{c}| - |\mathbf{b}+\mathbf{c}| - |\mathbf{c}+\mathbf{a}| - |\mathbf{a}+\mathbf{b}| + |\mathbf{a}+\mathbf{b}+\mathbf{c}| \geqq 0.$$

[The left member equals

$$\{|\mathbf{a}| + |\mathbf{b}| - |\mathbf{a}+\mathbf{b}|\}\left\{1 - \frac{|\mathbf{a}| + |\mathbf{b}| + |\mathbf{a}+\mathbf{b}|}{|\mathbf{a}| + |\mathbf{b}| + |\mathbf{c}| + |\mathbf{a}+\mathbf{b}+\mathbf{c}|}\right\} + \text{cycl},$$

in which each brace $\geqq 0$.]

18. If ABC is a spherical triangle on unit sphere about O, and $\mathbf{a} = \overrightarrow{OA}$, $\mathbf{b} = \overrightarrow{OB}$, $\mathbf{c} = \overrightarrow{OC}$, the vector $\mathbf{p} = x\mathbf{a} + y\mathbf{b} + z\mathbf{c}$ will pass through any given point P of the sphere for a suitable choice of x, y, z. Show that the vectors

$$\mathbf{u} = y\mathbf{b} + z\mathbf{c}, \qquad \mathbf{v} = z\mathbf{c} + x\mathbf{a}, \qquad \mathbf{w} = x\mathbf{a} + y\mathbf{b}$$

will pass through the points U, V, W where the great circles PA, PB, PC cut the sides BC, CA, AB of the triangle; and that

$$\frac{\sin(\mathbf{b},\mathbf{u})}{\sin(\mathbf{u},\mathbf{c})}\frac{\sin(\mathbf{c},\mathbf{v})}{\sin(\mathbf{v},\mathbf{a})}\frac{\sin(\mathbf{a},\mathbf{w})}{\sin(\mathbf{w},\mathbf{b})} = 1$$

(*Theorem of Ceva* for spherical triangles).

[From $\mathbf{w} = x\mathbf{a} + y\mathbf{b}$ and $|\mathbf{a}| = |\mathbf{b}| = 1$, we have

$$\frac{\mathbf{a}\times\mathbf{w}}{y} = \frac{\mathbf{w}\times\mathbf{b}}{x}, \qquad \frac{\sin(\mathbf{a},\mathbf{w})}{\sin(\mathbf{w},\mathbf{b})} = \frac{y}{x},$$

on taking account of signs.]

12. Vector Triple Product. The vector $(\mathbf{u} \times \mathbf{v}) \times \mathbf{w}$ is perpendicular to $\mathbf{u} \times \mathbf{v}$ and therefore coplanar with $\mathbf{u}$ and $\mathbf{v}$; hence (§4),

$$(\mathbf{u} \times \mathbf{v}) \times \mathbf{w} = \alpha \mathbf{u} + \beta \mathbf{v}.$$

But, since $(\mathbf{u} \times \mathbf{v}) \times \mathbf{w}$ is also perpendicular to $\mathbf{w}$,

$$\alpha \, \mathbf{u} \cdot \mathbf{w} + \beta \, \mathbf{v} \cdot \mathbf{w} = 0.$$

All numbers α, β that satisfy this equation must be of the form $\alpha = -\lambda \, \mathbf{v} \cdot \mathbf{w}$, $\beta = \lambda \, \mathbf{u} \cdot \mathbf{w}$, where λ is arbitrary. Thus we have

$$(\mathbf{u} \times \mathbf{v}) \times \mathbf{w} = \lambda \left\{ (\mathbf{u} \cdot \mathbf{w})\mathbf{v} - (\mathbf{v} \cdot \mathbf{w})\mathbf{u} \right\}.$$

In order to determine λ, we use a special basis in which $\mathbf{i}$ is collinear with $\mathbf{u}$, $\mathbf{j}$ coplanar with $\mathbf{u}$, $\mathbf{v}$; then

$$\mathbf{u} = u_1 \mathbf{i}, \qquad \mathbf{v} = v_1 \mathbf{i} + v_2 \mathbf{j}, \qquad \mathbf{w} = w_1 \mathbf{i} + w_2 \mathbf{j} + w_3 \mathbf{k}.$$

On substituting these values, we obtain, after a simple calculation, $\lambda = 1$. We therefore have the important expansion formulas,

(1)
$$(\mathbf{u} \times \mathbf{v}) \times \mathbf{w} = (\mathbf{u} \cdot \mathbf{w}) \, \mathbf{v} - (\mathbf{v} \cdot \mathbf{w}) \, \mathbf{u},$$
$$\mathbf{w} \times (\mathbf{u} \times \mathbf{v}) = (\mathbf{w} \cdot \mathbf{v}) \, \mathbf{u} - (\mathbf{w} \cdot \mathbf{u}) \, \mathbf{v}.$$

In the left-hand members of (1), one of the vectors in parenthesis is *adjacent* to the vector outside, the other *remote* from it. The right-hand members may be remembered as

(Outer dot Remote) Adjacent − (Outer dot Adjacent) Remote.

In general $(\mathbf{u} \times \mathbf{v}) \times \mathbf{w} \neq \mathbf{u} \times (\mathbf{v} \times \mathbf{w})$; for the former is coplanar with $\mathbf{u}$ and $\mathbf{v}$, the latter with $\mathbf{v}$ and $\mathbf{w}$. *Vector multiplication is not associative.*

From (1) we see that the sum of a vector triple product and its two cyclical permutations is zero:

(2) $$(\mathbf{a} \times \mathbf{b}) \times \mathbf{c} + (\mathbf{b} \times \mathbf{c}) \times \mathbf{a} + (\mathbf{c} \times \mathbf{a}) \times \mathbf{b} = 0.$$

If l is a directed line carrying the unit vector $\mathbf{e}$, we may express any vector $\mathbf{u}$ as the sum of its orthogonal projections on l and on a plane p perpendicular to l:

(3) $$\operatorname{proj}_l \mathbf{u} = \mathbf{e} \operatorname{comp}_l \mathbf{u} = (\mathbf{e} \cdot \mathbf{u})\mathbf{e}, \qquad\qquad (10.8),$$

(4) $$\operatorname{proj}_p \mathbf{u} = \mathbf{u} - (\mathbf{e} \cdot \mathbf{u}) \, \mathbf{e} = \mathbf{e} \times (\mathbf{u} \times \mathbf{e}).$$

13. Scalar Triple Product. Let the noncoplanar vectors

$$\mathbf{u} = \overrightarrow{OU}, \qquad \mathbf{v} = \overrightarrow{OV}, \qquad \mathbf{w} = \overrightarrow{OW}$$

be drawn from a common origin O. Then **u, v, w** form a *dextral* or *sinistral* set according as the circuit around the triangle UVW, *as viewed from O, is clockwise or counterclockwise.**

In Fig. 13*a*, **u, v, w** form a dextral set; for the circuit UVW is counterclockwise as viewed by the reader and therefore clockwise as viewed from O (which lies behind the plane UVW). The set **u, w, v** is sinistral.

Consider now the scalar product of **u** × **v** and **w**, written **u** × **v** · **w** or [**uvw**]. No ambiguity can arise from the omission of parentheses for **u** × (**v** · **w**) is not defined (the cross is only used between *vectors*). We shall also see that positions of the dot and cross are immaterial.

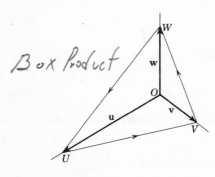

Fig. 13*a*. A dextral set: **u, v, w**.

THEOREM.   *The product* **u** × **v** · **w** *is numerically equal to the volume V of a parallelepiped having* **u, v, w** *as concurrent edges.   Its sign is positive or negative according as* **u, v, w** *form a dextral or a sinistral set.*

Proof.   We may write the vector product **u** × **v** = A**n**, where

$$A = |\mathbf{u} \times \mathbf{v}| = |\mathbf{u}|\,|\mathbf{v}|\,\sin(\mathbf{u}, \mathbf{v})$$

is the area of the parallelogram having **u** and **v** as adjacent sides and **n** is a unit vector perpendicular to **u** and **v** pointing as a right-handed screw would advance when turned from **u** to **v**.   When the set **u, v, w** is dextral (as in Fig. 13*b*) the angle $\theta = (\mathbf{n}, \mathbf{w})$ is acute, and

$$\mathbf{u} \times \mathbf{v} \cdot \mathbf{w} = A\mathbf{n} \cdot \mathbf{w} = A\,|\mathbf{w}|\cos\theta$$
$$= Ah = V,$$

where h is the altitude of the box. When the set **u, v, w** is sinistral, θ is obtuse, $\cos\theta$ is negative, and **u** × **v** · **w** $= -V$.

On account of the geometric meaning of the scalar triple product we shall call it the *box product*.†

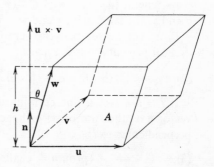

Fig. 13*b*. Box product.

* Our previous definition of a dextral set in §8 applied to orthogonal sets such as **i, j, k**.   This more general definition also shows that **i, j, k** form a dextral set.

† The name proposed by J. H. Taylor, *Vector Analysis*, Prentice-Hall, 1939, p. 46.

The dextral or sinistral character of a set **u**, **v**, **w** is not altered by a cyclical change in their order; hence

(1) $$\mathbf{u} \times \mathbf{v} \cdot \mathbf{w} = \mathbf{v} \times \mathbf{w} \cdot \mathbf{u} = \mathbf{w} \times \mathbf{u} \cdot \mathbf{v}.$$

But a dextral set becomes sinistral, and vice versa, when the cyclical order is changed:

(2) $$\mathbf{u} \times \mathbf{w} \cdot \mathbf{v} = -\mathbf{u} \times \mathbf{v} \cdot \mathbf{w}.$$

Thus, if the set **u**, **v**, **w** is dextral, the products in (1) all equal V, while the products

$$\mathbf{u} \times \mathbf{w} \cdot \mathbf{v} = \mathbf{w} \times \mathbf{v} \cdot \mathbf{u} = \mathbf{v} \times \mathbf{u} \cdot \mathbf{w}$$

all equal $-V$.

If **u**, **v**, **w** are proper vectors, $V = 0$ when and only when the vectors are coplanar (parallel to the same plane). Therefore, for proper vectors,

(3) $$\mathbf{u} \times \mathbf{v} \cdot \mathbf{w} = 0 \quad \text{implies} \quad \mathbf{u}, \mathbf{v}, \mathbf{w} \text{ coplanar}.$$

In particular, a box product containing two parallel vectors is zero; for example, $\mathbf{u} \times \mathbf{v} \cdot \mathbf{u} = 0$.

The value of a box product is not altered by an interchange of the dot and cross. For, from (1),

(4) $$\mathbf{u} \times \mathbf{v} \cdot \mathbf{w} = \mathbf{v} \times \mathbf{w} \cdot \mathbf{u} = \mathbf{u} \cdot \mathbf{v} \times \mathbf{w}$$

as dot multiplication is commutative. The notation [**uvw**] often is used for the box product, as the omission of dot and cross causes no ambiguity.

From (10.3) and (11.3), we have

(5) $$(\alpha\mathbf{u}) \times (\beta\mathbf{v}) \cdot (\gamma\mathbf{w}) = \alpha\beta\gamma\, \mathbf{u} \times \mathbf{v} \cdot \mathbf{w}.$$

Finally, the distributive law for scalar and vector products shows that a box product of vector sums may be expanded just as in ordinary algebra, provided that the order of the vector factors is not altered. Thus, if we expand the product $\mathbf{u} \times \mathbf{v} \cdot \mathbf{w}$ when the vectors are referred to the basis **i**, **j**, **k**, we obtain 27 terms of which all but 6 vanish as they contain box products with two or three equal vectors. The remaining 6 terms are those containing

$$[\mathbf{ijk}] = [\mathbf{jki}] = [\mathbf{kij}] = 1, \qquad [\mathbf{ikj}] = [\mathbf{kji}] = [\mathbf{jik}] = -1,$$

and constitute the expansion of the determinant

(6) $$[\mathbf{uvw}] = \begin{vmatrix} u_1 & u_2 & u_3 \\ v_1 & v_2 & v_3 \\ w_1 & w_2 & w_3 \end{vmatrix}.$$

= Box Product determinant

This result also follows at once from (11.8).

$i\,j\,k\,i\,j$

PROBLEMS

1. If $\mathbf{u} = [-1, 0, 2]$, $\mathbf{v} = [2, 1, -1]$, $\mathbf{w} = [1, 2, -2]$, compute

(a) $\mathbf{u} \times \mathbf{v}$, $\mathbf{v} \times \mathbf{w}$, $\mathbf{w} \times \mathbf{u}$;

(b) $\mathbf{u} \times \mathbf{v} \cdot \mathbf{w}$, $\mathbf{v} \times \mathbf{w} \cdot \mathbf{u}$, $\mathbf{w} \times \mathbf{u} \cdot \mathbf{v}$;

(c) $(\mathbf{u} \times \mathbf{v}) \times \mathbf{w}$, $(\mathbf{v} \times \mathbf{w}) \times \mathbf{u}$, $(\mathbf{w} \times \mathbf{u}) \times \mathbf{v}$; and find their sum.

(d) Verify the results of (c) by using (12.1). $(u \times v) \times w = (u \cdot w)v - (v \cdot w)u$

2. Given the points $A(3, 2, 1)$, $B(2, 3, -1)$, $C(-1, 2, 3)$, find

(a) the area of the triangle ABC;

(b) the distance p of O from the plane ABC;

(c) the volume of the tetrahedron $OABC$;

(d) the volume of the box whose edges are OA, OB, OC.

14. Products of Four Vectors. We first consider the scalar product $(\mathbf{a} \times \mathbf{b}) \cdot (\mathbf{c} \times \mathbf{d})$. If we interchange the first cross and dot, it becomes $\mathbf{a} \cdot \{\mathbf{b} \times (\mathbf{c} \times \mathbf{d})\}$; and, since

$$\mathbf{b} \times (\mathbf{c} \times \mathbf{d}) = (\mathbf{b} \cdot \mathbf{d})\mathbf{c} - (\mathbf{b} \cdot \mathbf{c})\mathbf{d}, \qquad (12.1),$$

(1) $(\mathbf{a} \times \mathbf{b}) \cdot (\mathbf{c} \times \mathbf{d}) = (\mathbf{a} \cdot \mathbf{c})(\mathbf{b} \cdot \mathbf{d}) - (\mathbf{a} \cdot \mathbf{d})(\mathbf{b} \cdot \mathbf{c})$.

This is *Lagrange's identity*; it may also be written

(1)′ $(\mathbf{a} \times \mathbf{b}) \cdot (\mathbf{c} \times \mathbf{d}) = \begin{vmatrix} \mathbf{a} \cdot \mathbf{c} & \mathbf{a} \cdot \mathbf{d} \\ \mathbf{b} \cdot \mathbf{c} & \mathbf{b} \cdot \mathbf{d} \end{vmatrix}$.

The special case

(2) $(\mathbf{a} \times \mathbf{b}) \cdot (\mathbf{a} \times \mathbf{b}) = (\mathbf{a} \cdot \mathbf{a})(\mathbf{b} \cdot \mathbf{b}) - (\mathbf{a} \cdot \mathbf{b})^2$

is also important.

We turn now to the vector product $(\mathbf{a} \times \mathbf{b}) \times (\mathbf{c} \times \mathbf{d})$. If we expand it as the triple product of $\mathbf{a}$, $\mathbf{b}$, $\mathbf{c} \times \mathbf{d}$ by (12.1),

(3) $(\mathbf{a} \times \mathbf{b}) \times (\mathbf{c} \times \mathbf{d}) = [\mathbf{acd}]\mathbf{b} - [\mathbf{bcd}]\mathbf{a}$.

But, if we expand it as the triple product of $\mathbf{a} \times \mathbf{b}$, $\mathbf{c}$, $\mathbf{d}$,

(4) $(\mathbf{a} \times \mathbf{b}) \times (\mathbf{c} \times \mathbf{d}) = [\mathbf{abd}]\mathbf{c} - [\mathbf{abc}]\mathbf{d}$.

On equating the right-hand members of (3) and (4), we obtain an equation connecting any four vectors:

(5) $\mathbf{a}[\mathbf{bcd}] - \mathbf{b}[\mathbf{cda}] + \mathbf{c}[\mathbf{dab}] - \mathbf{d}[\mathbf{abc}] = 0$.

When $\mathbf{a}$, $\mathbf{b}$, $\mathbf{c}$ are noncoplanar, $[\mathbf{abc}] \neq 0$ and the formula

(6) $[\mathbf{abc}]\mathbf{d} = [\mathbf{dbc}]\mathbf{a} + [\mathbf{adc}]\mathbf{b} + [\mathbf{abd}]\mathbf{c}$

gives $\mathbf{d}$ explicitly in terms of $\mathbf{a}$, $\mathbf{b}$, $\mathbf{c}$. This is an analytic solution of the problem solved geometrically in §4.

Example. Spherical Trigonometry. The unit vectors $\mathbf{a} = \overrightarrow{OA}$, $\mathbf{b} = \overrightarrow{OB}$, $\mathbf{c} = \overrightarrow{OC}$ define a spherical triangle ABC on a unit sphere about O; and let $[\mathbf{abc}] > 0$. Let α, β, γ denote the *sides* (arcs of great circles) opposite the interior (dihedral) angles A, B, C; and let all sides and angles be $< \pi$. Now

(7) $\mathbf{b} \cdot \mathbf{c} = \cos \alpha$, $\mathbf{c} \cdot \mathbf{a} = \cos \beta$, $\mathbf{a} \cdot \mathbf{b} = \cos \gamma$;

(8) $\mathbf{b} \times \mathbf{c} = \sin \alpha \, \mathbf{a}'$, $\mathbf{c} \times \mathbf{a} = \sin \beta \, \mathbf{b}'$, $\mathbf{a} \times \mathbf{b} = \sin \gamma \, \mathbf{c}'$.

Here $\mathbf{a}'$, $\mathbf{b}'$, $\mathbf{c}'$ are unit vectors normal to the planes BOC, COA, AOB, respectively (Fig. 14), and include the angles

$$(\mathbf{b}', \mathbf{c}') = \pi - A = \alpha', \quad (\mathbf{c}', \mathbf{a}') = \pi - B = \beta', \quad (\mathbf{a}', \mathbf{b}') = \pi - C = \gamma'.$$

Thus α', β', γ' are the *exterior* dihedral angles at A, B, C. Moreover

$$\mathbf{b}' \times \mathbf{c}' = \frac{(\mathbf{c} \times \mathbf{a}) \times (\mathbf{a} \times \mathbf{b})}{\sin \beta \sin \gamma} = \frac{[\mathbf{abc}]}{\sin \beta \sin \gamma} \mathbf{a},$$

a *positive* multiple of $\mathbf{a}$. Thus we have the equations

(9) $\mathbf{b}' \cdot \mathbf{c}' = \cos \alpha'$, $\mathbf{c}' \cdot \mathbf{a}' = \cos \beta'$, $\mathbf{a}' \cdot \mathbf{b}' = \cos \gamma'$;

(10) $\mathbf{b}' \times \mathbf{c}' = \sin \alpha' \mathbf{a}$, $\mathbf{c}' \times \mathbf{a}' = \sin \beta' \mathbf{b}$, $\mathbf{a}' \times \mathbf{b}' = \sin \gamma' \mathbf{c}$.

Thus there is complete reciprocity between the sets $(\mathbf{a}, \mathbf{b}, \mathbf{c})$ and $(\mathbf{a}', \mathbf{b}', \mathbf{c}')$, and also between the spherical triangles ABC, $A'B'C'$ that they determine. Whereas ABC has α, β, γ for sides and α', β', γ' for exterior angles, $A'B'C'$ has α', β', γ' for sides and α, β, γ for exterior angles. Since the vertices A', B', C' are the poles of the sides BC, CA, AB, and vice versa, the triangles ABC, $A'B'C'$ are said to be *polar*.

From (8) and (10) we have

$$[\mathbf{abc}] = \sin \alpha \, \mathbf{a} \cdot \mathbf{a}' = \sin \beta \, \mathbf{b} \cdot \mathbf{b}'$$

$$= \sin \gamma \, \mathbf{c} \cdot \mathbf{c}',$$

$$[\mathbf{a}'\mathbf{b}'\mathbf{c}'] = \sin \alpha' \, \mathbf{a} \cdot \mathbf{a}' = \sin \beta' \, \mathbf{b} \cdot \mathbf{b}'$$

$$= \sin \gamma' \, \mathbf{c} \cdot \mathbf{c}';$$

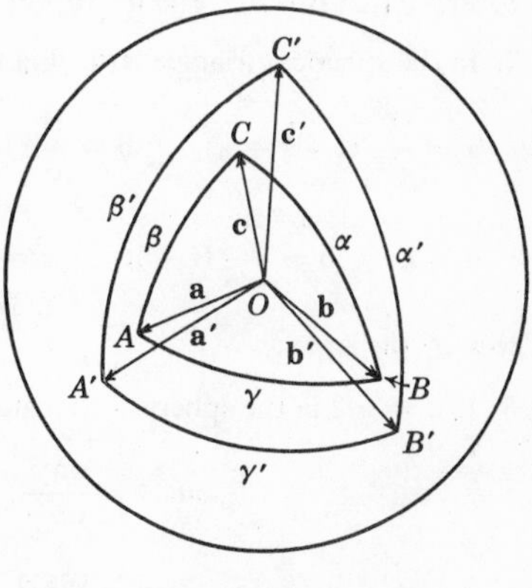

Fig. 14. Spherical triangle.

hence, on division, we obtain the *sine law* for spherical triangles:

(11) $$\frac{\sin \alpha}{\sin \alpha'} = \frac{\sin \beta}{\sin \beta'} = \frac{\sin \gamma}{\sin \gamma'}.$$

From (8) we have

$$\sin \beta \sin \gamma \, \mathbf{b}' \cdot \mathbf{c}' = (\mathbf{c} \times \mathbf{a}) \cdot (\mathbf{a} \times \mathbf{b}) = (\mathbf{c} \cdot \mathbf{a})(\mathbf{a} \cdot \mathbf{b}) - \mathbf{b} \cdot \mathbf{c};$$

hence, from (7) and (9), we obtain the *cosine law* for the spherical triangle ABC:

(12) $\cos \alpha = \cos \beta \cos \gamma - \sin \beta \sin \gamma \cos \alpha'$.

For the polar triangle this becomes

(13) $\cos \alpha' = \cos \beta' \cos \gamma' - \sin \beta' \sin \gamma' \cos \alpha$.

Of course α, β, γ may be cyclically permuted in (12) and (13).

Since α', β', γ' are exterior angles, $\alpha' = \pi - A$, $\beta' = \pi - B$, $\gamma' = \pi - C$; hence the sine and cosine laws may be written

$(11)'$ $$\frac{\sin \alpha}{\sin A} = \frac{\sin \beta}{\sin B} - \frac{\sin \gamma}{\sin C},$$

$(12)'$ $$\cos \alpha = \cos \beta \cos \gamma + \sin \beta \sin \gamma \cos A,$$

$(13)'$ $$\cos A = -\cos B \cos C + \sin B \sin C \cos \alpha.$$

In this version of the cosine laws the structural similarity of (12) and (13) is lost.

PROBLEMS

Prove the formulas:

1. $(\mathbf{a} \times \mathbf{b}) \times (\mathbf{b} \times \mathbf{c}) \cdot (\mathbf{c} \times \mathbf{a}) = [\mathbf{abc}]^2$.

2. $(\mathbf{b} \times \mathbf{c}) \cdot (\mathbf{a} \times \mathbf{d}) + (\mathbf{c} \times \mathbf{a}) \cdot (\mathbf{b} \times \mathbf{d}) + (\mathbf{a} \times \mathbf{b}) \cdot (\mathbf{c} \times \mathbf{d}) = 0$.

3. $(\mathbf{b} \times \mathbf{c}) \times (\mathbf{a} \times \mathbf{d}) + (\mathbf{c} \times \mathbf{a}) \times (\mathbf{b} \times \mathbf{d}) + (\mathbf{a} \times \mathbf{b}) \times (\mathbf{c} \times \mathbf{d}) = -2[\mathbf{abc}]\mathbf{d}$.

4. $(\mathbf{a} - \mathbf{d}) \cdot (\mathbf{b} - \mathbf{c}) + (\mathbf{b} - \mathbf{d}) \cdot (\mathbf{c} - \mathbf{a}) + (\mathbf{c} - \mathbf{d}) \cdot (\mathbf{a} - \mathbf{b}) = 0$.

5. $(\mathbf{a} - \mathbf{d}) \times (\mathbf{b} - \mathbf{c}) + (\mathbf{b} - \mathbf{d}) \times (\mathbf{c} - \mathbf{a}) + (\mathbf{c} - \mathbf{d}) \times (\mathbf{a} - \mathbf{b}) =$

$$2(\mathbf{a} \times \mathbf{b} + \mathbf{b} \times \mathbf{c} + \mathbf{c} \times \mathbf{a}).$$

6. Prove that $(\mathbf{a} \times \mathbf{b}) \times \mathbf{c} = \mathbf{a} \times (\mathbf{b} \times \mathbf{c})$ when, and only when, $(\mathbf{c} \times \mathbf{a}) \times \mathbf{b} = \mathbf{0}$.

7. In the spherical triangle ABC find the interior angles A, B, C when

(i) $\quad \mathbf{a} = \dfrac{1}{\sqrt{3}}(\mathbf{i} + \mathbf{j} + \mathbf{k}), \quad \mathbf{b} = \dfrac{1}{\sqrt{3}}(-\mathbf{i} + \mathbf{j} + \mathbf{k}), \quad \mathbf{c} = \dfrac{1}{\sqrt{3}}(-\mathbf{i} - \mathbf{j} + \mathbf{k});$

(ii) $\quad \mathbf{a} = \mathbf{i}, \quad \mathbf{b} = \dfrac{1}{\sqrt{2}}(\mathbf{i} + \mathbf{j}), \quad \mathbf{c} = \dfrac{1}{\sqrt{3}}(\mathbf{i} + \mathbf{j} + \mathbf{k}).$

Check by the sine law.

8. If $C = \pi/2$ in the spherical triangle ABC, prove that

$$\sin A = \frac{\sin \alpha}{\sin \gamma}, \qquad \sin B = \frac{\sin \beta}{\sin \gamma};$$

$$\cos \alpha = \frac{\cos A}{\sin B}, \qquad \cos \beta = \frac{\cos B}{\sin A};$$

$$\cos \gamma = \cos \alpha \cos \beta = \cot A \cot B,$$

in which A, B, C are interior angles.

9. Prove that an equilateral spherical triangle is equiangular; and that $\cos \alpha + \cos \alpha' + \cos \alpha \cos \alpha' = 0$.

10. Prove *Hero's formula* for the area of a plane triangle with sides a, b, c:

$$A = \sqrt{s(s - a)(s - b)(s - c)} \quad \text{where} \quad s = \tfrac{1}{2}(a + b + c).$$

[From $\mathbf{a} + \mathbf{b} + \mathbf{c} = \mathbf{0}$, $c^2 = a^2 + b^2 + 2\mathbf{a} \cdot \mathbf{b}$; now

$$4A^2 = (\mathbf{a} \times \mathbf{b}) \cdot (\mathbf{a} \times \mathbf{b}) = a^2 b^2 - (\mathbf{a} \cdot \mathbf{b})^2 = (ab + \mathbf{a} \cdot \mathbf{b})(ab - \mathbf{a} \cdot \mathbf{b}).]$$

15. Reciprocal Bases. We call a set of three noncoplanar vectors a
basis for space of three dimensions; for *all* vectors may be expressed
linearly in terms of them (§4).† Thus, if **a**, **b**, **c** form a basis, $[\mathbf{abc}] \neq 0$,
and we can express any vector **d** as

$$\mathbf{d} = \alpha\mathbf{a} + \beta\mathbf{b} + \gamma\mathbf{c},$$

where the numbers α, β, γ are given explicitly in (14.6).

Now let $\mathbf{e}_1$, $\mathbf{e}_2$, $\mathbf{e}_3$ form a basis in 3-space; then $[\mathbf{e}_1\mathbf{e}_2\mathbf{e}_3] \neq 0$. We proceed
to define a second basis $\mathbf{e}^1$, $\mathbf{e}^2$, $\mathbf{e}^3$ closely related to the first; here the
superscripts are not exponents, but mere identification tags.

DEFINITION. Two bases $\mathbf{e}_1$, $\mathbf{e}_2$, $\mathbf{e}_3$ and $\mathbf{e}^1$, $\mathbf{e}^2$, $\mathbf{e}^3$ are said to be *reciprocal*
when they satisfy the nine equations:

(1)
$$\begin{array}{lll}
\mathbf{e}_1 \cdot \mathbf{e}^1 = 1, & \mathbf{e}_1 \cdot \mathbf{e}^2 = 0, & \mathbf{e}_1 \cdot \mathbf{e}^3 = 0, \\
\mathbf{e}_2 \cdot \mathbf{e}^1 = 0, & \mathbf{e}_2 \cdot \mathbf{e}^2 = 1, & \mathbf{e}_2 \cdot \mathbf{e}^3 = 0, \\
\mathbf{e}_3 \cdot \mathbf{e}^1 = 0, & \mathbf{e}_3 \cdot \mathbf{e}^2 = 0, & \mathbf{e}_3 \cdot \mathbf{e}^3 = 1.
\end{array}$$

By use of the *Kronecker delta* δ_i^j defined as

(2)
$$\delta_i^j = \begin{cases} 1 & \text{when } i = j \\ 0 & \text{when } i \neq j, \end{cases}$$

equations (1) condense to

(3)
$$\mathbf{e}_i \cdot \mathbf{e}^j = \delta_i^j \qquad (i, j = 1, 2, 3).$$

Consider the three equations in the first column of (1). The second
and third state that $\mathbf{e}^1$ is perpendicular to both $\mathbf{e}_2$ and $\mathbf{e}_3$: that is, parallel
to $\mathbf{e}_2 \times \mathbf{e}_3$. Hence $\mathbf{e}^1 = \lambda\,\mathbf{e}_2 \times \mathbf{e}_3$; and, from the first equation, we have
$1 = \lambda\,\mathbf{e}_1 \cdot \mathbf{e}_2 \times \mathbf{e}_3$. We thus obtain

(4)
$$\mathbf{e}^1 = \frac{\mathbf{e}_2 \times \mathbf{e}_3}{[\mathbf{e}_1\mathbf{e}_2\mathbf{e}_3]}, \qquad \mathbf{e}^2 = \frac{\mathbf{e}_3 \times \mathbf{e}_1}{[\mathbf{e}_1\mathbf{e}_2\mathbf{e}_3]}, \qquad \mathbf{e}^3 = \frac{\mathbf{e}_1 \times \mathbf{e}_2}{[\mathbf{e}_1\mathbf{e}_2\mathbf{e}_3]},$$

$\mathbf{e}^2$ and $\mathbf{e}^3$ being derived from $\mathbf{e}^1$ by cyclical permutation. From the
symmetry of equations (1) in the two sets $\mathbf{e}_i$, $\mathbf{e}^i$, we have also

(5)
$$\mathbf{e}_1 = \frac{\mathbf{e}^2 \times \mathbf{e}^3}{[\mathbf{e}^1\mathbf{e}^2\mathbf{e}^3]}, \qquad \mathbf{e}_2 = \frac{\mathbf{e}^3 \times \mathbf{e}^1}{[\mathbf{e}^1\mathbf{e}^2\mathbf{e}^3]}, \qquad \mathbf{e}_3 = \frac{\mathbf{e}^1 \times \mathbf{e}^2}{[\mathbf{e}^1\mathbf{e}^2\mathbf{e}^3]}.$$

Thus, either basis is expressed in terms of the other by precisely the same
formulas.

† *Two* nonparallel vectors **a**, **b** ($\mathbf{a} \times \mathbf{b} \neq \mathbf{0}$) form a basis for all vectors in their plane.

$$\bar{e}_1 \cdot \bar{e}^1 + e_1 \cdot e^2 + c_3 \cdot e^3 = 3$$

From (4) and (5), we have

$$\mathbf{e}^1 \cdot \mathbf{e}_1 = \frac{(\mathbf{e}_2 \times \mathbf{e}_3) \cdot (\mathbf{e}^2 \times \mathbf{e}^3)}{[\mathbf{e}_1\mathbf{e}_2\mathbf{e}_3]\,[\mathbf{e}^1\mathbf{e}^2\mathbf{e}^3]} = \frac{1}{[\mathbf{e}_1\mathbf{e}_2\mathbf{e}_3]\,[\mathbf{e}^1\mathbf{e}^2\mathbf{e}^3]},$$

on making use of (14.1) and equations (1); hence

(6) $$[\mathbf{e}_1\mathbf{e}_2\mathbf{e}_3]\,[\mathbf{e}^1\mathbf{e}^2\mathbf{e}^3] = 1,$$

an equation that gives further justification for the name *reciprocal* applied to the *sets*. Since the box products in (6) must have the same sign, a basis and its reciprocal are both dextral or both sinistral.

On dividing the identity

$$\mathbf{e}_1 \times (\mathbf{e}_2 \times \mathbf{e}_3) + \mathbf{e}_2 \times (\mathbf{e}_3 \times \mathbf{e}_1) + \mathbf{e}_3 \times (\mathbf{e}_1 \times \mathbf{e}_2) = 0 \qquad (12.2)$$

by $[\mathbf{e}_1\mathbf{e}_2\mathbf{e}_3]$, we obtain the further relation

(7) $$\mathbf{e}_1 \times \mathbf{e}^1 + \mathbf{e}_2 \times \mathbf{e}^2 + \mathbf{e}_3 \times \mathbf{e}^3 = 0.$$

When a basis and its reciprocal are identical, $\mathbf{e}_i = \mathbf{e}^i$ and equations (3) give

$$\mathbf{e}_1 \cdot \mathbf{e}_1 = \mathbf{e}_2 \cdot \mathbf{e}_2 = \mathbf{e}_3 \cdot \mathbf{e}_3 = 1, \qquad \mathbf{e}_1 \cdot \mathbf{e}_2 = \mathbf{e}_2 \cdot \mathbf{e}_3 = \mathbf{e}_3 \cdot \mathbf{e}_1 = 0.$$

These equations characterize an orthogonal triple of unit vectors; hence:

A basis is self-reciprocal when and only when it consists of a mutually orthogonal triple of unit vectors.

The triple will be dextral if $[\mathbf{e}_1\mathbf{e}_2\mathbf{e}_3] = 1$, sinistral if $[\mathbf{e}_1\mathbf{e}_2\mathbf{e}_3] = -1$. Thus **i, j, k** and **i, j, −k** are typical dextral and sinistral self-reciprocal bases. *All* such bases may be derived by revolving these types about axes through the origin.

We can now readily solve the problem of expressing a vector **u** in terms of a basis $\mathbf{e}_1, \mathbf{e}_2, \mathbf{e}_3$. If we write

$$\mathbf{u} = u^1\mathbf{e}_1 + u^2\mathbf{e}_2 + u^3\mathbf{e}_3$$

(the upper indices are not exponents), and dot-multiply this equation by $\mathbf{e}^1, \mathbf{e}^2, \mathbf{e}^3$ in turn, we find

(8) $$u^i = \mathbf{u} \cdot \mathbf{e}^i \qquad (i = 1, 2, 3).$$

Similarly if we write

$$\mathbf{u} = u_1\mathbf{e}^1 + u_2\mathbf{e}^2 + u_3\mathbf{e}^3,$$

we find

(9) $$u_i = \mathbf{u} \cdot \mathbf{e}_i \qquad (i = 1, 2, 3).$$

When the basis is self-reciprocal

$$u^i = u_i = \mathbf{u} \cdot \mathbf{e}_i = |\mathbf{u}|\, \cos(\mathbf{e}_i, \mathbf{u}),$$

and we obtain the components of (8.2). For an arbitrary basis, we shall also call the three scalars

$$\left. \begin{aligned} u^i &= \mathbf{u} \cdot \mathbf{e}^i \\ u_i &= \mathbf{u} \cdot \mathbf{e}_i \end{aligned} \right\} \text{ components of } \mathbf{u} \text{ for the basis } \left\{ \begin{aligned} \mathbf{e}_i \\ \mathbf{e}^i \end{aligned} \right. .$$

The base vectors now are not in general *unit* vectors (as $\mathbf{i}, \mathbf{j}, \mathbf{k}$); but the *formulas* for general components are analogous to those for rectangular components:

(10) $$u_1 = \mathbf{u} \cdot \mathbf{i}, \qquad u_2 = \mathbf{u} \cdot \mathbf{j}, \qquad u_3 = \mathbf{u} \cdot \mathbf{k}.$$

With a self-reciprocal basis the distinctions implied by upper and lower indices vanish and only subscripts need be used.

PROBLEMS

1. Find the set of vectors reciprocal to

$$\mathbf{e}_1 = [1, 0, 0], \qquad \mathbf{e}_2 = [1, 1, 0], \qquad \mathbf{e}_3 = [1, 1, 1].$$

Find the components of $\mathbf{u} = [1, 2, 3]$ relative to the bases $\mathbf{e}_1, \mathbf{e}_2, \mathbf{e}_3$ and $\mathbf{e}^1, \mathbf{e}^2, \mathbf{e}^3$, and verify that $|\mathbf{u}|^2 = u^1 u_1 + u^2 u_2 + u^3 u_3$.

2. If $\mathbf{a}, \mathbf{b}$ are vectors in the xy plane, $\mathbf{a} \times \mathbf{b} = \lambda \mathbf{k}$. Prove that the set reciprocal to

$$\mathbf{a}, \mathbf{b}, \mathbf{k} \text{ is } \frac{\mathbf{b} \times \mathbf{k}}{\lambda}, \frac{\mathbf{k} \times \mathbf{a}}{\lambda}, \mathbf{k}.$$

3. If $\mathbf{e}_1, \mathbf{e}_2, \mathbf{e}_3$ is a set of mutually orthogonal vectors, show that the reciprocal set is $\mathbf{e}_1/|\mathbf{e}_1|^2, \mathbf{e}_2/|\mathbf{e}_2|^2, \mathbf{e}_3/|\mathbf{e}_3|^2$.

4. If the sets $\mathbf{e}_1, \mathbf{e}_2, \mathbf{e}_3$ and $\mathbf{e}^1, \mathbf{e}^2, \mathbf{e}^3$ are reciprocal, show that the following sets are also:

(i) $\alpha \mathbf{e}_1, \beta \mathbf{e}_2, \gamma \mathbf{e}_3$ and $\mathbf{e}^1/\alpha, \mathbf{e}^2/\beta, \mathbf{e}^3/\gamma$;

(ii) $\mathbf{e}_2 \times \mathbf{e}_3, \mathbf{e}_3 \times \mathbf{e}_1, \mathbf{e}_1 \times \mathbf{e}_2$ and $\mathbf{e}^2 \times \mathbf{e}^3, \mathbf{e}^3 \times \mathbf{e}^1, \mathbf{e}^1 \times \mathbf{e}^2$.

5. Find the set reciprocal to $\mathbf{a}, \mathbf{b}, \mathbf{a} \times \mathbf{b}$.

6. Solve the equations for $\mathbf{r}$ if $[\mathbf{abc}] \neq 0$:

$$\mathbf{r} \cdot \mathbf{a} = \alpha, \qquad \mathbf{r} \cdot \mathbf{b} = \beta, \qquad \mathbf{r} \cdot \mathbf{c} = \gamma.$$

16. General Bases. With a general basis $\mathbf{e}_1, \mathbf{e}_2, \mathbf{e}_3$, it is convenient to express vectors in two forms:

(1)
(2)
$$\mathbf{u} = \begin{cases} u^1 \mathbf{e}_1 + u^2 \mathbf{e}_2 + u^3 \mathbf{e}_3 = [u^1, u^2, u^3] \\ u_1 \mathbf{e}^1 + u_2 \mathbf{e}^2 + u_3 \mathbf{e}^3 = [u_1, u_2, u_3]. \end{cases}$$

To add such vectors or multiply them by numbers, we have

(3) $$\lambda \mathbf{u} = [\lambda u^1, \lambda u^2, \lambda u^3],$$

(4) $$\mathbf{u} + \mathbf{v} = [u^1 + v^1, u^2 + v^2, u^3 + v^3],$$

just as in §8.

In order to retain the simplicity of the formula (10.13) for $\mathbf{u} \cdot \mathbf{v}$, we must refer the vectors to different bases that are reciprocal. Thus, if we expand

$$\mathbf{u} \cdot \mathbf{v} = \begin{cases} (u^1\mathbf{e}_1 + u^2\mathbf{e}_2 + u^3\mathbf{e}_3) \cdot (v_1\mathbf{e}^1 + v_2\mathbf{e}^2 + v_3\mathbf{e}^3) \\ (u_1\mathbf{e}^1 + u_2\mathbf{e}^2 + u_3\mathbf{e}^3) \cdot (v^1\mathbf{e}_1 + v^2\mathbf{e}_2 + v^3\mathbf{e}_3) \end{cases}$$

and use the relations $\mathbf{e}_i \cdot \mathbf{e}^j = \delta_i^j$, we find

$$(5) \qquad \mathbf{u} \cdot \mathbf{v} = \begin{cases} u^1v_1 + u^2v_2 + u^3v_3 \\ u_1v^1 + u_2v^2 + u_3v^3. \end{cases}$$

In computing $\mathbf{u} \times \mathbf{v}$, we refer both vectors to the same basis. Taking $\mathbf{e}^1$, $\mathbf{e}^2$, $\mathbf{e}^3$ as basis, we have

$$\mathbf{u} \times \mathbf{v} = (u_1\mathbf{e}^1 + u_2\mathbf{e}^2 + u_3\mathbf{e}^3) \times (v_1\mathbf{e}^1 + v_2\mathbf{e}^2 + v_3\mathbf{e}^3)$$

$$= \begin{vmatrix} u_2 & u_3 \\ v_2 & v_3 \end{vmatrix} \mathbf{e}^2 \times \mathbf{e}^3 + \begin{vmatrix} u_3 & u_1 \\ v_3 & v_1 \end{vmatrix} \mathbf{e}^3 \times \mathbf{e}^1 + \begin{vmatrix} u_1 & u_2 \\ v_1 & v_2 \end{vmatrix} \mathbf{e}^1 \times \mathbf{e}^2.$$

Equations (15.5) now give

$$\mathbf{e}^2 \times \mathbf{e}^3 = \frac{\mathbf{e}_1}{[\mathbf{e}_1\mathbf{e}_2\mathbf{e}_3]}, \qquad \mathbf{e}^3 \times \mathbf{e}^1 = \frac{\mathbf{e}_2}{[\mathbf{e}_1\mathbf{e}_2\mathbf{e}_3]}, \qquad \mathbf{e}^1 \times \mathbf{e}^2 = \frac{\mathbf{e}_3}{[\mathbf{e}_1\mathbf{e}_2\mathbf{e}_3]}.$$

With these values $\mathbf{u} \times \mathbf{v}$ assumes the compact determinant form

$$(6) \qquad \mathbf{u} \times \mathbf{v} = \frac{1}{[\mathbf{e}_1\mathbf{e}_2\mathbf{e}_3]} \begin{vmatrix} \mathbf{e}_1 & \mathbf{e}_2 & \mathbf{e}_3 \\ u_1 & u_2 & u_3 \\ v_1 & v_2 & v_3 \end{vmatrix}$$

analogous to (11.9).

If we dot-multiply (6) by $\mathbf{w}$ and note that $\mathbf{w} \cdot \mathbf{e}_i = w_i$, we obtain a determinant on the right with w_1, w_2, w_3 in the first row. This can also be written

$$(7) \qquad \mathbf{u} \times \mathbf{v} \cdot \mathbf{w} = \frac{1}{[\mathbf{e}_1\mathbf{e}_2\mathbf{e}_3]} \begin{vmatrix} u_1 & u_2 & u_3 \\ v_1 & v_2 & v_3 \\ w_1 & w_2 & w_3 \end{vmatrix}$$

analogous to (13.6).

When $\mathbf{u}$, $\mathbf{v}$, $\mathbf{w}$ are referred to the basis $\mathbf{e}_1$, $\mathbf{e}_2$, $\mathbf{e}_3$, formulas (6) and (7) have precisely the same form with *upper* indices. With the self-reciprocal basis $\mathbf{i}$, $\mathbf{j}$, $\mathbf{k}$, $[\mathbf{ijk}] = 1$, and we obtain our previous results.

If we refer **u**, **v**, **w** to the basis **a**, **b**, **c**, we have

$$u_1 = \mathbf{u} \cdot \mathbf{a}, \qquad u_2 = \mathbf{u} \cdot \mathbf{b}, \qquad u_3 = \mathbf{u} \cdot \mathbf{c},$$

etc., and (7) yields the formula

$$(8) \qquad [\mathbf{uvw}][\mathbf{abc}] = \begin{vmatrix} \mathbf{u} \cdot \mathbf{a} & \mathbf{u} \cdot \mathbf{b} & \mathbf{u} \cdot \mathbf{c} \\ \mathbf{v} \cdot \mathbf{a} & \mathbf{v} \cdot \mathbf{b} & \mathbf{v} \cdot \mathbf{c} \\ \mathbf{w} \cdot \mathbf{a} & \mathbf{w} \cdot \mathbf{b} & \mathbf{w} \cdot \mathbf{c} \end{vmatrix}.$$

If we refer **a**, **b**, **c** and **u**, **v**, **w** to the basis **i**, **j**, **k**, the left member of (8) becomes a product of determinants:

$$\begin{vmatrix} u_1 & u_2 & u_3 \\ v_1 & v_2 & v_3 \\ w_1 & w_2 & w_3 \end{vmatrix} \begin{vmatrix} a_1 & a_2 & a_3 \\ b_1 & b_2 & b_3 \\ c_1 & c_2 & c_3 \end{vmatrix},$$

and (8) is equivalent to the "row-row" rule for multiplying determinants.

17. Equations of Line and Plane. A straight line through the point R_1 and parallel to the vector **a** contains only the points R for which $\overrightarrow{R_1R}$ is parallel to **a**. Therefore its equation is $(\mathbf{r} - \mathbf{r}_1) \times \mathbf{a} = \mathbf{0}$, or, on writing $\mathbf{r}_1 \times \mathbf{a} = \mathbf{a}_O$,

$$(1) \qquad \mathbf{r} \times \mathbf{a} = \mathbf{a}_O.$$

The vectors **a**, $\mathbf{a}_O$ must satisfy the relation

$$(2) \qquad \mathbf{a} \cdot \mathbf{a}_O = 0.$$

Since they determine the line, $(\mathbf{a}, \mathbf{a}_O)$ are called coordinates of the line—its *Plücker coordinates*. When the origin is shifted from O to Q, $\mathbf{a}_O$ changes from

$$\mathbf{a}_O = \overrightarrow{OR_1} \times \mathbf{a} \quad \text{to} \quad \mathbf{a}_Q = \overrightarrow{QR_1} \times \mathbf{a};$$

and, since $\overrightarrow{QR_1} = \overrightarrow{OR_1} - \overrightarrow{OQ}$, we obtain the *shift formula*

$$(3) \qquad \mathbf{a}_Q = \mathbf{a}_O - \overrightarrow{OQ} \times \mathbf{a}.$$

The Plücker coordinates are *homogeneous*; that is, $(\lambda\mathbf{a}, \lambda\mathbf{a}_O)$ determines the same line as $(\mathbf{a}, \mathbf{a}_O)$, for equation (1) is unaltered. Thus a line is given by the ratios of six numbers (the components of **a** and $\mathbf{a}_O$) connected by a relation $(\mathbf{a} \cdot \mathbf{a}_O = 0)$ and therefore depends on *four* independent numbers. This is often expressed by saying: *There are ∞^4 lines in space.*

A plane through the point R_1 and perpendicular to the vector $\mathbf{a}$ contains only the points R for which $\overrightarrow{R_1R}$ is perpendicular to $\mathbf{a}$. Therefore its equation is $(\mathbf{r} - \mathbf{r}_1) \cdot \mathbf{a} = 0$; or, on writing $\mathbf{r}_1 \cdot \mathbf{a} = \alpha_O$,

$$(4) \qquad \mathbf{r} \cdot \mathbf{a} = \alpha_O.$$

Since $\mathbf{a}$ and α_O determine the plane, $(\mathbf{a}, \alpha_O)$ are called coordinates of the plane. When the origin is shifted from O to Q, α_O changes from

$$\alpha_O = \overrightarrow{OR_1} \cdot \mathbf{a} \quad \text{to} \quad \alpha_Q = \overrightarrow{QR_1} \cdot \mathbf{a};$$

and, since $\overrightarrow{QR_1} = \overrightarrow{OR_1} - \overrightarrow{OQ}$, we obtain the *shift formula*,

$$(5) \qquad \alpha_Q = \alpha_O - \overrightarrow{OQ} \cdot \mathbf{a}.$$

These coordinates are also homogeneous for $(\lambda\mathbf{a}, \lambda\alpha_O)$ determines the same plane as $(\mathbf{a}, \alpha_O)$, for equation (4) is unaltered. Thus, a plane is given by the ratios of four numbers (the components of $\mathbf{a}$ and α_O) and therefore depends on *three* independent numbers. *There are ∞^3 planes in space.*

A point R given by its position vector $\mathbf{r} = \overrightarrow{OR}$. If we write $\mathbf{r} = \mathbf{a}_O/\alpha$, we may regard $(\alpha, \mathbf{a}_O)$ as the homogeneous coordinates of a point whose "equation" is

$$(6) \qquad \alpha\mathbf{r} = \mathbf{a}_O.$$

When the origin is shifted from O to Q, $\mathbf{a}_O$ changes from

$$\mathbf{a}_O = \alpha \, \overrightarrow{OR} \quad \text{to} \quad \mathbf{a}_Q = \alpha \, \overrightarrow{QR};$$

and, since $\overrightarrow{QR} = \overrightarrow{OR} - \overrightarrow{OQ}$, we obtain a shift formula

$$(7) \qquad \mathbf{a}_Q = \mathbf{a}_O - \alpha \overrightarrow{OQ}$$

analogous to (3) and (5). The point coordinates $(\alpha, \mathbf{a}_O)$ are also homogeneous since $(\lambda\alpha, \lambda\mathbf{a}_O)$ represents the same point. Thus a point in space depends on *three* independent numbers. *There are ∞^3 points in space.*

In the homogeneous coordinates for a

$$\text{Point } (\alpha, \mathbf{a}_O), \qquad \text{Line } (\mathbf{a}, \mathbf{a}_O), \qquad \text{Plane } (\mathbf{a}, \alpha_O),$$

the first cannot vanish, and the second (with subscript O) depends upon the choice of origin. A change of origin $O \rightarrow Q$ entails the shift formulas

$$(8) \quad \mathbf{a}_Q = \mathbf{a}_O - \overrightarrow{OQ}\,\alpha, \qquad \mathbf{a}_Q = \mathbf{a}_O - \overrightarrow{OQ} \times \mathbf{a}, \qquad \alpha_Q = \alpha_O - \overrightarrow{OQ} \cdot \mathbf{a}$$

which have the same general form.

The point, line, and plane,

(9) $$\mathbf{r}\alpha = \mathbf{a}_O, \qquad \mathbf{r} \times \mathbf{a} = \mathbf{a}_O, \qquad \mathbf{r} \cdot \mathbf{a} = \alpha_O,$$

are at the distances

(10) $$d_O = \frac{|\mathbf{a}_O|}{|\alpha|}, \qquad \frac{|\mathbf{a}_O|}{|\mathbf{a}|}, \qquad \frac{|\alpha_O|}{|\mathbf{a}|}$$

from the origin O.   The first is obvious, and the others are easily proved. Thus, if $\mathbf{p}$ is the perpendicular vector from O to the line,

$$\mathbf{p} \times \mathbf{a} = \mathbf{a}_O, \qquad \mathbf{p} \cdot \mathbf{a} = 0;$$

hence

$$\mathbf{a} \times (\mathbf{p} \times \mathbf{a}) = (\mathbf{a} \cdot \mathbf{a})\mathbf{p} - (\mathbf{a} \cdot \mathbf{p})\mathbf{a} = \mathbf{a} \times \mathbf{a}_O,$$

$$\mathbf{p} = \frac{\mathbf{a} \times \mathbf{a}_O}{\mathbf{a} \cdot \mathbf{a}}, \qquad |\mathbf{p}| = \frac{|\mathbf{a}_O|}{|\mathbf{a}|}.$$

To find the distances from a point Q, change O to Q in (10) and use the shift formulas (8).   Thus, if $\overrightarrow{OQ} = \mathbf{q}$,

(11) $$d_Q = \frac{|\mathbf{a}_O - \mathbf{q}\alpha|}{|\alpha|}, \qquad \frac{|\mathbf{a}_O - \mathbf{q} \times \mathbf{a}|}{|\mathbf{a}|}, \qquad \frac{|\alpha_O - \mathbf{q} \cdot \mathbf{a}|}{|\mathbf{a}|}.$$

Example 1.   *Two lines* $(\mathbf{a}, \mathbf{a}_O)$, $(\mathbf{b}, \mathbf{b}_O)$ *are coplanar when and only when*

(12) $$\mathbf{a} \cdot \mathbf{b}_O + \mathbf{b} \cdot \mathbf{a}_O = 0.$$

Proof.   If R_1, R_2 are points on $(\mathbf{a}, \mathbf{a}_O)$, $(\mathbf{b}, \mathbf{b}_O)$, the lines are coplanar when and only when the vectors $\mathbf{r}_1 - \mathbf{r}_2$, $\mathbf{a}$, $\mathbf{b}$ are coplanar: that is, when

$$(\mathbf{r}_1 - \mathbf{r}_2) \cdot \mathbf{a} \times \mathbf{b} = \mathbf{r}_1 \times \mathbf{a} \cdot \mathbf{b} + \mathbf{r}_2 \times \mathbf{b} \cdot \mathbf{a} = \mathbf{a}_O \cdot \mathbf{b} + \mathbf{b}_O \cdot \mathbf{a} = 0.$$

Example 2.   *The shortest distance between the nonparallel lines* $(\mathbf{a}, \mathbf{a}_O)$, $(\mathbf{b}, \mathbf{b}_O)$ *is*

(13) $$d = \frac{|\mathbf{a} \cdot \mathbf{b}_O + \mathbf{b} \cdot \mathbf{a}_O|}{|\mathbf{a} \times \mathbf{b}|}.$$

Proof.   If R_1, R_2 are points on the lines $(\mathbf{a}, \mathbf{a}_O)$, $(\mathbf{b}, \mathbf{b}_O)$, d has the same numerical value as the component of $\overrightarrow{R_2 R_1}$ on their common normal $\mathbf{a} \times \mathbf{b}$, namely

$$(\mathbf{r}_1 - \mathbf{r}_2) \cdot \frac{\mathbf{a} \times \mathbf{b}}{|\mathbf{a} \times \mathbf{b}|} = \frac{\mathbf{r}_1 \times \mathbf{a} \cdot \mathbf{b} + \mathbf{r}_2 \times \mathbf{b} \cdot \mathbf{a}}{|\mathbf{a} \times \mathbf{b}|} = \frac{\mathbf{a}_O \cdot \mathbf{b} + \mathbf{b}_O \cdot \mathbf{a}}{|\mathbf{a} \times \mathbf{b}|}.$$

PROBLEMS

1. Show that the line AB has the coordinates $(\mathbf{b} - \mathbf{a}, \mathbf{a} \times \mathbf{b})$.
2. Show that the plane ABC has the coordinates $(\mathbf{a} \times \mathbf{b} + \mathbf{b} \times \mathbf{c} + \mathbf{c} \times \mathbf{a}, [\mathbf{abc}])$.
3. If the lines $(\mathbf{a}, \mathbf{a}_O)$ and $(\mathbf{b}, \mathbf{b}_O)$ are coplanar, show that they meet in the point

$$\mathbf{r} = \frac{\mathbf{a}_O \times \mathbf{b}_O}{\mathbf{a}_O \cdot \mathbf{b}} \quad \text{if} \quad \mathbf{a}_O \cdot \mathbf{b} \neq 0.$$

4. Show that the lines AA' and BB' are coplanar, and find their point of intersection, given

$$A(4, 5, 1), \quad A'(3, 9, 4); \qquad B(-4, 4, 4), \quad B'(0, -1, -1).$$

5. Show that the nonparallel planes $(\mathbf{a}, \alpha_0)$, $(\mathbf{b}, \beta_0)$ intersect in the line $(\mathbf{a} \times \mathbf{b}, \beta_0\mathbf{a} - \alpha_0\mathbf{b})$.

6. Show that the line $(\mathbf{a}, \mathbf{a}_0)$ cuts the plane $(\mathbf{b}, \beta_0)$ in the point

$$\mathbf{r} = \frac{\beta_0\mathbf{a} + \mathbf{b} \times \mathbf{a}_0}{\mathbf{a} \cdot \mathbf{b}} \quad \text{if} \quad \mathbf{a} \cdot \mathbf{b} \neq 0.$$

[Solve $\mathbf{r} \times \mathbf{a} = \mathbf{a}_0, \mathbf{r} \cdot \mathbf{b} = \beta_0$ for $\mathbf{r}$.]

7. If the lines $(\mathbf{a}, \mathbf{a}_0)$ and $(\mathbf{b}, \mathbf{b}_0)$ are parallel and $\mathbf{b} = \mathbf{a}$, show that their distance apart is $|\mathbf{b}_0 - \mathbf{a}_0|/|\mathbf{a}|$.

8. Find the point of intersection of the three planes

$$\mathbf{r} \cdot \mathbf{a} = \alpha_0, \qquad \mathbf{r} \cdot \mathbf{b} = \beta_0, \qquad \mathbf{r} \cdot \mathbf{c} = \gamma_0 \quad \text{if} \quad [\mathbf{abc}] \neq 0.$$

[Cf. Prob. 15.6.]

9. Show that the line $(\mathbf{a}, \mathbf{a}_0)$ lies in the plane $(\mathbf{b}, \beta_0)$ when and only when

$$\beta_0\mathbf{a} - \mathbf{a}_0 \times \mathbf{b} = 0.$$

[Eliminate $\mathbf{r}$ from $\mathbf{r} \times \mathbf{a} = \mathbf{a}_0, \mathbf{r} \cdot \mathbf{b} = \beta_0$ when $\mathbf{a} \cdot \mathbf{b} = 0$.]

10. If the three *points* $(\alpha, \mathbf{a}_0)$, $(\beta, \mathbf{b}_0)$, $(\gamma, \mathbf{c}_0)$ lie on a line, Theorem 5.1 states that there are three numbers x, y, z such that

$$x\frac{\mathbf{a}_0}{\alpha} + y\frac{\mathbf{b}_0}{\beta} + z\frac{\mathbf{c}_0}{\gamma} = 0, \qquad x + y + z = 0.$$

If three *planes* $(\mathbf{a}, \alpha_0)$, $(\mathbf{b}, \beta_0)$, $(\mathbf{c}, \gamma_0)$ pass through a line, is it true that there are three numbers x, y, z such that

$$x\frac{\mathbf{a}}{\alpha_0} + y\frac{\mathbf{b}}{\beta_0} + z\frac{\mathbf{c}}{\gamma_0} = 0, \qquad x + y + z = 0?$$

18. Summary of Vector Algebra.

Sum: $\mathbf{a} + \mathbf{b}$ by triangle construction.

$$\mathbf{a} + \mathbf{b} = \mathbf{b} + \mathbf{a}; \qquad (\mathbf{a} + \mathbf{b}) + \mathbf{c} = \mathbf{a} + (\mathbf{b} + \mathbf{c}).$$

$$\mathbf{a} + \mathbf{b} = 0 \quad \rightarrow \quad \mathbf{b} = -\mathbf{a}.$$

Difference: $\mathbf{a} - \mathbf{b} = \mathbf{a} + (-\mathbf{b})$.

Numerical Factor: If $\lambda > 0$, $\pm\,\lambda\,\mathbf{a}$ has $\begin{cases} \text{length } \lambda\,|\mathbf{a}| \\ \text{direction } \pm\mathbf{a}. \end{cases}$

$$\alpha(\beta\mathbf{a}) = (\alpha\beta)\mathbf{a}, \qquad (\alpha + \beta)\mathbf{a} = \alpha\mathbf{a} + \beta\mathbf{a};$$

$$\lambda(\mathbf{a} + \mathbf{b}) = \lambda\mathbf{a} + \lambda\mathbf{b}.$$

Dot Product: $\mathbf{a} \cdot \mathbf{b} = |\mathbf{a}|\,|\mathbf{b}| \cos(\mathbf{a}, \mathbf{b})$.

$$\mathbf{a} \cdot \mathbf{b} = \mathbf{b} \cdot \mathbf{a}; \qquad \mathbf{a} \cdot (\mathbf{b} + \mathbf{c}) = \mathbf{a} \cdot \mathbf{b} + \mathbf{a} \cdot \mathbf{c};$$

$$\mathbf{a} \cdot \mathbf{b} = 0 \quad \rightarrow \quad \mathbf{a} \perp \mathbf{b} \quad \text{if} \neq 0.$$

Cross Product: $\mathbf{a} \times \mathbf{b} = |\mathbf{a}|\,|\mathbf{b}|\,\sin(\mathbf{a}, \mathbf{b})\mathbf{e}$,

$$|\mathbf{e}| = 1, \qquad \mathbf{e} \perp \mathbf{a} \text{ and } \mathbf{b}, \qquad \text{set } \mathbf{a}, \mathbf{b}, \mathbf{e} \text{ dextral.}$$

$$\mathbf{a} \times \mathbf{b} = -\mathbf{b} \times \mathbf{a}; \qquad \mathbf{a} \times (\mathbf{b} + \mathbf{c}) = \mathbf{a} \times \mathbf{b} + \mathbf{a} \times \mathbf{c}.$$

$$\mathbf{a} \times \mathbf{b} = 0 \qquad \longrightarrow \qquad \mathbf{a} \parallel \mathbf{b} \quad \text{if} \neq 0.$$

Triple Product: $\mathbf{a} \times (\mathbf{b} \times \mathbf{c}) = (\mathbf{a} \cdot \mathbf{c})\mathbf{b} - (\mathbf{a} \cdot \mathbf{b})\mathbf{c}$.

Box Product: $\mathbf{a} \times \mathbf{b} \cdot \mathbf{c} = \begin{cases} V, & \mathbf{a}, \mathbf{b}, \mathbf{c} \text{ dextral,} \\ -V, & \mathbf{a}, \mathbf{b}, \mathbf{c} \text{ sinistral;} \end{cases}$

$$V = \text{volume of box } \mathbf{a}, \mathbf{b}, \mathbf{c}.$$

$$[\mathbf{abc}] = \begin{cases} \mathbf{a} \times \mathbf{b} \cdot \mathbf{c} = \mathbf{b} \times \mathbf{c} \cdot \mathbf{a} = \mathbf{c} \times \mathbf{a} \cdot \mathbf{b} \\ \mathbf{a} \cdot \mathbf{b} \times \mathbf{c}. \end{cases}$$

$$[\mathbf{abc}] = 0 \qquad \longrightarrow \qquad \mathbf{a}, \mathbf{b}, \mathbf{c} \text{ coplanar if} \neq 0.$$

Reciprocal Bases: $\mathbf{e}_1, \mathbf{e}_2, \mathbf{e}_3$ and $\mathbf{e}^1, \mathbf{e}^2, \mathbf{e}^3$;

$$\mathbf{e}_i \cdot \mathbf{e}^j = \delta_i^j, \qquad [\mathbf{e}_1\mathbf{e}_2\mathbf{e}_3][\mathbf{e}^1\mathbf{e}^2\mathbf{e}^3] = 1.$$

Basis $\mathbf{i}, \mathbf{j}, \mathbf{k}$ is self-reciprocal, and $[\mathbf{ijk}] = 1$.

Components: $\mathbf{a} = \begin{cases} a^1\mathbf{e}_1 + a^2\mathbf{e}_2 + a^3\mathbf{e}_3 \\ a_1\mathbf{e}^1 + a_2\mathbf{e}^2 + a_3\mathbf{e}^3; \end{cases}$

$$a_i = \mathbf{a} \cdot \mathbf{e}_i, \qquad a^i = \mathbf{a} \cdot \mathbf{e}^i.$$

$$\mathbf{a} \cdot \mathbf{b} = a_1 b^1 + a_2 b^2 + a_3 b^3;$$

$$\mathbf{a} \times \mathbf{b} = \frac{1}{[\mathbf{e}_1\mathbf{e}_2\mathbf{e}_3]} \begin{vmatrix} \mathbf{e}_1 & \mathbf{e}_2 & \mathbf{e}_3 \\ a_1 & a_2 & a_3 \\ b_1 & b_2 & b_3 \end{vmatrix};$$

$$\mathbf{a} \times \mathbf{b} \cdot \mathbf{c} = \frac{1}{[\mathbf{e}_1\mathbf{e}_2\mathbf{e}_3]} \begin{vmatrix} a_1 & a_2 & a_3 \\ b_1 & b_2 & b_3 \\ c_1 & c_2 & c_3 \end{vmatrix}.$$

Equations in Homogeneous Coordinates:

Point $(\alpha, \mathbf{a}_O)$: $\mathbf{r}\alpha = \mathbf{a}_O$;

Line $(\mathbf{a}, \mathbf{a}_O)$: $\mathbf{r} \times \mathbf{a} = \mathbf{a}_O$, $(\mathbf{a} \cdot \mathbf{a}_O = 0)$;

Plane $(\mathbf{a}, \alpha_O)$: $\mathbf{r} \cdot \mathbf{a} = \alpha_O$.

Chapter 2 _____

Line Vectors

19. Moment of a Line Vector. A vector which is restricted to lie in definite line is called a *line vector* (§1).   Two line vectors are equal when they have the same length, direction, and line of action.

If **u** is a line vector whose line of action passes through the point R_1, the equation of the line is

(1) $$\mathbf{r} \times \mathbf{u} = \mathbf{u}_O,$$

where $\mathbf{u}_O = \overrightarrow{OR_1} \times \mathbf{u}$.

DEFINITION 1.   If R_1 is any point of **u**'s line of action, the vector

(2) $$\mathbf{u}_O = \overrightarrow{OR_1} \times \mathbf{u}$$

is called the *moment of* **u** *about the point O.*

The moment of **u** about the point Q is therefore

$$\mathbf{u}_Q = \overrightarrow{QR_1} \times \mathbf{u} = (\overrightarrow{OR_1} - \overrightarrow{OQ}) \times \mathbf{u}$$

and is given by the *shift formula*

(3) $$\mathbf{u}_Q = \mathbf{u}_O - \overrightarrow{OQ} \times \mathbf{u}.$$

We have also

(4) $$\mathbf{u}_Q \cdot \mathbf{u} = \mathbf{u}_O \cdot \mathbf{u} = 0.$$

A line vector is always perpendicular to its moment about a point.

We denote the line vector by the symbol $(\mathbf{u}, \mathbf{u}_O)$ giving the coordinates of its line of action.   Any pair of vectors $(\mathbf{u}, \mathbf{u}_O)$ such that $\mathbf{u} \neq \mathbf{0}, \mathbf{u} \cdot \mathbf{u}_O = 0$ determines uniquely a proper line vector.

46

In accordance with (1), the vector $\mathbf{u} = \mathbf{0}$ has also a zero moment $\mathbf{u}_O = \mathbf{0}$. The symbol $(\mathbf{0}, \mathbf{0})$ thus represents the zero line vector with an arbitrary line of action.

A *unit* vector $\mathbf{e}$ acting in the line $(\mathbf{e}, \mathbf{e}_O)$ is called an *axis*. Thus $(\mathbf{i}, \mathbf{0})$, $(\mathbf{j}, \mathbf{0})$, $(\mathbf{k}, \mathbf{0})$ represent the rectangular axes of coordinates.

DEFINITION 2.   If l is an axis through P with unit vector $\mathbf{e}$, the rectangular component of $\mathbf{u}_P$ on l is called the *moment of* $\mathbf{u}$ *about the axis*.

This axial moment is therefore

$$\mathrm{comp}_l\, \mathbf{u}_P = \mathbf{e} \cdot \mathbf{u}_P \tag{10.8}$$

$$= \mathbf{e} \cdot (\mathbf{u}_O - \overrightarrow{OP} \times \mathbf{u})$$

$$= \mathbf{e} \cdot \mathbf{u}_O + \mathbf{u} \cdot \overrightarrow{OP} \times \mathbf{e};$$

or, since $\overrightarrow{OP} \times \mathbf{e} = \mathbf{e}_O$,

$$\text{(5)} \qquad \text{Mom }(\mathbf{u}, \mathbf{u}_O) \text{ about } (\mathbf{e}, \mathbf{e}_O) = \mathbf{e} \cdot \mathbf{u}_O + \mathbf{u} \cdot \mathbf{e}_O,$$

a number entirely independent of the choice of P on the axis.

If d is the perpendicular distance between $(\mathbf{u}, \mathbf{u}_O)$ and the axis,

$$d = \frac{|\mathbf{e} \cdot \mathbf{u}_O + \mathbf{u} \cdot \mathbf{e}_O|}{|\mathbf{e} \times \mathbf{u}|} = \frac{|\mathbf{e} \cdot \mathbf{u}_O + \mathbf{u} \cdot \mathbf{e}_O|}{|\mathbf{u}| \sin (\mathbf{e}, \mathbf{u})} \tag{17.13}$$

Hence the numerical value of the moment (5) is

$$|\mathbf{e} \cdot \mathbf{u}_O + \mathbf{u} \cdot \mathbf{e}_O| = |\mathbf{u}|\, d \sin (\mathbf{e}, \mathbf{u}).$$

This becomes $|\mathbf{u}|d$ when $\mathbf{u}$ is perpendicular to $\mathbf{e}$.

To summarize: If the line of a vector $\mathbf{u}$ passes through Q, its moment about the point P is

$$\text{(6)} \qquad\qquad \mathbf{u}_P = \overrightarrow{PQ} \times \mathbf{u}.$$

If s is an axis through P with the unit vector $\mathbf{e}$, the moment of $\mathbf{u}$ about s is the component of $\mathbf{u}_P$ on this axis:

$$\text{(7)} \qquad\qquad \text{Mom}_s\, \mathbf{u} = \mathbf{e} \cdot \mathbf{u}_P.$$

The vector moment $\mathbf{u}_P$ *represents a synthesis of the scalar moments of* $\mathbf{u}$ *about all axes through* P. The various axial moments assume all values between $\pm|\mathbf{u}_P|$; and these extreme values correspond to axes having the direction of $\mathbf{u}_P$ and $-\mathbf{u}_P$.

Example. Consider the line vector $\mathbf{u} = [1, -1, 2]$ acting through the point $A(2, 4, -1)$. Find the moment of $\mathbf{u}$
(a)   about the point $P(3, -1, 2)$,
(b)   about an axis through P in the direction $[2, -1, 2]$.

Since $\overrightarrow{PA} = [-1, 5, -3]$, we have

$$\mathbf{u}_P = \overrightarrow{PA} \times \mathbf{u} = [-1, 5, -3] \times [1, -1, 2] = [7, -1, -4].$$

A unit vector along the axis is $\mathbf{e} = \frac{1}{3}[2, -1, 2]$; hence the moment of $\mathbf{u}$ about this axis is

$$\mathbf{e} \cdot \mathbf{u}_P = \frac{1}{3}[2, -1, 2] \cdot [7, -1, -4] = \frac{7}{3}.$$

Or we may compute

$$\mathbf{u}_O = [2, 4, -1] \times [1, -1, 2] = [7, -5, -6],$$

$$\mathbf{e}_O = [3, -1, 2] \times \frac{1}{3}[2, -1, 2] = \frac{1}{3}[0, -2, -1],$$

and use (5):

$$\mathbf{e} \cdot \mathbf{u}_O + \mathbf{u} \cdot \mathbf{e}_O = \frac{1}{3}(14 + 5 - 12) + \frac{1}{3}(2 - 2) = \frac{7}{3}.$$

PROBLEMS

1. The vector $\mathbf{f} = [2, 2, -3]$ acts through the point $A(1, -2, 1)$. Compute its moment

  (i)   about the origin $(0, 0, 0)$;
  (ii) about the coordinate axes;
  (iii) about an axis through $B(1, 3. -2)$ in the direction of the vector $[2, 2, 1]$.

2. Find the moment of the vector $\overrightarrow{PQ}$ about the points A and B and about the axis AB, given

$$P(2, 3, 0), \quad Q(-1, 2, 4); \qquad A(3, 1, -1), \quad B(5, -1, 0).$$

3. If $\mathbf{f}_1$ and $\mathbf{f}_2$ are unit forces acting at R_1 and R_2, prove that the moment of either force about the axis of the other is $(\mathbf{r}_1 - \mathbf{r}_2) \cdot \mathbf{f}_1 \times \mathbf{f}_2$.

20. Addition of Line Vectors. The sum of two line vectors $(\mathbf{u}, \mathbf{u}_O)$ and $(\mathbf{v}, \mathbf{v}_O)$ is defined by

$$(1) \qquad\qquad (\mathbf{u}, \mathbf{u}_O) + (\mathbf{v}, \mathbf{v}_O) = (\mathbf{u} + \mathbf{v}, \mathbf{u}_O + \mathbf{v}_O).$$

If $\mathbf{u} + \mathbf{v} = 0$, (1) is the zero line vector when $\mathbf{u}_O + \mathbf{v}_O = 0$. If R_1 and R_2 are points on the lines of $\mathbf{u}$ and $\mathbf{v}$,

$$\mathbf{u}_O + \mathbf{v}_O = \mathbf{r}_1 \times \mathbf{u} + \mathbf{r}_2 \times \mathbf{v} = (\mathbf{r}_1 - \mathbf{r}_2) \times \mathbf{u}.$$

Since $\mathbf{u}_O + \mathbf{v}_O = 0$ only when R_1 and R_2 lie on the line of $(\mathbf{u}, \mathbf{u}_O)$, we have

THEOREM 1. *The sum of two line vectors is zero when and only when the vectors have the same length and opposite directions and act along the same line.*

If $\mathbf{u} + \mathbf{v} \neq 0$, (1) represents a line vector only when $\mathbf{u} + \mathbf{v}$ is perpendicular to $\mathbf{u}_O + \mathbf{v}_O$ (§19); then

$$(2) \qquad\qquad (\mathbf{u} + \mathbf{v}) \cdot (\mathbf{u}_O + \mathbf{v}_O) = \mathbf{u} \cdot \mathbf{v}_O + \mathbf{v} \cdot \mathbf{u}_O = 0,$$

and $(\mathbf{u}, \mathbf{u}_O)$ and $(\mathbf{v}, \mathbf{v}_O)$ are coplanar (Ex. 17.1).   Hence we have

THEOREM 2. *The sum of two line vectors $(\mathbf{u}, \mathbf{u}_O)$, $(\mathbf{v}, \mathbf{v}_O)$ is a proper line vector when and only when $\mathbf{u} + \mathbf{v} \neq 0$ and their lines of action are coplanar.*

Assume now that $\mathbf{u} + \mathbf{v} \neq \mathbf{0}$ and the lines of action intersect at R_1. Then we may take $\mathbf{u}_O = \mathbf{r}_1 \times \mathbf{u}$, $\mathbf{v}_O = \mathbf{r}_1 \times \mathbf{v}$. Since the line of $(\mathbf{u} + \mathbf{v}, \mathbf{u}_O + \mathbf{v}_O)$ has the equation

$$\mathbf{r} \times (\mathbf{u} + \mathbf{v}) = \mathbf{u}_O + \mathbf{v}_O = \mathbf{r}_1 \times (\mathbf{u} + \mathbf{v}),$$

which is satisfied when $\mathbf{r} = \mathbf{r}_1$, the line passes through R_1. Thus we have

THEOREM 3. *If two line vectors intersect, their sum is a line vector through their point of intersection.*

The construction, shown in Fig. 20a, is aptly called the *parallelogram law.*

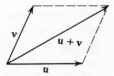

Fig. 20a. Sum of intersecting line vectors

Next assume that $\mathbf{u} + \mathbf{v} \neq \mathbf{0}$ and the lines of action are parallel; then $\mathbf{v} = \lambda\mathbf{u}$ $(\lambda \neq -1)$. If R_1, R_2 are points on the lines of $\mathbf{u}$ and $\mathbf{v}$,

$$\mathbf{u} + \mathbf{v} = (1 + \lambda)\mathbf{u}, \qquad \mathbf{u}_O + \mathbf{v}_O = (\mathbf{r}_1 + \lambda\mathbf{r}_2) \times \mathbf{u}.$$

Since the line of $(\mathbf{u} + \mathbf{v}, \mathbf{u}_O + \mathbf{v}_O)$ has the equation

$$\mathbf{r} \times (\mathbf{u} + \mathbf{v}) = \mathbf{u}_O + \mathbf{v}_O$$

or
$$(1 + \lambda)\mathbf{r} \times \mathbf{u} = (\mathbf{r}_1 + \lambda\mathbf{r}_2) \times \mathbf{u},$$

which is satisfied when

$$\mathbf{r} = \frac{\mathbf{r}_1 + \lambda\mathbf{r}_2}{1 + \lambda},$$

the line passes through the point R which divides R_1R_2 in the ratio $\lambda/1$ (5.2). We thus obtain

THEOREM 4. *If $(\mathbf{u}, \mathbf{u}_O)$, $(\mathbf{v}, \mathbf{v}_O)$ are parallel line vectors and $\mathbf{v} = \lambda\mathbf{u}$ $(\lambda \neq -1)$, the line of action of their sum is parallel to both and divides any segment from $(\mathbf{u}, \mathbf{u}_O)$ to $(\mathbf{v}, \mathbf{v}_O)$ in the ratio $\lambda/1$.*

The constructions when $\lambda = 2$ and $\lambda = -2$ are shown in Fig. 20b.

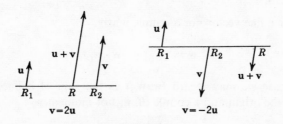

Fig. 20b. Sum of parallel line vectors.

21. Couples.   The simplest case in which the sum

(1) $$(\mathbf{u}, \mathbf{u}_O) + (\mathbf{v}, \mathbf{v}_O) = (\mathbf{u} + \mathbf{v}, \mathbf{u}_O + \mathbf{v}_O)$$

is not a line vector occurs when

(2) $$\mathbf{u} + \mathbf{v} = \mathbf{0}, \qquad \mathbf{u}_O + \mathbf{v}_O \neq \mathbf{0};$$

for a zero vector must also have a zero moment.   In this case the given vectors are *equal in magnitude, opposite in direction, and act along different parallel lines*.   Their sum has the form $(\mathbf{0}, \mathbf{m} \neq \mathbf{0})$; and the line vectors are said to form a *couple of moment* **m**.

If the moments $\mathbf{u}_O$, $\mathbf{v}_O$ are referred to another point A, the moment of the couple is not changed; for, from (19.3),

$$\mathbf{u}_A + \mathbf{v}_A = \mathbf{u}_O + \mathbf{v}_O - \overrightarrow{OA} \times (\mathbf{u} + \mathbf{v}) = \mathbf{u}_O + \mathbf{v}_O.$$

The moment of a couple is independent of the point about which moments are taken.

If $\mathbf{u} + \mathbf{v} = \mathbf{0}$, all pairs of line vectors $(\mathbf{u}, \mathbf{u}_O)$, $(\mathbf{v}, \mathbf{v}_O)$ which have the same sum $(\mathbf{0}, \mathbf{u}_O + \mathbf{v}_O)$ are regarded as equivalent couples of moment $\mathbf{m} = \mathbf{u}_O + \mathbf{v}_O$.   Their moment may be computed about any point.   Thus, if $\overrightarrow{AB}$, $\overrightarrow{CD}$ form a couple, $ABCD$ is a parallelogram (Fig. 21); the moment

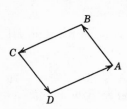

Fig. 21. Equivalent couples.

of the couple (about D) is $\overrightarrow{DA} \times \overrightarrow{AB}$ and equals the vector area of $ABCD$ (11.10).   The couple $\overrightarrow{BC}$, $\overrightarrow{DA}$ has the same moment $\overrightarrow{BA} \times \overrightarrow{DA}$ (about B).

Thus $\overrightarrow{AB}$, $\overrightarrow{CD}$ and $\overrightarrow{BC}$, $\overrightarrow{DA}$ are equivalent couples.   The sum

$$(\mathbf{u}, \mathbf{u}_O) + (\mathbf{v}, \mathbf{v}_O) = (\mathbf{w}, \mathbf{w}_O)$$

is neither a line vector nor a couple when

(3) $$\mathbf{w} \neq \mathbf{0}, \qquad \mathbf{w} \cdot \mathbf{w}_O \neq 0.$$

In this case we may regard $(\mathbf{w}, \mathbf{w}_O)$ as the sum of a line vector $(\mathbf{w}, \mathbf{0})$ through the origin and a couple $(\mathbf{0}, \mathbf{w}_O)$ of moment $\mathbf{w}_O$:

(4) $$(\mathbf{w}, \mathbf{w}_O) = (\mathbf{w}, \mathbf{0}) + (\mathbf{0}, \mathbf{w}_O).$$

The symbol $(\mathbf{w}, \mathbf{w}_O)$ now represents a new entity called a *motor* which includes the line vector and couple as special cases.†

Example. Consider the line vectors $\overrightarrow{AB}, \overrightarrow{BC}, \overrightarrow{CA}$ forming the triangle ABC. Their vector sum is zero; and their moment sum, computed about A, is

$$\overrightarrow{AB} \times \overrightarrow{BC} = (\mathbf{b} - \mathbf{a}) \times (\mathbf{c} - \mathbf{b}) = \mathbf{a} \times \mathbf{b} + \mathbf{b} \times \mathbf{c} + \mathbf{c} \times \mathbf{a}.$$

Thus the three line vectors $\overrightarrow{AB}, \overrightarrow{BC}, \overrightarrow{CA}$ are equivalent to a couple whose moment is twice the vector area of the triangle ABC.

PROBLEMS

Warning: Line vectors must be added in accordance with §20. To emphasize this point we use $\equiv$ to denote equality of line vectors when their moments are omitted.

1. If $\overrightarrow{AB}, \overrightarrow{BC}, \overrightarrow{CA}$ are line vectors and

$$\overrightarrow{AB} + \overrightarrow{BC} + \overrightarrow{CA} \equiv 0.$$

prove that the points A, B, C are collinear.

2. If A, B, C, D are the vertices of a quadrilateral in circuital order and P, Q are the mid-points of the diagonals AC, BD, prove that the line vectors

$$\overrightarrow{AB} + \overrightarrow{AD} + \overrightarrow{CB} + \overrightarrow{CD} \equiv 4\,\overrightarrow{PQ}.$$

3. In a triangle ABC, three forces of magnitude AB, BC, CA are directed along the inward normals to these sides at their mid-points. Show that they form a system in equilibrium.

[The force $\mathbf{k} \times (\mathbf{b} - \mathbf{a})$ acts at the point $\frac{1}{2}(\mathbf{a} + \mathbf{b})$.]

4. Generalize the result of Prob. 3 to any plane polygon by dissecting it into triangles.

5. $ABCD$ are the vertices of a parallelogram taken in circuital order. Prove that the sum of the line vectors

(*a*)
$$\overrightarrow{AB} + \overrightarrow{BD} + \overrightarrow{DC} + \overrightarrow{CA} \equiv 0;$$

(*b*)
$$\overrightarrow{AB} + \overrightarrow{CD} + \overrightarrow{BD} + \overrightarrow{CA} \equiv 2\,\overrightarrow{CD}.$$

6. If A, B, C, D are vertices of a plane quadrilateral taken in circuital order, prove that the line vectors $\overrightarrow{AB}, \overrightarrow{BC}, \overrightarrow{CD}, \overrightarrow{DA}$ are equivalent to a couple whose moment is twice the vector area of the quadrilateral.

Generalize this result.

† See Louis Brand, *Vector and Tensor Analysis*, Wiley, 1947, Chapter II, for a systematic account of the algebra of motors.

For the application of motors to line geometry consult

W. Blaschke, *Vorlesungen uber Differential Geometrie*, Springer, Bd. 1, 1924, Kap. 7; and

E. A. Weiss, *Einführung in die Linien-geometrie und Kinematik*, Teubner, 1935, p. 85.

A comprehensive account of the application of motor calculus to mechanics is given in the fundamental paper of

R. von Mises, "Motorrechnung, ein neues Hilfsmittel der Mechanik," *Z. angew. Math. u. Mech.*, Bd. 4, 1924.

7. If A, B, C, D are vertices of a skew quadrilateral and $PQRS$ are the mid-points of its sides taken in order, prove that the line vectors $\overrightarrow{AB}$, $\overrightarrow{BC}$, $\overrightarrow{CD}$, $\overrightarrow{DA}$ are equivalent to four times the couple formed by $\overrightarrow{PQ}$ and $\overrightarrow{RS}$.

8. The forces $X\mathbf{i}$, $Y\mathbf{j}$, $Z\mathbf{k}$ act through the points $(0, 0, c)$, $(a, 0, 0)$, $(0, b, 0)$ respectively. Show that they reduce to a single force if $a/X + b/Y + c/Z = 0$.

9. If the forces $\mathbf{i}$, $2\mathbf{j}$, $-\mathbf{k}$ acting at $(0, 0, 2)$, $(1, 0, 0)$, $(0, 2, 0)$ respectively have a resultant, find its magnitude and axis.

10. The parallel forces $\lambda_i\mathbf{e}$ act through the points R_i $(i = 1, 2, \cdots, n)$. Show that their resultant is as follows:

(i) If $\Sigma\,\lambda_i \neq 0$, the system reduces to a single force acting through the centroid of the weighted points $\lambda_i R_i$.

(ii) If $\Sigma\,\lambda_i = 0$, the system reduces to zero or a couple according as the set of weighted points $\lambda_i R_i$ is self-centroidal or not (§7).

11. The *plane* system of forces $\mathbf{F}_i$ acting through the points R_i has the resultant $\mathbf{F} = \Sigma\mathbf{F}_i \neq \mathbf{0}$. When all the forces $\mathbf{F}_i$ are revolved about these points through the same angle θ, show that their resultant $\mathbf{F}$ also revolves through θ about a point $\bar{R}$ (the *astatic center*) given by

$$\bar{\mathbf{r}} = \frac{\mathbf{F} \times \mathbf{M} + (\Sigma\,\mathbf{r}_i \cdot \mathbf{F}_i)\mathbf{F}}{\mathbf{F} \cdot \mathbf{F}} \quad \text{where} \quad \mathbf{M} = \Sigma\,\mathbf{r}_i \times \mathbf{F}_i.$$

When the forces are parallel ($\mathbf{F}_i = \lambda_i\mathbf{e}$) show that the astatic center is the centroid of the weighted points $\lambda_i R_i$.

22. Coplanar Line Vectors.
If the set of line vectors $(\mathbf{f}^i, \mathbf{f}_O^i)$ is *coplanar*, we have, from (17.2) and (17.12),

$$\mathbf{f}^i \cdot \mathbf{f}_O^i = 0, \qquad \mathbf{f}^i \cdot \mathbf{f}_O^j + \mathbf{f}^j \cdot \mathbf{f}_O^i = 0.$$

Hence, if

$$\mathbf{f} = \sum \mathbf{f}^i, \qquad \mathbf{f}_O = \sum \mathbf{f}_O^i$$

give the sum or *resultant* of the set, we obtain

$$(1) \qquad\qquad\qquad\qquad \mathbf{f} \cdot \mathbf{f}_O = 0$$

on expanding $(\sum \mathbf{f}^i) \cdot (\sum \mathbf{f}_O^i)$. Therefore:

The resultant $(\mathbf{f}, \mathbf{f}_O)$ of a set of coplanar line vectors is

$$
\begin{array}{lll}
\text{a line vector} & & \mathbf{f} \neq \mathbf{0}, \\
\text{a couple} & \text{when} & \mathbf{f} = \mathbf{0}, \quad \mathbf{f}_O \neq \mathbf{0}, \\
\text{zero} & & \mathbf{f} = \mathbf{0}, \quad \mathbf{f}_O = \mathbf{0}.
\end{array}
$$

This resultant may be obtained graphically by a succession of the constructions of §20. But, when the lines of action are parallel or nearly parallel, the following construction is much more convenient.

Consider the case of three line vectors $\mathbf{f}^1$, $\mathbf{f}^2$, $\mathbf{f}^3$ acting along the lines shown in the space diagram Fig. 22a. First construct the sum

$$\mathbf{f}^1 + \mathbf{f}^2 + \mathbf{f}^3 = \mathbf{f}$$

by means of the vector polygon $ABCD$ (Fig. 22b). Select any convenient point O in the plane $ABCD$ as *pole* and draw the vectors

$$\mathbf{a} = \overrightarrow{OA}, \qquad \mathbf{b} = \overrightarrow{OB}, \qquad \mathbf{c} = \overrightarrow{OC}, \qquad \mathbf{d} = \overrightarrow{OD}.$$

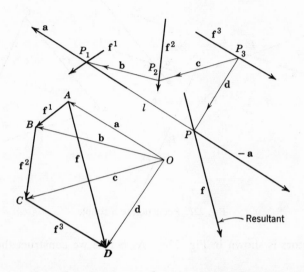

Fig. 22b. Vector polygon.   Fig. 22a. Link polygon.

Now introduce the line vectors $\mathbf{a}$ and $-\mathbf{a}$ acting along a line $l \parallel OA$ into the space diagram. The lines of action of

$$\mathbf{a} + \mathbf{f}_1 = \mathbf{b}, \qquad \mathbf{b} + \mathbf{f}_2 = \mathbf{c}, \qquad \mathbf{c} + \mathbf{f}_3 = \mathbf{d}, \qquad \mathbf{d} + (-\mathbf{a}) = \mathbf{f}$$

are drawn in turn through P_1, P_2, P_3, P parallel to $\mathbf{b}$, $\mathbf{c}$, $\mathbf{d}$, $\mathbf{f}$ in Fig. 22b. The resultant line vector

$$\begin{aligned}
\mathbf{f} &= \mathbf{d} - \mathbf{a} \\
&= \mathbf{c} + \mathbf{f}_3 - \mathbf{a} \\
&= \mathbf{b} + \mathbf{f}_2 + \mathbf{f}_3 - \mathbf{a} \\
&= \mathbf{a} + \mathbf{f}_1 + \mathbf{f}_2 + \mathbf{f}_3 - \mathbf{a} = \mathbf{f}_1 + \mathbf{f}_2 + \mathbf{f}_3
\end{aligned}$$

acts along the line through P where the lines of $\mathbf{d}$ and $-\mathbf{a}$ intersect.

The figure $PP_1P_2P_3$, whose sides are parallel to the rays OA, OB, OC, OD drawn from the pole to the vertices of the vector polygon (Fig. 22b), is called a *link* (or *funicular*) polygon. Note that the sides of the link polygon that meet on the line of $\mathbf{f}^i$ are parallel to the rays that subtend $\mathbf{f}^i$ in the vector polygon.

The construction above corresponds to the case $\sum \mathbf{f}^i \neq \mathbf{0}$. If, however, $\sum \mathbf{f}^i = \mathbf{0}$, the polygon formed by the vectors $\mathbf{f}^i$ will close ($D = A$), and the system will reduce to a couple or to zero. The construction for

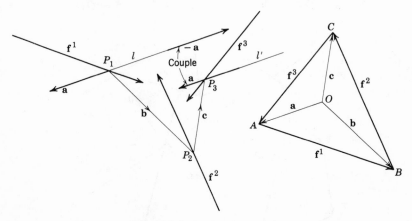

Fig. 22c. Reduction to a couple.

three vectors is shown in Fig. 22c. As before we construct the lines of action of

$$\mathbf{a} + \mathbf{f}_1 = \mathbf{b}, \qquad \mathbf{b} + \mathbf{f}_2 = \mathbf{c}, \qquad \mathbf{c} + \mathbf{f}_3 = \mathbf{d},$$

where $\mathbf{d} = \mathbf{a}$ but acts along the line l' parallel to l. The system now reduces to the *couple* $-\mathbf{a}$ in l, $\mathbf{d} = \mathbf{a}$ in l'.

If the lines l and l' had coincided, the system would have reduced to the zero line vector $(\mathbf{0}, \mathbf{0})$.

The line vectors and couples of the xy plane when written

$$(\mathbf{u}, \mathbf{u}_O) = (u_1\mathbf{i} + u_2\mathbf{j}, u_3\mathbf{k}),$$

suggest the one-to-one correspondence

(2) $$(\mathbf{u}, \mathbf{u}_O) \leftrightarrow [u_1, u_2, u_3] = \mathbf{U}$$

with the space vectors $\mathbf{U}$ drawn from the origin; thus

Line vectors $(\mathbf{u} \neq \mathbf{0}, \mathbf{u}_O) \leftrightarrow [u_1, u_2, u_3],$

Couples $(\mathbf{0}, \mathbf{u}_O \neq \mathbf{0}) \leftrightarrow [0, 0, u_3],$

Zero vectors $(\mathbf{0}, \mathbf{0}) \qquad \leftrightarrow [0, 0, 0].$

Of the space vectors localized at the origin, those lying on the z axis correspond to couples, all others to line vectors. Addition of coplanar line vectors now corresponds to the addition of free space vectors:

$$(3) \qquad (\mathbf{u}, \mathbf{u}_O) + (\mathbf{v}, \mathbf{v}_O) \leftrightarrow [u_1 + v_1, u_2 + v_2, u_3 + v_3] = \mathbf{U} + \mathbf{V}$$

All line vectors parallel to $(\mathbf{u}, \mathbf{u}_O)$ are given by $(\lambda\mathbf{u}, \lambda'\mathbf{u}_O)$; hence the corresponding space vectors lie in plane parallel to $\mathbf{u}$ through the z axis.

If the line vector $(\mathbf{u}, \mathbf{u}_O)$ passes through the point (x, y), the corresponding

$$\mathbf{U} = [u_1, u_2, xu_2 - yu_1]$$

is a space vector perpendicular to $[y, -x, 1]$; hence all line vectors through the point (x, y) correspond to space vectors $\mathbf{U}$ lying in the plane perpendicular to $[y, -x, 1]$.

We can now readily solve the following important problem:†

Express a given line vector as the sum of three coplanar line vectors acting along specified lines, not concurrent and not all parallel.

Solution. Write the given line vector $(\mathbf{u}, \mathbf{u}_O)$ in the form (2), and let the three lines given by their Plücker coordinates

$$(\mathbf{a}, \mathbf{a}_O) \leftrightarrow \mathbf{A}, \qquad (\mathbf{b}, \mathbf{b}_O) \leftrightarrow \mathbf{B}, \qquad (\mathbf{c}, \mathbf{c}_O) \leftrightarrow \mathbf{C}.$$

Since the lines are not concurrent and not all parallel, the corresponding space vectors $\mathbf{A}$, $\mathbf{B}$, $\mathbf{C}$ are not coplanar and admit a reciprocal set $\mathbf{A}'$, $\mathbf{B}'$, $\mathbf{C}'$. Now

$$\mathbf{U} = \alpha\mathbf{A} + \beta\mathbf{B} + \gamma\mathbf{C},$$

where, from (15.8), $\alpha = \mathbf{U} \cdot \mathbf{A}'$, $\beta = \mathbf{U} \cdot \mathbf{B}'$, $\gamma = \mathbf{U} \cdot \mathbf{C}'$. This equality corresponds to

$$(\mathbf{u}, \mathbf{u}_O) = \alpha(\mathbf{a}, \mathbf{a}_O) + \beta(\mathbf{b}, \mathbf{b}_O) + \gamma(\mathbf{c}, \mathbf{c}_O),$$

and the problem is solved. The solution, moreover, is unique.

Example. Resolve the force $\mathbf{f} = [1, 2]$ acting through the point $(-3, 0)$ in the xy-plane into forces acting along the lines $y = 0$, $x = 0$, $x + y = 2$.

Since $\mathbf{f}$ has the moment -6 about the z-axis, $\mathbf{F} = [1, 2, -6]$. The three lines correspond to space vectors

$$\mathbf{A} = [1, 0, 0], \qquad \mathbf{B} = [0, 1, 0]. \qquad \mathbf{C} = [-1, 1, 2].$$

† In statics this is the *problem of three forces.* For a graphical solution see Brand, *Vectorial Mechanics*, Wiley, 1930, §54.

Since $[\mathbf{ABC}] = 2$, their reciprocal set is

$$\mathbf{A}' = \tfrac{1}{2}[2, 0, 1], \qquad \mathbf{B}' = \tfrac{1}{2}[0, 2, -1], \qquad \mathbf{C}' = \tfrac{1}{2}[0, 0, 1];$$

hence

$$\alpha = \mathbf{F} \cdot \mathbf{A}' = -2, \qquad \beta = \mathbf{F} \cdot \mathbf{B}' = 5, \qquad \gamma = \mathbf{F} \cdot \mathbf{C}' = -3,$$

$$\mathbf{F} = -2\mathbf{A} + 5\mathbf{B} - 3\mathbf{C}.$$

Thus the given force $\mathbf{f}$ is equivalent to the force $-2\mathbf{i}$ along the x-axis, $5\mathbf{j}$ along the y-axis, $3\mathbf{i} - 3\mathbf{j}$ along the line $x + y = 2$. Let the reader make a graphical check.

23. Statics. The forces acting on a rigid body may be treated as line vectors and replaced by their sum.† If the forces $(\mathbf{f}^i, \mathbf{f}_O^i)$ are coplanar, there are *three* possibilities, for their sum may represent a line vector, a couple, or zero (§22). In this case the link polygon gives a simple graphical method for obtaining the resultant.

With a general distribution of forces in space there are *four* possibilities, for the sum

$$\mathbf{f} = \sum \mathbf{f}^i, \qquad \mathbf{f}_O = \sum \mathbf{f}_O^i,$$

represents

     a line vector + couple   when $\mathbf{f} \neq 0, \quad \mathbf{f} \cdot \mathbf{f}_O \neq 0,$

     a line vector   when $\mathbf{f} \neq 0, \quad \mathbf{f} \cdot \mathbf{f}_O = 0,$

     a couple   when $\mathbf{f} = 0, \qquad \mathbf{f}_O \neq 0,$

     zero   when $\mathbf{f} = 0, \qquad \mathbf{f}_O = 0.$

The rigid body is in equilibrium only in the last case:

A rigid body at rest will remain at rest when and only when the system of forces acting on it, treated as line vectors, have the zero line vector as their sum.

PROBLEMS

1. The line of action of a force $\mathbf{f} = [1, -1, 2]$ passes through the point $P(2, 4, -1)$. Find the moment of $\mathbf{f}$ about

(a)   the point $A(3, -1, 2)$;

(b)   an axis through A in the direction $[2, -1, 2]$;

(c)   about the coordinate axes.

2. The forces $\mathbf{f}_1, \mathbf{f}_2$ are equal in magnitude and act at the points P_1, P_2. Prove that the moment of $\mathbf{f}_1$ about the axis of $\mathbf{f}_2$ is equal to the moment of $\mathbf{f}_2$ about the axis of $\mathbf{f}_1$.

3. Forces $\mathbf{f}_1 = 30\mathbf{j}, \mathbf{f}_2 = -15\mathbf{j}, \mathbf{f}_3 = -10\mathbf{j}, \mathbf{f}_4 = 15\mathbf{j}$ at the points $(0, 0), (2, 0), (3, 0), (4, 0)$ on the x-axis. Find their resultant analytically and graphically.

---

† See *Vectorial Mechanics*, Chapter II, for a development of statics from four fundamental principles.

4. Forces of 1, 2, and 3 lb, acting at the vertices A, B, C, of an equilateral triangle having sides of 3 ft, are perpendicular to the sides AB, BC, CA. Each force tends to turn the triangle in the sense ABC about its center. Show that their resultant is a force of $\sqrt{3}$ lb in the direction BC and cutting AB produced 8 ft from A.

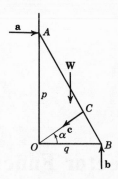

5. The base plate of a crane is bolted to the floor by four bolts at the corners $A(1, 1)$, $B(-1, 1)$, $C(-1, -1)$, $D(1, -1)$ of a 2-ft square. If the crane load of 2000 lb acts vertically downward through the point $P(0, 10)$, find the reactions on the plate exerted by the bolts.

6. A uniform rod of weight W rests on smooth planes at A and B and is supported by a cord at C (Fig. 23). Show that the normal reactions at A, B and the tension of the cord at C are given by

Fig. 23. Rod supported by a cord.

$$a = \frac{\tfrac{1}{2}qW \cos\alpha}{d}, \qquad b = \frac{W(p \cos\alpha - \tfrac{1}{2}q \sin\alpha)}{d}, \qquad c = \frac{\tfrac{1}{2}qW}{d},$$

where $d = p \cos\alpha - q \sin\alpha$.

[Resolve the load $\mathbf{F} = [0, -W, -\tfrac{1}{2}qW]$ along the *unit* line vectors

$$\mathbf{A} = [-1, 0, p], \qquad \mathbf{B} = [0, -1, -q], \qquad \mathbf{C} = [\cos\alpha, \sin\alpha, 0]$$

opposed to $\mathbf{a}$, $\mathbf{b}$, $\mathbf{c}$. Then $a = \mathbf{F} \cdot \mathbf{A}'$, etc. (§22).]

7. Solve Prob. 6 graphically when $W = 100$ lb, $p = 8$ ft, $q = 4$ ft, $\alpha = 30°$, by means of a link polygon. Use the results of Prob. 6 to check the answers.

Chapter 3

Vector Functions
of One Variable

24. Derivative of a Vector. Let $\mathbf{u}(t)$ denote a vector function of a scalar variable t over the interval $a \leq t \leq b$; that is, when t is given, $\mathbf{u}(t)$ is uniquely determined.† Then $\mathbf{u}(t)$ is said to be continuous for a value t_0 if

$$(1) \qquad\qquad \lim_{t \to t_0} \mathbf{u}(t) = \mathbf{u}(t_0).$$

The derivative of $u(t)$ is defined as

$$(2) \qquad u'(t) \frac{d\mathbf{u}}{dt} = \lim_{\Delta t \to 0} \frac{\mathbf{u}(t + \Delta t) - \mathbf{u}(t)}{\Delta t},$$

and is also denoted by $\mathbf{u}'(t)$.

If $\mathbf{u}'(t)$ exists when $t = t_0$, $\mathbf{u}(t)$ is said to be *differentiable* at t_0. Then we may write

$$\frac{\mathbf{u}(t_0 + \Delta t) - \mathbf{u}(t_0)}{\Delta t} = \mathbf{u}'(t_0) + \varepsilon$$

where $\varepsilon \to 0$ as $\Delta t \to 0$; hence

$$\mathbf{u}(t_0 + \Delta t) = \mathbf{u}(t_0) + (\mathbf{u}'(t_0) + \varepsilon)\Delta t,$$

and, as $\Delta t \to 0$, $\mathbf{u}(t_0 + \Delta t) \to \mathbf{u}(t_0)$. Therefore:

If the function $\mathbf{u}(t)$ is differentiable at t_0, it is also continuous there.

† *Function* is always used in the sense of *single-valued* function.

58

Derivatives of higher order are defined as in the calculus:

$$\frac{d^2\mathbf{u}}{dt^2} = \mathbf{u}''(t) = \frac{d\mathbf{u}'}{dt},$$

$$\frac{d^3\mathbf{u}}{dt^3} = \mathbf{u}'''(t) = \frac{d\mathbf{u}''}{dt}, \qquad \text{etc.}$$

25. Derivatives of Sums and Products. If $\mathbf{u}(t)$, $\mathbf{v}(t)$ are differentiable vector functions, and $f(t)$ a differentiable scalar function, we can readily prove that

(1) $$\frac{d\mathbf{c}}{dt} = \mathbf{0} \qquad (\mathbf{c}\ \text{const}),$$

(2) $$\frac{d}{dt}(\mathbf{u} + \mathbf{v}) = \frac{d\mathbf{u}}{dt} + \frac{d\mathbf{v}}{dt},$$

(3) $$\frac{d}{dt}(f\mathbf{u}) = f\frac{d\mathbf{u}}{dt} + \frac{df}{dt}\mathbf{u},$$

(4) $$\frac{d}{dt}(\mathbf{u}\cdot\mathbf{v}) = \mathbf{u}\cdot\frac{d\mathbf{v}}{dt} + \frac{d\mathbf{u}}{dt}\cdot\mathbf{v},$$

(5) $$\frac{d}{dt}(\mathbf{u}\times\mathbf{v}) = \mathbf{u}\times\frac{d\mathbf{v}}{dt} + \frac{d\mathbf{u}}{dt}\times\mathbf{v}.$$

Formulas (3), (4), and (5) depend essentially on the distributive law for the respective products. Since the proofs follow the same lines as in the calculus of scalars, it will suffice to prove (5):

$$\frac{d}{dt}(\mathbf{u}\times\mathbf{v}) = \lim_{\Delta t \to 0} \frac{(\mathbf{u}+\Delta\mathbf{u})\times(\mathbf{v}+\Delta\mathbf{v}) - \mathbf{u}\times\mathbf{v}}{\Delta t}$$

$$= \lim_{\Delta t \to 0}\left(\mathbf{u}\times\frac{\Delta\mathbf{v}}{\Delta t} + \frac{\Delta\mathbf{u}}{\Delta t}\times\mathbf{v} + \frac{\Delta\mathbf{u}}{\Delta t}\times\Delta\mathbf{v}\right)$$

$$= \mathbf{u}\times\frac{d\mathbf{v}}{dt} + \frac{d\mathbf{u}}{dt}\times\mathbf{v},$$

in which the *order* of the factors must be preserved.

If $\mathbf{u}(t)$ is referred to the constant basis $\mathbf{e}_1$, $\mathbf{e}_2$, $\mathbf{e}_3$

$$\mathbf{u} = u^1\mathbf{e}_1 + u^2\mathbf{e}_2 + u^3\mathbf{e}_3,$$

we have from (1) and (3)

(6) $$\frac{d\mathbf{u}}{dt} = \frac{du^1}{dt}\mathbf{e}_1 + \frac{du^2}{dt}\mathbf{e}_2 + \frac{du^3}{dt}\mathbf{e}_3.$$

The components of $d\mathbf{u}/dt$ are the derivatives of the components of $\mathbf{u}$.

THEOREM 1.   *A necessary and sufficient condition that a proper vector* **u** *have a constant length is that*

(7) $$\mathbf{u} \cdot \frac{d\mathbf{u}}{dt} = 0.$$

Proof.   Since $|\mathbf{u}|^2 = \mathbf{u} \cdot \mathbf{u}$, we have from (4)

$$\frac{d}{dt}|\mathbf{u}|^2 = 2\mathbf{u} \cdot \frac{d\mathbf{u}}{dt}.$$

Hence $|\mathbf{u}| = $ const implies (7), and conversely.

THEOREM 2.   *A necessary and sufficient condition that a proper vector* **u** *always remains parallel to fixed line is that*

(8) $$\mathbf{u} \times \frac{d\mathbf{u}}{dt} = \mathbf{0}.$$

Proof.   Let $\mathbf{u} = u(t)\mathbf{e}$, where $\mathbf{e}$ is a *unit* vector;   then

$$\mathbf{u} \times \frac{d\mathbf{u}}{dt} = u\mathbf{e} \times \left(\frac{du}{dt}\mathbf{e} + u\frac{d\mathbf{e}}{dt}\right) = u^2\mathbf{e} \times \frac{d\mathbf{e}}{dt}.$$

If **e** is constant, $d\mathbf{e}/dt = \mathbf{0}$, and the condition follows.   Conversely, since $\mathbf{u} \neq \mathbf{0}$, the condition implies that $\mathbf{e} \times (d\mathbf{e}/dt) = \mathbf{0}$;   but, since $\mathbf{e} \cdot (d\mathbf{e}/dt) = 0$ from Theorem 1, these equations are contradictory unless $d\mathbf{e}/dt = \mathbf{0}$;   that is, **e** is constant.

When **u** is a function of the scalar variable s, and s in turn a function of t, we have the familiar *chain rule* of the calculus:

(9) $$\frac{d\mathbf{u}}{dt} = \frac{d\mathbf{u}}{ds}\frac{ds}{dt}.$$

26. Curves.   *A curve is an aggregate of points whose coordinates are functions of a single variable.*   Thus the equations

(1) $$x = x(t), \qquad y = y(t), \qquad z = z(t)$$

represent a curve in space.   The variable t is called a *parameter*, and each value of the parameter within a certain range T: $a \leq t \leq b$ corresponds to a definite point $P(x, y, z)$ of the curve.   If $x(t)$, $y(t)$, $z(t)$ are continuous functions in T, the curve is said to be *continuous* in this interval.

To avoid having the curve degenerate into a point we exclude the case in which all three functions are constants.   We also restrict the interval T so that each t in $a \leq t < b$ corresponds to a different point of the curve. Then equations (1) set up a one-to-one correspondence between the points of the curve and the values of t in $a \leq t < b$. When $t = a$ and $t = b$ correspond to the same point, the curve is said to be *closed*.

A parameter value t corresponds to an *ordinary point* of a curve when the three derivatives $x'(t)$, $y'(t)$, $z'(t)$ exist and are continuous at t and at least one is not zero. An arc of a curve that consists entirely of ordinary points is said to be *smooth*.

We can make the change of parameter

$$t = \varphi(u) \quad \text{where} \quad a = \varphi(\alpha), \quad b = \varphi(\beta),$$

provided

(i) $\varphi'(u) > 0$ in $U: \alpha \leq u \leq \beta$,

(ii) $\varphi'(u)$ is continuous in U.†

Then $\varphi(u)$ is an increasing function in U, and $t = \varphi(u)$ sets up a one-to-one correspondence between the u-values in U and the t-values in T. On putting $t = \varphi(u)$ in (i), we get another set of parametric equations; and, since

$$\frac{dx}{du} = \frac{dx}{dt}\,\varphi'(u), \qquad \frac{dy}{du} = \frac{dy}{dt}\,\varphi'(u), \qquad \frac{dz}{du} = \frac{dz}{dt}\,\varphi'(u),$$

the ordinary points are the same as before.

We may combine equations (1) into the single vector equation

(2) $\mathbf{r} = x(t)\mathbf{i} + y(t)\mathbf{j} + z(t)\mathbf{k} = \mathbf{r}(t).$

Now each value to t corresponds to a point P of the curve whose position vector is $\overrightarrow{OP} = \mathbf{r}(t)$.

Example.   The equations

$$x = \cos t, \qquad y = \sin t, \qquad z = 0 \qquad (-\pi \leq t \leq \pi)$$

are parametric equations of a unit circle with origin as center. Since $t = \pm\pi$ give the same point $(-1, 0, 0)$ the curve is closed. It is obviously also continuous and smooth. If we make the change of parameter

$$t = 2 \tan^{-1} u \quad (-\infty \leq u \leq \infty), \qquad \frac{dt}{du} = \frac{2}{1 + u^2} > 0,$$

and we obtain the new parametric equations for the circle:

$$x = \frac{1 - u^2}{1 + u^2}, \qquad y = \frac{2u}{1 + u^2}, \qquad z = 0, \qquad (-\infty \leq u \leq \infty).$$

† We may replace (i) by $\varphi'(u) < 0$; then $\varphi(u)$ is a decreasing function, and the interval U becomes $\beta \leq u \leq \alpha$.

27. Tangent Vector.   If P_0 and P are neighboring points of a curve

(1) $$\mathbf{r} = \mathbf{r}(t) \qquad (a \leq t \leq b),$$

and the line P_0P tends to a limiting position as P approaches P_0 along the curve, the limiting line is called the *tangent* to the curve at P_0. Now, if

$$\overrightarrow{OP_0} = \mathbf{r}(t_0), \qquad \overrightarrow{OP} = \mathbf{r}(t),$$

$$\frac{\overrightarrow{P_0P}}{t - t_0} = \frac{\Delta\mathbf{r}}{\Delta t} = \frac{\Delta x}{\Delta t}\mathbf{i} + \frac{\Delta y}{\Delta t}\mathbf{j} + \frac{\Delta z}{\Delta t}\mathbf{k};$$

and, as $t \to t_0$, we have

(2) $$\frac{d\mathbf{r}}{dt} = \frac{dx}{dt}\mathbf{i} + \frac{dy}{dt}\mathbf{j} + \frac{dz}{dt}\mathbf{k} \neq \mathbf{0}$$

at all ordinary points of the curve;   for the derivatives on the right exist, and not all are zero.   Thus the limiting position of the line P_0P as $t \to t_0$

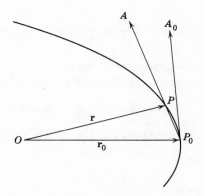

Fig. 27. Tangent vector.

is a line through P_0 parallel to $d\mathbf{r}/dt$.   Therefore $d\mathbf{r}/dt$ is a vector tangent to the curve at P_0.   If $\Delta t > 0$ in Fig. 27, $\Delta\mathbf{r}/\Delta t = \overrightarrow{P_0A}$ is a positive multiple of $\overrightarrow{P_0P}$; but, if $\Delta t < 0$, $\Delta\mathbf{r}/\Delta t$ is a negative multiple of $\overrightarrow{P_0P}$, and $\overrightarrow{P_0A}$ in the figure must be reversed.   In any case $\overrightarrow{P_0A}$ approaches a limiting vector $\overrightarrow{P_0A_0}$ which points in the direction of increasing t.

The vector $d\mathbf{r}/dt$ is a tangent vector to the curve $\mathbf{r} = \mathbf{r}(t)$ at all ordinary points and points in the direction of increasing t.

Example.   Find the equations of the tangent to the curve

$$x = 3t, \qquad y = 3t^2, \qquad z = 2t^3$$

at the point $t = 1$.

The point of tangency is $P_0(3, 3, 2)$, and the tangent vector at this point is

$$[3, 6t, 6t^2]_{t=1} = 3[1, 2, 2].$$

Every vector along the tangent line is a multiple of $[1, 2, 2]$; and, if $P(x, y, z)$ is any point on the tangent,

$$\overrightarrow{P_0P} = [x - 3, y - 3, z - 2] = \lambda[1, 2, 2].$$

Hence the equations of the tangent at $(3, 3, 2)$ are

$$\frac{x - 3}{1} = \frac{y - 3}{2} = \frac{z - 2}{2}.$$

28. Unit Tangent Vector.   It is proved in the calculus that an arc of a *smooth* curve $\mathbf{r} = \mathbf{r}(t)$ is rectifiable, and its length from $t = a$ to $t = b$ is given by†

$$ds = \sqrt{dx^2 + dy^2 + dz^2}$$

(1) $$L = \int_a^b \sqrt{x'(t)^2 + y'(t)^2 + z'(t)^2}\, dt = \int_a^b \left|\frac{d\mathbf{r}}{dt}\right| dt.$$

The arc s between points corresponding to the parameter values a and t is therefore

(2) $$s = \int_a^t \left|\frac{d\mathbf{r}}{dt}\right| dt, \qquad a \leq t \leq b,$$

and

(3) $$\frac{ds}{dt} = \left|\frac{d\mathbf{r}}{dt}\right| > 0.$$

Thus s is a continuous increasing function of t.   The same is true of the inverse function $t = \varphi(s)$, and consequently we can write the equation of the curve $\mathbf{r} = \mathbf{r}(s)$ with the arc s as parameter.

We can now prove the important

THEOREM.   *If $\mathbf{r} = \mathbf{r}(s)$ is the vector equation of a smooth curve with the arc $s = P_0P$ as parameter, then*

(4) $$\frac{d\mathbf{r}}{ds} = \mathbf{T}$$

a unit vector tangent to the curve at P and pointing in the direction of increasing arcs.

Proof.   From §27 we know that $d\mathbf{r}/ds$ is a tangent vector to the curve in the direction of increasing s; and from (3)

$$\left|\frac{d\mathbf{r}}{ds}\right| = \frac{ds}{ds} = 1.$$

† See Louis Brand, *Advanced Calculus*, Wiley, 1955, pp. 284–285.

COROLLARY. *The ratio of the chord of a smooth curve to the arc it subtends approaches 1 as the arc approaches zero.*

Proof: $|\Delta \mathbf{r}|/|\Delta s| = |\Delta \mathbf{r}/\Delta s| \to |d\mathbf{r}/ds| = 1$ as $\Delta s \to 0$.

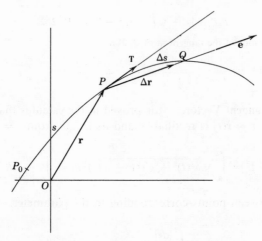

Fig. 28a. Unit tangent vector: $d\mathbf{r}/ds = \mathbf{T}$.

If we *assume* this corollary, the result (4) is evident from Fig. 28a.   For, if $\mathbf{e}$ denotes a unit vector along $\overrightarrow{PQ}$,

$$\frac{\Delta \mathbf{r}}{\Delta s} = \frac{\overrightarrow{PQ}}{\text{arc } PQ} = \frac{\overrightarrow{PQ}}{\text{chord } PQ} \frac{\text{chord } PQ}{\text{arc } PQ} = \mathbf{e} \frac{\text{chord } PQ}{\text{arc } PQ}.$$

Now let $Q \to P$; then, as $\Delta s \to 0$, $\mathbf{e} \to \mathbf{T}$ and chord/arc $\to 1$ on the right; hence $d\mathbf{r}/ds = \mathbf{T}$.

If the position vector of the curve is

$$\mathbf{r} = x\mathbf{i} + y\mathbf{j} + z\mathbf{k},$$

(5) $\dfrac{d\mathbf{r}}{ds} = \mathbf{T} = \dfrac{dx}{ds}\mathbf{i} + \dfrac{dy}{ds}\mathbf{j} + \dfrac{dz}{ds}\mathbf{k}.$

On dot-multiplying (5) by $\mathbf{i}$, $\mathbf{j}$, $\mathbf{k}$ in turn, we get

(6) $\dfrac{dx}{ds} = \cos (\mathbf{i}, \mathbf{T}),$ $\dfrac{dy}{ds} = \cos (\mathbf{j}, \mathbf{T}),$ $\dfrac{dz}{ds} = \cos (\mathbf{k}, \mathbf{T}).$

An important special case arises when $\mathbf{r} = \mathbf{R}(\theta)$, a variable unit vector in a *plane* making an angle of θ radians with some fixed line as x-axis.   If

$R(\theta)$ is drawn from the origin, the locus of its end point is a circle of unit radius (Fig. 28b), and $s = \theta$. Now (4) becomes $\frac{dr}{ds} = T$ *in direction of increasing arc length*

(7) $\quad \dfrac{d\mathbf{R}}{d\theta} = \mathbf{R}(\theta + \tfrac{1}{2}\pi) = \mathbf{P}, \; = T$

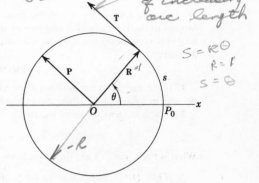

Fig. 28b. Derivative of revolving unit vector: $d\mathbf{R}/d\theta = \mathbf{P}$.

$S = R\theta$, $R = 1$, $S = \theta$

a unit vector perpendicular to $\mathbf{R}$ in the direction of increasing angles. Using this result, we have also

(8) $\quad \dfrac{d\mathbf{P}}{d\theta} = \mathbf{R}(\theta + \pi) = -\mathbf{R}.$

If we put

(9) $\quad \mathbf{R} = \mathbf{i} \cos\theta + \mathbf{j} \sin\theta$

in (7), we find at one stroke the derivatives of both sine and cosine:

$$\frac{d}{d\theta} \cos\theta = \cos(\theta + \tfrac{1}{2}\pi), \qquad \frac{d}{d\theta} \sin\theta = \sin(\theta + \tfrac{1}{2}\pi).$$

If $r = f(\theta)$ is the equation of a plane curve in polar coordinates, its vector equation is

$$\mathbf{r} = r\, \mathbf{R}(\theta);$$

hence, on differentiating with respect to s,

$$\mathbf{T} = \frac{dr}{ds}\mathbf{R} + r\frac{d\mathbf{R}}{d\theta}\frac{d\theta}{ds} = \frac{dr}{ds}\mathbf{R} + r\frac{d\theta}{ds}\mathbf{P}.$$

On dot-multiplying by $\mathbf{R}$ and $\mathbf{P}$, we find

(10) $\qquad \dfrac{dr}{ds} = \cos(\mathbf{R}, \mathbf{T}), \qquad r\dfrac{d\theta}{ds} = \sin(\mathbf{R}, \mathbf{T}).$

Example. Focal Properties of Conic Sections. If r_1 and r_2 are the focal distances of a point P on the ellipse,

$$r_1 + r_2 = 2a, \quad \text{the major axis.}$$

If we differentiate this with respect to s, we have from (10)

$$(\mathbf{R}_1 + \mathbf{R}_2) \cdot \mathbf{T} = 0,$$

where $\mathbf{R}_1$ and $\mathbf{R}_2$ are unit vectors along the focal radii. Thus $\mathbf{R}_1 + \mathbf{R}_2$ is normal to the ellipse at P and bisects the interior angle between the focal radii at P (draw the figure).

For the hyperbola

$$r_1 - r_2 = 2a, \qquad (\mathbf{R}_1 - \mathbf{R}_2) \cdot \mathbf{T} = 0.$$

Thus $\mathbf{R}_1 - \mathbf{R}_2$ is normal to the hyperbola at P and bisects the exterior angle between the focal radii at P (draw the figure).

For a parabola whose axis is the x-axis and directrix the y-axis,

$$r = x, \qquad \frac{dr}{ds} = \frac{dx}{ds}, \qquad (\mathbf{R} - \mathbf{i}) \cdot \mathbf{T} = 0,$$

where $\mathbf{R}$ is a unit vector along the focal radius to the point P. Therefore $\mathbf{R} - \mathbf{i}$ is normal to the parabola at P and bisects the angle between $\mathbf{R}$ and $-\mathbf{i}$. This is also an angle between focal radii if we regard the parabola as having a second focus on its axis at infinity.

PROBLEMS

1. If the proper vector $\mathbf{u}(t)$ is not parallel to a fixed line, prove that it will remain parallel to a fixed plane when and only when $[\mathbf{u}\,\mathbf{u}'\,\mathbf{u}''] = 0$.

2. Find a tangent vector of the curve

$$x = x_0 + at, \qquad y = y_0 + bt, \qquad z = z_0 + ct.$$

What is the curve? Find its length from $t = 0$ to $t = 1$.

3. If $\mathbf{r} = \overrightarrow{OP}$ is the position vector to the

ellipse: $\qquad x = a \cos t, \qquad y = b \sin t,$

or $\qquad$ hyperbola: $\qquad x = a \cosh t, \qquad y = b \sinh t,$

prove that $d\mathbf{r}/dt = \mathbf{r}' = \overrightarrow{OP'}$, where OP and OP' are conjugate semidiameters.

4. Show that the plane curve $f(x, y) = 0$ has the normal vector

$$\mathbf{i}\,f_x(x, y) + \mathbf{j}\,f_y(x, y).$$

[Differentiate the equation with respect to s.]

5. Show that the plane curve $f(r, \theta) = 0$ has the normal vector

$$\mathbf{R}\,f_r(r, \theta) + \mathbf{P}\,\frac{f_\theta(r, \theta)}{r}.$$

[Differentiate the equation with respect to s.]

29. Frenet's Formulas.

For a rectifiable curve

$$\mathbf{r} = \overrightarrow{OP} = \mathbf{r}(s), \qquad \frac{d\mathbf{r}}{ds} = \mathbf{T},$$

the unit tangent at P. Since the length of $\mathbf{T}$ is constant, $d\mathbf{T}/ds$, if not zero, must be perpendicular to $\mathbf{T}$ (Theorem 25.1). A directed line through P in the direction of $d\mathbf{T}/ds$ is called the *principal normal* of the curve at P. Let $\mathbf{N}$ denote a unit vector in the direction of the principal normal; then we may write

$$(1) \qquad \frac{d\mathbf{T}}{ds} = \kappa \mathbf{N},$$

where κ is a non-negative scalar called the *curvature* of the curve at P.

Now $\mathbf{B} = \mathbf{T} \times \mathbf{N}$ is third unit vector such that $\mathbf{T}$, $\mathbf{N}$, $\mathbf{B}$ form a dextral set of orthogonal unit vectors at each point of the curve where $\kappa \neq 0$.

As P traverses the curve, we speak of the *moving trihedral* **TNB**. A directed line through P in the direction of **B** is called the *binormal* to the curve at P.

Since **B** is a unit vector, $d\mathbf{B}/ds$, if not zero, must be perpendicular to **B**. Differentiating $\mathbf{B} = \mathbf{T} \times \mathbf{N}$, we have $\kappa N \times N = 0$

$$\frac{d\mathbf{B}}{ds} = \frac{d\mathbf{T}}{ds} \times \mathbf{N} + \mathbf{T} \times \frac{d\mathbf{N}}{ds} = \mathbf{T} \times \frac{d\mathbf{N}}{ds}$$

in view of (1). Hence $d\mathbf{B}/ds$ is perpendicular to **T** as well as **B** and therefore must be parallel to **N**. We therefore may write

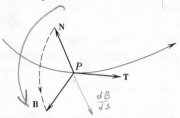

Fig. 29. Moving trihedral.

$$(2) \qquad \frac{d\mathbf{B}}{ds} = -\tau\mathbf{N}$$

where τ is a scalar called the *torsion* of the curve at P. The minus sign in (2) has this purpose: when $\tau > 0$, $d\mathbf{B}/ds$ has the direction of $-\mathbf{N}$; then, as P moves along the curve in a positive direction, **B** revolves about **T** in the same sense as a right-handed screw advancing in the direction of **T** (Fig. 29).

We may now compute $d\mathbf{N}/ds$ by differentiating $\mathbf{N} = \mathbf{B} \times \mathbf{T}$ and using (1) and (2):

$$(3) \qquad \frac{d\mathbf{N}}{ds} = \frac{d\mathbf{B}}{ds} \times \mathbf{T} + \mathbf{B} \times \frac{d\mathbf{T}}{ds} = -\tau\mathbf{N} \times \mathbf{T} + \kappa\mathbf{B} \times \mathbf{N}.$$

dextral set

TNB

$N = B \times T$

$\frac{d}{ds}\bar{N} = \frac{d}{ds} B \times T$

Collecting (1), (2), and (3) we have the set of equations

$$(4) \qquad \begin{cases} d\mathbf{T}/ds = & \kappa\mathbf{N}, \\ d\mathbf{N}/ds = -\kappa\mathbf{T} & +\tau\mathbf{B}, \\ d\mathbf{B}/ds = & -\tau\mathbf{N}, \end{cases}$$

known as *Frenet's formulas*.† They are fundamental in the theory of space curves.

From (4) we see that both κ and τ have the dimensions of the reciprocal of length; hence

$$(5)(6) \qquad \rho = 1/\kappa, \qquad \sigma = 1/\tau$$

have the dimensions of length and are called the *radius of curvature* and *radius of torsion*, respectively.

Since **N**, by definition, has the same direction as $d\mathbf{T}/ds$, the curvature κ is never negative. If $\kappa = 0$ (identically), $d\mathbf{T}/ds = \mathbf{0}$, and **T** is a unit vector of

† Or *Frenet-Serret formulas*.

constant direction; the curve is therefore a straight line. Conversely for a straight line $\mathbf{T}$ is constant, $d\mathbf{T}/ds = \mathbf{0}$ and $\kappa = 0$. *The only curves of zero curvature are straight lines.*

The torsion may be positive or negative. As P traverses the curve in a positive direction, the trihedral $\mathbf{TNB}$ will resolve about $\mathbf{T}$ as a right-handed or left-handed screw according as τ is positive or negative. The sign of τ is independent of the choice of positive direction along the curve; for, if we reverse the positive direction, we must replace

$$s, \mathbf{T}, \frac{d\mathbf{T}}{ds}, \mathbf{N}, \mathbf{B}, \frac{d\mathbf{B}}{ds} \qquad \text{by} \qquad -s, -\mathbf{T}, \frac{d\mathbf{T}}{ds}, \mathbf{N}, -\mathbf{B}, \frac{d\mathbf{B}}{ds},$$

and equations (4) maintain their form with unaltered κ and τ.

If $\tau = 0$ (identically), $d\mathbf{B}/ds = \mathbf{0}$, and $\mathbf{B}$ is a constant vector; hence, from

$$\mathbf{B} \cdot \mathbf{T} = \mathbf{B} \cdot \frac{d\mathbf{r}}{ds} = 0, \qquad \mathbf{B} \cdot (\mathbf{r} - \mathbf{r}_0) = 0,$$

and the curve lies in a plane normal to $\mathbf{B}$. Conversely, for a plane curve, $\mathbf{T}$ and $\mathbf{N}$ always lie in a fixed plane while $\mathbf{B}$ is a unit normal to that plane; hence $d\mathbf{B}/ds = \mathbf{0}$ at all points where $\mathbf{N}$ is defined ($\kappa \neq 0$) and $\tau = 0$. *The only curves of zero torsion are plane.*†

By introducing *Darboux's vector*

(7) $$\boldsymbol{\delta} = \tau \mathbf{T} + \kappa \mathbf{B},$$

Frenet's formulas take on the memorable form

(8) $$d\mathbf{T}/ds = \boldsymbol{\delta} \times \mathbf{T}, \qquad d\mathbf{N}/ds = \boldsymbol{\delta} \times \mathbf{N}, \qquad d\mathbf{B}/ds = \boldsymbol{\delta} \times \mathbf{B}.$$

Darboux's vector proves to be the angular velocity of the moving trihedral $\mathbf{TNB}$ when the curve is traversed with constant speed (§34).

30. Curvature and Torsion. By use of Frenet's formulas we may compute the curvature and torsion of a curve from its parametric equations. Thus on differentiating $\mathbf{r} = \mathbf{r}(t)$ three times and denoting t-derivatives by dots, we have

$$\dot{\mathbf{r}} = \frac{d\mathbf{r}}{ds}\frac{ds}{dt} = \dot{s}\mathbf{T},$$

$$\ddot{\mathbf{r}} = \ddot{s}\mathbf{T} + \dot{s}^2\kappa\mathbf{N},$$

$$\dddot{\mathbf{r}} = \dddot{s}\mathbf{T} + \ddot{s}\dot{s}\kappa\mathbf{N} + (2\dot{s}\ddot{s}\kappa + \dot{s}^2\dot{\kappa})\mathbf{N} + \dot{s}^3\kappa(-\kappa\mathbf{T} + \tau\mathbf{B})$$

$$= (\dddot{s} - \dot{s}^3\kappa^2)\mathbf{T} + (3\dot{s}\ddot{s}\kappa + \dot{s}^2\dot{\kappa})\mathbf{N} + \dot{s}^3\kappa\tau\mathbf{B}.$$

† For a straight line ($\kappa = 0$), $\mathbf{N}$ is not determined. We then agree to give $\mathbf{N}$ any fixed direction normal to $\mathbf{T}$ and, as before, define $\mathbf{B} = \mathbf{T} \times \mathbf{N}$. Then $\mathbf{B}$ is constant, $d\mathbf{B}/ds = \mathbf{0}$ and $\tau = 0$.

Hence

$$\dot{\mathbf{r}} \times \ddot{\mathbf{r}} = \dot{s}^3 \kappa \mathbf{B}, \qquad \dot{\mathbf{r}} \times \ddot{\mathbf{r}} \cdot \dddot{\mathbf{r}} = \dot{s}^6 \kappa^2 \tau,$$

$$|\dot{\mathbf{r}} \times \ddot{\mathbf{r}}| = |\dot{s}|^3 \kappa, \qquad \dot{\mathbf{r}} \times \ddot{\mathbf{r}} \cdot \dddot{\mathbf{r}} = |\dot{\mathbf{r}} \times \ddot{\mathbf{r}}|^2 \tau,$$

and, since $|\dot{\mathbf{r}}| = |\dot{s}| \neq 0$ at an ordinary point,

(1)(2)
$$\kappa = \frac{|\dot{\mathbf{r}} \times \ddot{\mathbf{r}}|}{|\dot{\mathbf{r}}|^3}, \qquad \tau = \frac{\dot{\mathbf{r}} \times \ddot{\mathbf{r}} \cdot \dddot{\mathbf{r}}}{|\dot{\mathbf{r}} \times \ddot{\mathbf{r}}|^2}.$$

If the positive direction on the curve is that of increasing t, $\dot{s} = ds/dt > 0$; and the preceding equations show that

(3) **T, B, N** have the directions of $\dot{\mathbf{r}}$, $\dot{\mathbf{r}} \times \ddot{\mathbf{r}}$, $(\dot{\mathbf{r}} \times \ddot{\mathbf{r}}) \times \dot{\mathbf{r}}$.

The planes through a point $\mathbf{r}(t)$ of the curve and perpendicular to **T, N,** or **B** are called, respectively, the *normal, rectifying,* and *osculating* planes to the curve. Their equations are readily obtained from (3). Thus, if **q** is a variable position vector to the osculating plane, its equation is

(4)
$$(\mathbf{q} - \mathbf{r}) \cdot \dot{\mathbf{r}} \times \ddot{\mathbf{r}} = 0.$$

If the parametric equations of a plane curve are $x = x(t)$, $y = y(t)$, we have

$$\mathbf{r} = x\mathbf{i} + y\mathbf{j}, \qquad \dot{\mathbf{r}} = \dot{x}\mathbf{i} + \dot{y}\mathbf{j}, \qquad \ddot{\mathbf{r}} = \ddot{x}\mathbf{i} + \ddot{y}\mathbf{j};$$

and from (1) and (2)

(5)
$$\kappa = \frac{|\dot{x}\ddot{y} - \dot{y}\ddot{x}|}{(\dot{x}^2 + \dot{y}^2)^{3/2}}, \qquad \tau = 0.$$

If the curve has the Cartesian equation $y = f(x)$, we can regard x as the parameter: $x = t$, $y = f(t)$. Then κ in (5) becomes

(6)
$$\kappa = \frac{|y''|}{(1 + y'^2)^{3/2}},$$

where the primes denote x derivatives.

If the curve has the polar equation $r = f(\theta)$, we take $t = \theta$ as parameter. Then

$$\mathbf{r} = r\mathbf{R}, \qquad \dot{\mathbf{r}} = \dot{r}\mathbf{R} + r\mathbf{P}, \qquad \ddot{\mathbf{r}} = (\ddot{r} - r)\mathbf{R} + 2\dot{r}\mathbf{P};$$

and since

$$|\dot{\mathbf{r}}| = (\dot{r}^2 + r^2)^{1/2}, \qquad |\dot{\mathbf{r}} \times \ddot{\mathbf{r}}| = |2\dot{r}^2 - r(\ddot{r} - r)|,$$

we have from (1)

(7)
$$\kappa = \frac{|r^2 + 2\dot{r}^2 - r\ddot{r}|}{(r^2 + \dot{r}^2)^{3/2}}.$$

Example 1. At the point $t = 1$ of the twisted cubic

$$x = 2t, \qquad y = t^2, \qquad z = t^3/3,$$

find T, N, B, κ, τ and the equation of its osculating plane.
Since $\mathbf{r}(t) = [2t, t^2, t^3/3]$,

$$\dot{\mathbf{r}} = [2, 2t, t^2], \qquad \ddot{\mathbf{r}} = [0, 2, 2t], \qquad \dddot{\mathbf{r}} = [0, 0, 2];$$

hence, when $t = 1$,

$$\dot{\mathbf{r}} = [2, 2, 1], \qquad \ddot{\mathbf{r}} = [0, 2, 2], \qquad \dddot{\mathbf{r}} = [0, 0, 2],$$

$$\dot{\mathbf{r}} \times \ddot{\mathbf{r}} = [2, -4, 4], \qquad \dot{\mathbf{r}} \times \ddot{\mathbf{r}} \cdot \dddot{\mathbf{r}} = 8.$$

From (3)

$$\text{T} = \tfrac{1}{3}[2, 2, 1], \qquad \text{B} = \tfrac{1}{3}[1, -2, 2], \qquad \text{N} = \tfrac{1}{3}[-2, 1, 2];$$

the osculating plane is

$$(x - 2) - 2(y - 1) + 2(z - \tfrac{1}{3}) = 0;$$

and, from (1) and (2), $\kappa = \tfrac{2}{9}$, $\tau = \tfrac{2}{9}$.
Since $\dot{\mathbf{r}} = \dot{s}\text{T}$, the length of the curve is found from the equation

$$ds/dt = |\dot{\mathbf{r}}| = \sqrt{4 + 4t^2 + t^4}.$$

Example 2. The Circular Helix. A screw thread or helix, on a circular cylinder of radius a, has the parametric equations

$$x = a \cos t, \qquad y = a \sin t, \qquad z = bt,$$

where t is the angle measured counterclockwise from the x-axis.
In order to find its curvature and torsion we compute

$$\dot{\mathbf{r}} = [-a \sin t, a \cos t, b],$$

$$\ddot{\mathbf{r}} = [-a \cos t, -a \sin t, 0],$$

$$\dddot{\mathbf{r}} = [a \sin t, -a \cos t, 0],$$

$$\dot{\mathbf{r}} \times \ddot{\mathbf{r}} = [ab \sin t, -ab \cos t, a^2],$$

$$\dot{\mathbf{r}} \times \ddot{\mathbf{r}} \cdot \dddot{\mathbf{r}} = a^2 b,$$

and, since

$$|\dot{\mathbf{r}}|^2 = a^2 + b^2, \qquad |\dot{\mathbf{r}} \times \ddot{\mathbf{r}}|^2 = a^2(a^2 + b^2),$$

we have from (1) and (2)

$$\kappa = \frac{a}{a^2 + b^2}, \qquad \tau = \frac{b}{a^2 + b^2}.$$

Since τ has the sign of b, the helix is a right-handed if $b > 0$, left-handed if $b < 0$.
The length of the helix measured from $t = 0$ is

$$L = \int_0^t |\dot{\mathbf{r}}|\, dt = t \sqrt{a^2 + b^2} \qquad\qquad (28.1).$$

PROBLEM

1. Let $\mathbf{R} = \mathbf{R}(t)$ be a twisted curve on a unit sphere. If t is its arc length, prove that the curve

(i) $$\mathbf{r} = a \int_0^t \mathbf{R}(t)\, dt \qquad \text{has constant curvature} \qquad \kappa = \frac{1}{|a|}\,;$$

and, if t is an arbitrary parameter, the curve

(ii) $$\mathbf{r} = a \int_0^t \mathbf{R}(t) \times \frac{d\mathbf{R}}{dt}\, dt \qquad \text{has constant torsion} \qquad \tau = \frac{1}{a}.$$

Read

31. Plane Curves. For plane curves Frenet's formulas reduce to

(1)(2) $$\frac{d\mathbf{T}}{ds} = \kappa\mathbf{N}, \qquad \frac{d\mathbf{N}}{ds} = -\kappa\mathbf{T}.$$

Since $d\mathbf{T}/ds$ is always directed to the concave side of a plane curve, the same is true of $\mathbf{N}$. At points of inflection $d\mathbf{T}/ds = 0$, $\kappa = 0$, and $\mathbf{N}$ is not defined. When P passes through a point of inflection, $\mathbf{N}$ reverses its direction and $\mathbf{B} = \mathbf{T} \times \mathbf{N}$ does the same. To remedy this discontinuous behavior of $\mathbf{N}$ and $\mathbf{B}$ at points of inflection, the following convention often is adopted in the differential geometry of plane curves. Take $\mathbf{B}$ as a *fixed* unit vector normal to the plane of the curve, and define $\mathbf{N} = \mathbf{B} \times \mathbf{T}$. As before, $\mathbf{T}$, $\mathbf{N}$, $\mathbf{B}$ form a dextral set of orthogonal unit vectors. The curvature κ, defined by (1), is now positive or negative according as $d\mathbf{T}/ds$ has the direction of $\mathbf{N}$ or the opposite. Equation (2) still holds good; for

$$\frac{d\mathbf{N}}{ds} = \mathbf{B} \times \frac{d\mathbf{T}}{ds} = \mathbf{B} \times \kappa\mathbf{N} = -\kappa\mathbf{T}.$$

Let ψ be the angle from a fixed line in the plane to the tangent at P, taken positive in the sense determined by $\mathbf{B}$.† Then, from (28.7),

$$\frac{d\mathbf{T}}{ds} = \frac{d\mathbf{T}}{d\psi}\frac{d\psi}{ds} = \mathbf{B} \times \mathbf{T}\frac{d\psi}{ds} = \mathbf{N}\frac{d\psi}{ds},$$

and hence, from (1),

(3)(4) $$\kappa = \frac{d\psi}{ds}, \qquad \rho = \frac{ds}{d\psi}.$$

The *intrinsic equation* of a plane curve is the relation connecting s and ψ, say $s = f(\psi)$. When this relation is known, the radius of curvature $\rho = f'(\psi)$. For example, a circle of radius a has the intrinsic equation $s = a\psi$ when ψ is measured from the tangent at the point $s = 0$; hence, for a circle, $\rho = a$.

† A vector normal to a plane determines a positive sense of rotation by the right-handed screw convention. Thus, if $\mathbf{B}$ points *up* from the paper, the positive sense is counterclockwise; then $\mathbf{N}$ is always 90° *ahead* of $\mathbf{T}$.

Example 1. Evolute. At any point P of a plane curve where $\kappa \neq 0$, the *center of curvature* P_1 is given by

(5)
$$\mathbf{r}_1 = \mathbf{r} + \rho \mathbf{N}.$$

The locus of P_1 is called the *evolute* of the curve. If $s = AP$ and $s_1 = A_1P_1$ denote corresponding arcs on the curve Γ and its evolute Γ_1 (Fig. 31*a*), we have, on differentiating (5) with respect to s,

$$\mathbf{T}_1 \frac{ds_1}{ds} = \mathbf{T} + \rho \frac{d\mathbf{N}}{ds} + \frac{d\rho}{ds}\mathbf{N} = \frac{d\rho}{ds}\mathbf{N}.$$

Choose the positive direction on Γ_1 so that $\mathbf{T}_1 = \mathbf{N}$; then

$$\frac{ds_1}{ds} = \frac{d\rho}{ds}, \qquad s_1 = \rho + \text{const};$$

Fig. 31*a*. Evolute of a plane curve.

and, since $\Delta s_1 = \Delta \rho$, an arc of the evolute is equal to the difference in the values of ρ at its end points. These properties show that a curve Γ may be traced by the end P of a taut string unwound from its evolute Γ_1; the string is always tangent to Γ_1, and its free portion is equal to ρ. From this point of view, Γ is called the *involute* of Γ_1.

Since $\mathbf{T}_1 = \mathbf{N}$,

$$\psi_1 = (\mathbf{i}, \mathbf{T}_1) = (\mathbf{i}, \mathbf{T}) + \tfrac{1}{2}\pi = \psi + \tfrac{1}{2}\pi;$$

hence the radius of curvature of the evolute is

$$\rho_1 = \frac{ds_1}{d\psi_1} = \frac{d\rho}{d\psi} = \frac{d^2s}{d\psi^2}.$$

Example 2. Involute. An involute Γ_1 of a plane curve Γ is traced by the end P_1 of a taut string PP_1 unwound from Γ (Fig. 31*b*). If Γ has the equation $\mathbf{r} = \mathbf{r}(s)$, an involute is given by

(6)
$$\mathbf{r}_1 = \mathbf{r} - s\mathbf{T}$$

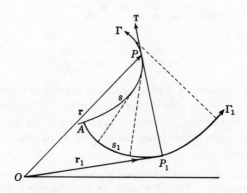

Fig. 31*b*. Involute of a plane curve.

if the arcs s and s_1 are measured from the point A where the curves meet. On differentiating (6) with respect to s,

$$\mathbf{T}_1 \frac{ds_1}{ds} = \mathbf{T} - \mathbf{T} - s\kappa\mathbf{N} = -s\kappa\mathbf{N}.$$

If we choose the positive direction on Γ_1 so that $\mathbf{T}_1 = -\mathbf{N}$,

$$\frac{ds_1}{ds} = s\kappa = s\frac{d\psi}{ds}, \qquad \text{or} \qquad \frac{ds_1}{d\psi} = s.$$

Thus, if Γ has the intrinsic equation $s = f(\psi)$ when ψ is measured from a tangent at A ($s = 0$), the arc of the involute

$$s_1 = \int_0^\psi s \, d\psi.$$

For example, from the intrinsic equation of a circle $s = a\psi$ we obtain

$$s_1 = \int_0^\psi a\psi \, d\psi = \tfrac{1}{2}a\psi^2$$

for the arc of its involute.

Example 3. Envelopes. Consider the plane vector function of two variables, $\mathbf{r} = \mathbf{f}(u, v)$. A one-parameter family of curves (with u as parameter) is given by

$$\mathbf{r}_1 = \mathbf{f}(u, v), \qquad u = \text{const.}$$

If this family has a curve envelope given by $v = \varphi(u)$, namely,

$$(7) \qquad\qquad \mathbf{p} = \mathbf{f}\{u, \varphi(u)\},$$

the vectors

$$\frac{d\mathbf{p}}{\partial u} = \frac{\partial \mathbf{f}}{\partial u} + \frac{\partial \mathbf{f}}{\partial v} \varphi'(u) \quad \text{and} \quad \frac{d\mathbf{r}_1}{\partial v} = \frac{\partial \mathbf{f}}{\partial v}$$

are parallel at the points of contact; that is,

$$(8) \qquad\qquad \frac{\partial \mathbf{f}}{\partial u} \times \frac{\partial \mathbf{f}}{\partial v} = \mathbf{0}.$$

This condition must be fulfilled if the envelope exists. If (8) leads to a relation $v = \varphi(u)$ (which does not make $\partial\mathbf{f}/\partial u$ or $\partial\mathbf{f}/\partial v$ zero), this relation gives the envelope (7).

Consider, for example, the one-parameter family of normals to the plane curve $\mathbf{r} = \mathbf{r}(s)$, namely,

$$\mathbf{r}_1 = \mathbf{r}(s) + v\,\mathbf{N}(s) \qquad (s = \text{const.}).$$

If they have an envelope,

$$\frac{\partial \mathbf{r}_1}{\partial s} \times \frac{\partial \mathbf{r}_1}{\partial v} = (\mathbf{T} - v\kappa\mathbf{T}) \times \mathbf{N} = (1 - v\kappa)\mathbf{B} = \mathbf{0}.$$

Hence the envelope is given by $v = 1/\kappa = \rho$, or

$$\mathbf{p} = \mathbf{r}(s) + \rho\mathbf{N}(s),$$

namely the locus of the centers of curvature of the curve.

PROBLEMS

1. At the points $t = 0$ and $t = 1$ of the twisted cubic

$$x = 3t, \qquad y = 3t^2, \qquad z = 2t^3$$

find

(a)   T, N, B;

(b) κ and τ;

(c)   the equations of the normal and osculating planes.

2. Find κ and τ at any point t of the curve

(a)   in Prob. 1;

(b) $x = a(3t - t^3)$, $y = 3at^2$, $z = a(3t + t^3)$.

3. Show that the radius of curvature of the ellipse

$$x = a \cos t, \qquad y = a \sin t, \qquad z = a \cos t$$

is $\rho = a(1 + \sin^2 t)^{3/2}/\sqrt{2}$.

4. If $\mathbf{r} = \mathbf{r}(s)$ is a plane curve Γ, show that $\mathbf{r}_1 = \mathbf{r} + c\mathbf{N}$ (c const) is a *parallel curve* ($\mathbf{T}_1 = \mathbf{T}$ at corresponding points); and

(a) $s_1 = s - c\psi$ if $s_1 = s = 0$ when $\psi = 0$;

(b) $\rho_1 = \rho - c$.

5. Prove that the intrinsic equation of the *catenary* $y = c \cosh (x/c)$ is $s = c \tan \psi$ when s is measured from the vertex ($\psi = 0$). $= \frac{c}{2}\left(e^{x/c} + e^{-x/c}\right)$

6. Prove that the intrinsic equation of the *cycloid*

$$x = a(t - \sin t), \qquad y = a(1 - \cos t),$$

formed by a circle of radius a rolling along the x-axis, is $s = 4a(1 - \sin \psi)$ where s and ψ are measured from the x-axis ($\psi = \pi/2$).

7. Show that the curvature and torsion of the curve

$$x = e^t, \qquad y = e^{-t}, \qquad z = \sqrt{2}\,t$$

are $\kappa = -\tau = \sqrt{2}/(e^t + e^{-t})^2$.

8. Find the envelope of the family of straight lines in the xy-plane

$$\mathbf{r} = p(\theta)\mathbf{R} + \lambda\mathbf{P},$$

where R, P are the unit vectors of §28, $\theta = $ angle (i, R), and $p\mathbf{R}$ is the normal vector from O to the line.

Show that the envelope is the curve

$$\mathbf{r}_1 = p(\theta)\mathbf{R} + p'(\theta)\mathbf{P}$$

and that

$$\mathbf{T}_1 = \mathbf{T}, \qquad \frac{ds_1}{d\theta} = p(\theta) + p''(\theta).$$

9. Find the envelope of the family of lines for which the segment included between the x-axis and y-axis is of constant length c.

[Put $p = c \sin \theta \cos \theta$ in Prob. 8.]

Show that the envelope has the parametric equations

$$x = c \sin^3 \theta, \qquad y = c \cos^3 \theta,$$

and that the entire length of the curve is $6c$.

10. Prove that the Darboux vector $\boldsymbol{\delta}$ is constant if κ and τ are constant, and that $\boldsymbol{\delta}$ has a fixed direction if κ/τ is constant.

11. A *helix* is a twisted curve whose tangent makes a constant angle with a fixed direction ($\mathbf{e} \cdot \mathbf{T} = \cos \alpha$ where $\mathbf{e}$ is a unit vector in the fixed direction). Prove that:

(a) Helices are the only twisted curves whose Darboux vector has a constant direction.

(b) Helices are the only twisted curves for which κ/τ is constant.

(c) Circular helices are the only twisted curves for which κ and τ (and also the Darboux vector) are constant.

(d) The curve in Problem 1 is a helix with $\mathbf{e} = (\mathbf{i} + \mathbf{k})/\sqrt{2}$, $\alpha = \pi/4$.

32. Kinematics of a Particle. Let $\mathbf{r} = \overrightarrow{OP}$ be the position vector of a moving particle P relative to some reference frame. If its path has the equation $\mathbf{r} = \mathbf{r}(t)$ in terms of the time t as parameter, the *velocity* $\mathbf{v}$ and *acceleration* $\mathbf{a}$ of P relative to this frame are defined as the time derivatives

$$(1)(2) \qquad \mathbf{v} = \frac{d\mathbf{r}}{dt}, \qquad \mathbf{a} = \frac{d\mathbf{v}}{dt} = \frac{d^2\mathbf{r}}{dt^2}.$$

By the chain rule

$$(3) \qquad \mathbf{v} = \frac{d\mathbf{r}}{ds}\frac{ds}{dt} = \mathbf{T}\frac{ds}{dt} = v\mathbf{T}, \qquad v = \frac{ds}{dt},$$

where the scalar v is a signed number whose absolute value, $|v| = |\mathbf{v}|$, is called the *speed* of the particle. *The velocity of P is a vector tangent to its path in the direction of motion and of length numerically equal to the speed.*

On differentiating (3) with respect to the time, we get

$$(4) \qquad \mathbf{a} = \frac{dv}{dt}\mathbf{T} + v\frac{d\mathbf{T}}{dt};$$

or, since $\mathbf{T}$ may be regarded as a function of the arc s along the curve,

$$\frac{d\mathbf{T}}{dt} = \frac{d\mathbf{T}}{ds}\frac{ds}{dt} = (\kappa\mathbf{N})v = \frac{v}{\rho}\mathbf{N}.$$

Therefore

$$(5) \qquad \left(\mathbf{a} = \frac{dv}{dt}\mathbf{T} + \frac{v^2}{\rho}\mathbf{N}: \right)$$

The acceleration of P is a vector in the plane of the tangent and principal normal to the path at P; its tangential and normal components are dv/dt and v^2/ρ.

The acceleration will be purely tangential when the motion is rectilinear ($\rho = \infty$); it will be purely normal when the speed is constant ($dv/dt = 0$).

The velocity and acceleration vectors are regarded as bound to the moving particle.

With rectangular coordinates

$$\mathbf{r} = x\mathbf{i} + y\mathbf{j} + z\mathbf{k},$$

and

(6) $$\mathbf{v} = \frac{dx}{dt}\mathbf{i} + \frac{dy}{dt}\mathbf{j} + \frac{dz}{dt}\mathbf{k},$$

(7) $$\mathbf{a} = \frac{d^2x}{dt^2}\mathbf{i} + \frac{d^2y}{dt^2}\mathbf{j} + \frac{d^2z}{dt^2}\mathbf{k}.$$

Thus the rectangular components of $\mathbf{v}$ and $\mathbf{a}$ are the first and second time derivatives of the coordinates.

Motion in a plane may be referred to polar coordinates r, θ; then

$$\mathbf{r} = r\mathbf{R}(\theta), \qquad |\mathbf{R}| = 1.$$

If we differentiate twice with respect to t and use the equations

$$\frac{d\mathbf{R}}{dt} = \frac{d\mathbf{R}}{d\theta}\frac{d\theta}{dt} = \mathbf{P}\frac{d\theta}{dt}, \qquad \frac{d\mathbf{P}}{dt} = \frac{d\mathbf{P}}{d\theta}\frac{d\theta}{dt} = -\mathbf{R}\frac{d\theta}{dt},$$

we find

(8) $$\mathbf{v} = \frac{dr}{dt}\mathbf{R} + r\frac{d\theta}{dt}\mathbf{P}, \qquad a = \frac{d\bar{v}}{dt} = \frac{d^2 r}{dt^2}\bar{R} + \frac{dr}{dt}\frac{d\bar{R}}{d\theta}\frac{d\theta}{dt} + \left(r\frac{d\theta}{dt}\right)\frac{d\bar{P}}{d\theta}\frac{d\theta}{dt}$$

(9) $$\mathbf{a} = \left[\frac{d^2r}{dt^2} - r\left(\frac{d\theta}{dt}\right)^2\right]\mathbf{R} + \left[r\frac{d^2\theta}{dt^2} + 2\frac{dr}{dt}\frac{d\theta}{dt}\right]\mathbf{P}.$$

The coefficients of $\mathbf{R}$ and $\mathbf{P}$ give the radial and transverse components of $\mathbf{v}$ and $\mathbf{a}$:

$$\bar{v} = \bar{v}_r + \bar{v}_p$$

$$v_r = \frac{dr}{dt}, \qquad\qquad v_p = r\frac{d\theta}{dt};$$

$$\bar{a} = \bar{a}_r + \bar{a}_p \qquad a_r = \frac{d^2r}{dt^2} - r\left(\frac{d\theta}{dt}\right)^2, \qquad a_p = r\frac{d^2\theta}{dt^2} + 2\frac{dr}{dt}\frac{d\theta}{dt}.$$

If the acceleration is purely radial, $\leftarrow$ same

$$a_p = \frac{1}{r}\frac{d}{dt}\left(r^2\frac{d\theta}{dt}\right) = 0, \qquad \frac{1}{r} \neq 0$$

and

$$r = r(\theta) \qquad r^2\frac{d\theta}{dt} = h \quad \text{(const).}$$

$$A(\theta) = \int_0^\theta \tfrac{1}{2} r^2 \, d\theta$$

$$\frac{dA}{dt} = \frac{dA}{d\theta}\frac{d\theta}{dt} = \tfrac{1}{2} r^2 \frac{d\theta}{dt} = \tfrac{1}{2} h$$

This means that the vector $\overrightarrow{OP}$ sweeps out area at a constant rate; for the sectorial area measured from the initial line is

$$A = \tfrac{1}{2} \int_0^\theta r^2 \, d\theta \quad \text{and} \quad \frac{dA}{dt} = \tfrac{1}{2} r^2 \frac{d\theta}{dt} = \tfrac{1}{2} h.$$

This result is known as the

LAW OF AREAS. *If the acceleration of a particle P is always directed towards a fixed point O, the position vector $\overrightarrow{OP}$ will sweep out area at a constant rate.*

Example 1. Circular Motion. A particle P moves in a circle of radius r, with variable angular speed $\omega = d\theta/dt$ (radians per second). Its position vector $\overrightarrow{OP}$ is

$$\mathbf{r} = r\,\mathbf{R}(\theta), \qquad |\mathbf{R}| = 1,$$

and, from (28.7–8),

$$\mathbf{v} = r\omega\mathbf{P}, \qquad \mathbf{a} = -r\omega^2\mathbf{R} + r\frac{d\omega}{dt}\mathbf{P}.$$

Its speed $v = r\omega$; and its acceleration components

$$a_r = -r\omega^2, \qquad a_p = r\frac{d\omega}{dt}.$$

Example 2. Uniformly Accelerated Motion. If a particle has a constant acceleration $\mathbf{g}$, and $\mathbf{r} = 0$, $\mathbf{v} = \mathbf{v}_0$ when $t = 0$, we have on integrating $d\mathbf{v}/dt = \mathbf{g}$ twice:

$$\mathbf{v} = \mathbf{v}_0 + \mathbf{g}t, \qquad \mathbf{r} = \mathbf{v}_0 t + \tfrac{1}{2}\mathbf{g}t^2.$$

The path is the result of superposing the displacement $\tfrac{1}{2}\mathbf{g}t^2$ due to the acceleration upon $\mathbf{v}_0 t$ due to motion at constant velocity $\mathbf{v}_0$. It is easily shown to be a parabola with axis parallel to $\mathbf{g}$.

To find the path of a projectile under gravity (neglecting air resistance), we put

$$\mathbf{v}_0 = \mathbf{i}v_0 \cos\alpha + \mathbf{j}v_0 \sin\alpha, \qquad \mathbf{g} = -\mathbf{j}g;$$

then the equations of the path are

$$x = (v_0 \cos\alpha)t, \qquad y = (v_0 \sin\alpha)t - \tfrac{1}{2}gt^2.$$

Since $y = 0$ at the time $t_1 = (2v_0/g)\sin\alpha$, the horizontal range $x_1 = (v_0{}^2/g)\sin 2\alpha$.

PROBLEMS

1. A particle has the velocity $\mathbf{v} = \omega\mathbf{k} \times \mathbf{r}$ where ω is constant; prove that it travels in a circle with constant angular speed ω.

[Put $\mathbf{r} = r\mathbf{R}$.]

2. A particle moves in an ellipse

$$x = a \cos\varphi, \qquad y = b \sin\varphi,$$

so that the eccentric angle φ increases at a constant rate $n\,(\varphi = nt)$. Prove that its acceleration $\mathbf{a} = -n^2\mathbf{r}$ where $\mathbf{r}$ issues from the center of the ellipse.

3. A particle has the constant acceleration **a**. If its velocity is $\mathbf{v}_1$ and $\mathbf{v}_2$ at the times t_1 and t_2, show that $\mathbf{a} = (\mathbf{v}_2 - \mathbf{v}_1)/(t_2 - t_1)$.

4. A particle moves along the curve

$$x = 3t^2, \qquad y = 2t^3, \qquad z = 3t.$$

When $t = 1$, find

(a) its velocity **v** and acceleration **a**;
(b) **T**, **N**, **B** of the path;
(c) κ and τ of the path;
(d) the tangential and normal components of **a**.

(handwritten: $T \sim \dot{r}$ $N \; (\dot{r} \times \ddot{r}) \times \dot{r}$ $B \; \dot{r} \times \ddot{r}$)

5. A particle moves along the helix

$$x = \sin t, \qquad y = \cos t, \qquad z = 2t.$$

When $t = \pi/2$, find the quantities required in Prob. 4.

6. A particle moves along the path

$$x = e^t, \qquad y = e^{-t}, \qquad z = \sqrt{2}\,t.$$

When $t = 0$, find the quantities required in Prob. 4.

33. Relative Velocity. In §32 we have defined the velocity **v** of a particle P relative to a given reference frame $\mathscr{F}$. If $\mathscr{F}'$ is a second reference frame, in motion with respect to $\mathscr{F}$, how is the velocity $\mathbf{v}'$ of P relative to $\mathscr{F}'$ related to **v**?

At the instant t let P coincide with the point Q *fixed in* $\mathscr{F}'$. Then on differentiating

$$\overrightarrow{OP} = \overrightarrow{OQ} + \overrightarrow{QP}$$

with respect to t, we have

$$\frac{d}{dt}\overrightarrow{OP} = \mathbf{v}_P, \qquad \frac{d}{dt}\overrightarrow{OQ} = \mathbf{v}_Q \qquad \text{referred to } \mathscr{F},$$

$$\frac{d}{dt}\overrightarrow{QP} = \mathbf{v}'_P, \qquad \text{referred to } \mathscr{F}',$$

in which the fixed point Q is taken as origin; for, if P is in motion with respect to $\mathscr{F}'$, $\overrightarrow{QP}$ (originally zero) changes with time. We thus obtain

(1) $$\mathbf{v}_P = \mathbf{v}_Q + \mathbf{v}'_P,$$

where $\mathbf{v}_Q$, the velocity of the point Q of $\mathscr{F}'$ relative to $\mathscr{F}$, is called the *transfer velocity* of P.

If we regard the frame $\mathscr{F}$ as "fixed" and velocities referred to it as "absolute," while velocities referred to $\mathscr{F}'$, are "relative," we may state (1) as follows:

The absolute velocity of a particle is equal to the sum of its transfer and relative velocities.

In many applications all points of the frame $\mathscr{F}'$ have the same velocity relative to $\mathscr{F}$; then $\mathbf{v}_Q$ is the *velocity of translation* of $\mathscr{F}'$, and we may write

(2) $$\mathbf{v}_P = \mathbf{v}_{\mathscr{F}'} + \mathbf{v}_P'.$$

Example 1. Wind Triangle. An airplane p has the velocity $\mathbf{v}$ relative to the ground (the *earth e*), $\mathbf{v}'$ relative to the air; and the air (the *wind w*) has the velocity $\mathbf{V}$ relative to the ground; then $\mathbf{v} = \mathbf{V} + \mathbf{v}'$, from (2). In Fig. 33a,

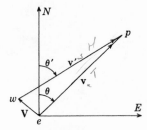

$$\mathbf{v} = \overrightarrow{ep}, \qquad \mathbf{V} = \overrightarrow{ew}, \qquad \mathbf{v}' = \overrightarrow{wp};$$

thus vectors from e and w represent velocities relative to the earth and wind, respectively. The magnitudes of $\mathbf{v}$ and $\mathbf{v}'$ give the *ground speed* (ep) and *air speed* (wp) of the plane. The directions of $\mathbf{v}$ and $\mathbf{v}'$, given as angles θ and θ' measured from the north around through the east (clockwise), determine the *track* and *heading* of the plane. The plane is pointed along its heading but travels over the ground along its track. The angle $(\mathbf{v}', \mathbf{v})$ from heading to track is the *drift angle*.

Fig. 33a. Wind triangle.

In this example $\mathscr{F}$ is the earth, $\mathscr{F}'$ the air in motion with respect to the earth.

Example 2. Interception. A plane p is flying over the track PX with the ground speed ep (Fig. 33b). As plane p passes the point P, a plane q departs from Q to

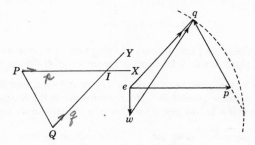

Fig. 33b. Interception.

intercept plane p. If the air speed of plane q is given, over what track shall q fly in order to intercept p?

Solution. In order that plane q may intercept plane p, the velocity of q relative to p must have the direction $\overrightarrow{QP}$.

Draw the vectors $\overrightarrow{ep}$ and $\overrightarrow{ew}$, giving the velocities of plane p and the wind w relative to earth e. With w as center describe a circle having the known air speed of plane q as radius. If a *ray* drawn through point p in the direction of $\overrightarrow{QP}$ cuts the circle at point q, plane q will intercept plane p on flying with the ground speed eq over the track QY parallel to $\overrightarrow{eq}$; for $\overrightarrow{pq}$, the velocity of plane q relative to plane p, has the direction $\overrightarrow{QP}$. Interception occurs at I after a flying time of QI/eq (or PI/ep) hours.

Interception is impossible if the air-speed circle of plane q fails to cut the ray. If the circle cuts the ray in just one point, as in Fig. 33b, plane q can intercept p on only one track. But, if the circle cuts the ray in two points, say q_1 and q_2, plane q can intercept p along two different tracks parallel to $\overrightarrow{eq_1}$ and $\overrightarrow{eq_2}$, respectively.

PROBLEMS

1. An airplane p leaves a carrier s at O and patrols along the track OY while the carrier follows the course OX with constant speed of v miles per hour (Fig. 33c). If the

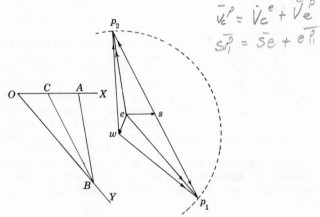

Fig. 33c. Plane returning to a carrier.

fuel in the tank allows the plane T hours of flying time at a given air speed, at what point B must the plane turn in order to rejoin the carrier at A, T hours after departure?

In Fig. 33c, $\overrightarrow{es}$ and $\overrightarrow{ew}$ give the velocities of carrier and wind, and the dotted circle, with center at w, is the *air-speed circle*. If a ray through e in the direction OY cuts this circle at p_1, show that p has the velocities relative to the earth and carrier:

$$\overrightarrow{ep_1}, \overrightarrow{sp_1} \quad \text{on leg out,} \qquad \overrightarrow{ep_2}, \overrightarrow{sp_2} \quad \text{on leg back.}$$

If the carrier is at A after T hours, the turning point B is the point where $AB \parallel ep_2$ cuts OY. The track of the plane is OBA; and the carrier is at C $(BC \parallel p_1sp_2)$ when the plane is at B.

2. A plane p, with T hours of flying time, departs from O along the track OY (Fig. 33c). Local bad weather makes landing at Y dangerous, and the plane is directed to land at an alternative airport A. Show that the farthest turning point B for the plane is located as in Fig. 33c if A is regarded as a carrier traveling from O to A with the uniform velocity $\overrightarrow{es} = \overrightarrow{OA}/T$.

3. In Prob. 1, $r = CB$ is called the *radius of action* of the plane. If the speeds of p relative to the carrier s are u_1 and u_2 (sp_1 and sp_2), show that $r = Tu_1u_2/(u_1 + u_2)$.

34. Angular Velocity Vector.
Consider first a rigid body having a *fixed line* or axis; its motion is then a rotation about this axis. The position

of the body at any instant may be specified by the angle θ (radians) between an axial plane fixed in our frame of reference $\mathscr{F}$ and an axial plane fixed in the body. By choosing a positive direction on the axis (unit vector $\mathbf{e}$), we fix the positive sense of θ by the right-handed screw convention. Then the *angular speed* ω of the body at any instant is defined as

$$\text{(1)} \qquad \omega = \frac{d\theta}{dt}.$$

Thus ω (radians per second) is positive or negative, according as θ is increasing or decreasing at the instant in question.

The velocity distribution in the revolving body may be simply expressed if we define the *angular velocity* as the vector,

$$\boldsymbol{\omega} = \frac{d\theta}{dt}\, \mathbf{e}.$$

Note that $\boldsymbol{\omega}$ always is related to the instantaneous sense of rotation by the rule of the right-hand screw.

Choose an origin O on the axis, and let $\mathbf{r} = \overrightarrow{OP}$ be the position vector of any particle of the body. Then (Fig. 34)

$$\mathbf{r} = \overrightarrow{OQ} + \overrightarrow{QP} = z\mathbf{e} + p\mathbf{R},$$

where $\mathbf{R}$ is a unit vector perpendicular to the axis and revolving with the body. Since $z\mathbf{e}$ and p are constant during the motion of P, the velocity of P is

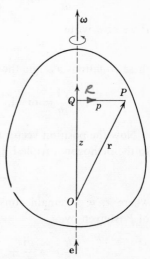

Fig. 34. Body revolving about a fixed axis.

$$\mathbf{v} = \frac{d\mathbf{r}}{dt} = p\,\frac{d\mathbf{R}}{d\theta}\frac{d\theta}{dt} = \left(p\,\frac{d\theta}{dt}\right)\mathbf{e} \times \mathbf{R} = \left(\frac{d\theta}{dt}\,\mathbf{e}\right) \times (z\mathbf{e} + p\mathbf{R});$$

that is,

$$\text{(2)} \qquad \mathbf{v} = \boldsymbol{\omega} \times \mathbf{r}.$$

The velocity of any particle of a body revolving about a fixed axis is equal to the vector product of the angular velocity and the position vector of the particle referred to any origin on the axis.

Let us next consider a rigid body having one fixed point O. Let $\mathbf{i}$ be a unit vector fixed in the body, $\mathbf{j}$ a unit vector in the direction of $d\mathbf{i}/dt$ (perpendicular to $\mathbf{i}$) and $\mathbf{k} = \mathbf{i} \times \mathbf{j}$.   Then we may write

$$\frac{d\mathbf{i}}{dt} = \alpha\mathbf{j}, \qquad \frac{d\mathbf{k}}{dt} = \frac{d\mathbf{i}}{dt} \times \mathbf{j} + \mathbf{i} \times \frac{d\mathbf{j}}{dt} = \mathbf{i} \times \frac{d\mathbf{j}}{dt}.$$

Hence $d\mathbf{k}/dt$ (perpendicular to $\mathbf{k}$) is also perpendicular to $\mathbf{i}$ and therefore parallel to $\mathbf{k} \times \mathbf{i} = \mathbf{j}$.   Thus we have

$$\frac{d\mathbf{k}}{dt} = \beta\mathbf{j}, \qquad \frac{d\mathbf{j}}{dt} = \frac{d}{dt}(\mathbf{k} \times \mathbf{i}) = \beta\mathbf{j} \times \mathbf{i} + \mathbf{k} \times \alpha\mathbf{j},$$

or, on collecting results,

$$\frac{d\mathbf{i}}{dt} = \alpha\mathbf{j}, \qquad \frac{d\mathbf{j}}{dt} = (\alpha\mathbf{k} - \beta\mathbf{i}) \times \mathbf{j}, \qquad \frac{d\mathbf{k}}{dt} = \beta\mathbf{j}.$$

If we now write

$$\boldsymbol{\omega} = \alpha\mathbf{k} - \beta\mathbf{i},$$

these equations assume the same form:

$$\frac{d\mathbf{i}}{dt} = \boldsymbol{\omega} \times \mathbf{i}, \qquad \frac{d\mathbf{j}}{dt} = \boldsymbol{\omega} \times \mathbf{j}, \qquad \frac{d\mathbf{k}}{dt} = \boldsymbol{\omega} \times \mathbf{k}.$$

Now the position vector $\mathbf{r}$ of any particle P in the body may be referred to the orthogonal triple $\mathbf{i}$, $\mathbf{j}$, $\mathbf{k}$ fixed in the body; thus

$$\mathbf{r} = \overrightarrow{OP} = x\mathbf{i} + y\mathbf{j} + z\mathbf{k},$$

where x, y, z remain constant during the motion.   Hence the velocity of P is given by

$$\frac{d\mathbf{r}}{dt} = x\frac{d\mathbf{i}}{dt} + y\frac{d\mathbf{j}}{dt} + z\frac{d\mathbf{k}}{dt} = \boldsymbol{\omega} \times (x\mathbf{i} + y\mathbf{j} + z\mathbf{k}),$$

(3) $$\mathbf{v} = \boldsymbol{\omega} \times \overrightarrow{OP}.$$

Thus, at any instant, the velocity distribution in a rigid body with one point O fixed is the same as if it were revolving about an axis through O with angular velocity $\boldsymbol{\omega}$.   The line through O in the direction of $\boldsymbol{\omega}$ is called the *instantaneous axis of rotation*, and $\boldsymbol{\omega}$ is called, as before, the *angular velocity*.   Now, however, $\boldsymbol{\omega}$ may change in direction as well as in magnitude.   With a fixed axis of rotation,

$$\boldsymbol{\omega} = \frac{d\theta}{dt}\mathbf{e} = \frac{d}{dt}(\theta\mathbf{e}),$$

so that $\boldsymbol{\omega}$ may be regarded as the time derivative of the vector angle $\theta\mathbf{e}$.

But with a variable axis of rotation $\boldsymbol{\omega}$ no longer can be expressed as a time derivative.

35. Kinematics of a Rigid Body. We next consider the motion of a free rigid body. If, at any instant, all points of the body have the same velocity $\mathbf{v}$, the motion is said to be an *instantaneous translation*. When the velocity distribution is given by $\mathbf{v} = \boldsymbol{\omega} \times \overrightarrow{AP}$, the motion is said to be an instantaneous rotation about an axis through A in the direction of $\boldsymbol{\omega}$. We now shall show that, in the most general motion of a rigid body, the velocities may be regarded as compounded of an instantaneous translation and rotation.

Let A be any point of the rigid body, and denote its velocity relative to a reference frame $\mathscr{F}$ by $\mathbf{v}_A$. Consider a second reference frame $\mathscr{F}'$ having a translation of velocity $\mathbf{v}_A$ relative to $\mathscr{F}$. Then the motion of the body relative to $\mathscr{F}'$ is an instantaneous rotation about an axis through A, since A has zero velocity relative to $\mathscr{F}'$. The velocity of any particle P of the body is therefore
$$\mathbf{v}'_P = \boldsymbol{\omega} \times \overrightarrow{AP},$$
relative to $\mathscr{F}'$, and, consequently,

(1)
$$\mathbf{v}_P = \mathbf{v}_A + \boldsymbol{\omega} \times \overrightarrow{AP},$$

relative to $\mathscr{F}$. Moreover, for any other point Q of the body,

(1)'
$$\mathbf{v}_Q = \mathbf{v}_A + \boldsymbol{\omega} \times \overrightarrow{AQ};$$

and, on subtracting this from (1), we get

(2)
$$\mathbf{v}_P = \mathbf{v}_Q + \boldsymbol{\omega} \times \overrightarrow{QP}.$$

The content of these equations is stated in the following

THEOREM. *If A is any point of a free rigid body, the velocities of its points are the same as if they were compounded of an instantaneous translation $\mathbf{v}_A$ and an instantaneous rotation $\boldsymbol{\omega}$ about an axis through A; and $\boldsymbol{\omega}$ is the same for any choice of A.*

From (2) we note that

$$\boldsymbol{\omega} \cdot \mathbf{v}_P = \boldsymbol{\omega} \cdot (\mathbf{v}_Q + \boldsymbol{\omega} \times \overrightarrow{QP}) = 0$$

(3)
$$\boldsymbol{\omega} \cdot \mathbf{v}_P = \boldsymbol{\omega} \cdot \mathbf{v}_Q; \qquad = \boldsymbol{\omega} \cdot \mathbf{v}_Q + [\boldsymbol{\omega}\,\boldsymbol{\omega}\,\overrightarrow{QP}]$$

All velocities of the rigid body have the same projection on $\boldsymbol{\omega}$, namely $(\mathbf{e} \cdot \mathbf{v}_A)\,\mathbf{e}$. This minimum velocity is actually attained at all points R of the line for which
$$(\mathbf{e} \cdot \mathbf{v}_A)\,\mathbf{e} = \mathbf{v}_A + \boldsymbol{\omega} \times \overrightarrow{AR}.$$
The vector equation of this line referred to A as origin is therefore
$$\overrightarrow{AR} \times \boldsymbol{\omega} = \mathbf{v}_A - (\mathbf{e} \cdot \mathbf{v}_A)\,\mathbf{e} = (\mathbf{e} \times \mathbf{v}_A) \times \mathbf{e},$$
or, since $\mathbf{e} = \boldsymbol{\omega}/|\boldsymbol{\omega}|$,

(4)
$$\mathbf{r} \times \boldsymbol{\omega} = \left(\frac{\boldsymbol{\omega} \times \mathbf{v}_A}{\boldsymbol{\omega} \cdot \boldsymbol{\omega}}\right) \times \boldsymbol{\omega}.$$

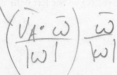
$$\left(\frac{\mathbf{v}_A \cdot \boldsymbol{\omega}}{|\boldsymbol{\omega}|}\right)\frac{\boldsymbol{\omega}}{|\boldsymbol{\omega}|}$$

The line, or *instantaneous axis*, is parallel to $\boldsymbol{\omega}$ and passes through the point R, given by

(5)
$$\overrightarrow{AR} = \frac{\boldsymbol{\omega} \times \mathbf{v}_A}{\boldsymbol{\omega} \cdot \boldsymbol{\omega}} \; ;$$

and all of its particles have the same (minimum) velocity

(6)
$$\mathbf{v}_R = (\mathbf{e} \cdot \mathbf{v}_A)\,\mathbf{e} = \left(\frac{\boldsymbol{\omega} \cdot \mathbf{v}_A}{\boldsymbol{\omega} \cdot \boldsymbol{\omega}}\right)\boldsymbol{\omega}$$

in the direction of $\boldsymbol{\omega}$.   Therefore:

At any instant the motion of a rigid body is a rotation $\boldsymbol{\omega}$ about the instantaneous axis combined with a translation $\mathbf{v}_R$ in the direction of $\boldsymbol{\omega}$; in other words, a screw motion.

When $\boldsymbol{\omega} \cdot \mathbf{v}_A = 0$, $\mathbf{v}_R = 0$ and the motion reduces to a pure rotation $\boldsymbol{\omega}$ about the instantaneous axis

(4)′
$$\mathbf{r} \times \boldsymbol{\omega} = \mathbf{v}_A.$$

When $\boldsymbol{\omega} = 0$, the motion of the body is a pure translation $\mathbf{v}_A$.

Example 1.   Plane Motion.   When the motion is plane, $\boldsymbol{\omega}$ is perpendicular to the plane and $\mathbf{v}_R = 0$.   Thus at every instant plane motion is a pure rotation about an *instantaneous center R* given by (5).   The velocities of the body at that instant are given by

(7)
$$\mathbf{v}_P = \boldsymbol{\omega} \times \overrightarrow{RP}.$$

Therefore $\mathbf{v}_P$ is perpendicular to RP and $v_P = \omega(RP.)$ A line perpendicular to $\mathbf{v}_P$ at P passes through R.   Similarly a line perpendicular to $\mathbf{v}_Q$ at Q passes through R.   We therefore have the following simple construction for the instantaneous center:

If the points P, Q of a figure in plane motion have nonparallel velocities $\mathbf{v}_P$, $\mathbf{v}_Q$, its instantaneous center is the point in which the normals to these velocities at P and Q meet.

In Fig. 35a, AB represents the connecting rod of an engine; A moves with the

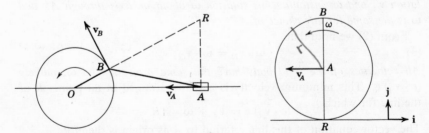

Fig. 35a. Connecting rod.   Fig. 35b. Rolling wheel.

cross-head in a straight line, B revolves with the crank in a circle.   The instantaneous center of the connecting rod is at R.

Example 2.   Rolling Wheel.   In Fig. 35b a wheel of radius r is rolling to the left with angular velocity $\boldsymbol{\omega} = \omega\mathbf{k}$. Its center has the velocity $\mathbf{v}_A = -\omega r\mathbf{i}$ and the instantaneous center R, given by

$$\overrightarrow{AR} = \frac{\boldsymbol{\omega} \times \mathbf{v}_A}{\boldsymbol{\omega} \cdot \boldsymbol{\omega}} = \frac{-\omega^2 r\,\mathbf{k} \times \mathbf{i}}{\omega^2} = -r\mathbf{j},$$

is at the point of contact with the track.   The velocity of B is therefore

$$\mathbf{v}_B = \mathbf{v}_R + \boldsymbol{\omega} \times \overrightarrow{RB} = 0 + (\omega\mathbf{k}) \times (2r\mathbf{j}) = -2\omega r\mathbf{i}.$$

PROBLEMS

1. A vane on the masthead of a ship, going due east at 10 miles per hour, points NNE. When the ship stops the vane points NW.   Find the speed of the wind.

2. At time zero ship A is d miles away from port and approaching it with the speed of u miles per hour while ship B is leaving port at the speed of v miles per hour.   If their courses are straight and include an angle α, show that the least distance D between the ships and the time T of reaching this position are given by

$$D = \frac{dv \sin \alpha}{w}, \qquad T = \frac{d(u + v \cos \alpha)}{w^2},$$

where $w = \sqrt{u^2 + v^2 + 2uv \cos \alpha}$ is the speed of A relative to B.

3. A ladder AB rests on a horizontal floor at A and against a vertical wall at B.   If it begins to slip down, find its instantaneous center R.   If the ladder makes an acute angle θ with the ground, show that the speeds of A and B are in the ratio $v_A/v_B = \tan \theta$.

4. The rigid frame $\mathscr{F}'$ has the angular velocity $\boldsymbol{\omega}$ referred to a frame $\mathscr{F}$.   If $\mathbf{u} = \overrightarrow{PQ}$ and P, Q coincide with A, B of $\mathscr{F}'$ at the instant t, show that

(8)
$$\frac{d\mathbf{u}}{dt} = \boldsymbol{\omega} \times \mathbf{u} + \frac{d'\mathbf{u}}{dt},$$

where $d'\mathbf{u}/dt$ is the rate of $\mathbf{u}$'s change referred to $\mathscr{F}'$.

$$\left[\frac{d\mathbf{u}}{dt} = \mathbf{v}_Q - \mathbf{v}_P = \mathbf{v}_B + \mathbf{v}'_Q - \mathbf{v}_A - \mathbf{v}'_P = \boldsymbol{\omega} \times \overrightarrow{AB} + \frac{d'\mathbf{u}}{dt}.\right]$$

5. If a point traverses a space curve with unit speed ($ds/dt = 1$), show that the moving trihedral TNB has the angular velocity $\boldsymbol{\omega} = \boldsymbol{\delta}$, the Darboux vector.   [Cf. (29.8).]

6. Coriolis Acceleration.   A particle P has the velocity and acceleration $\mathbf{v}$, $\mathbf{a}$ and $\mathbf{v}'$, $\mathbf{a}'$ referred to the frames $\mathscr{F}$ and $\mathscr{F}'$, respectively.   If $\mathscr{F}'$ has the angular velocity $\boldsymbol{\omega}$ relative to $\mathscr{F}$, and P momentarily coincides with the point Q in $\mathscr{F}'$, show that

(9)
$$\mathbf{v} = \mathbf{v}_Q + \mathbf{v}',$$

(10)
$$\mathbf{a} = \mathbf{a}_Q + 2\,\boldsymbol{\omega} \times \mathbf{v}' + \mathbf{a}'.$$

[Let A be a fixed origin in $\mathscr{F}'$.   Then, if $\mathbf{r} = \overrightarrow{OP}$, $\mathbf{r}' = \overrightarrow{AP}$, $\mathbf{r} = \overrightarrow{OA} + \mathbf{r}'$; hence, from (8),

$$\mathbf{v} = \frac{d\mathbf{r}}{dt} = \mathbf{v}_A + \boldsymbol{\omega} \times \mathbf{r}' + \mathbf{v}',$$

$$\mathbf{a} = \frac{d\mathbf{v}}{dt} = \mathbf{a}_A + \frac{d\boldsymbol{\omega}}{dt} \times \mathbf{r}' + \boldsymbol{\omega} \times (\boldsymbol{\omega} \times \mathbf{r}' + \mathbf{v}') + \boldsymbol{\omega} \times \mathbf{v}' + \mathbf{a}'.$$

When $\mathbf{v}' = 0$, $\mathbf{a}' = 0$ these formulas give $\mathbf{v}_Q$ and $\mathbf{a}_Q$.   The part $2\boldsymbol{\omega} \times \mathbf{v}'$ of $\mathbf{a}$ is called the *Coriolis acceleration* of P.]

(7.) The motion of a particle P along a plane curve may be referred to a system of rectangular axes $\mathscr{F}'$ revolving about O so that the x'-axis always passes through $P\,(\mathbf{i}' = \mathbf{R},\ \mathbf{j}' = \mathbf{P})$.   Let P have the plane polar coordinates r, θ referred to the fixed frame $\mathscr{F}$.   Deduce (32.8) and (32.9) from (9) and (10) by showing that:

(a) The motion of P relative of $\mathscr{F}'$ is given by

$$\mathbf{v}' = \frac{dr}{dt}\,\mathbf{R}, \qquad \mathbf{a}' = \frac{d^2 r}{dt^2}\,\mathbf{R};$$

(b) If P coincides with the point Q of $\mathscr{F}'$,

$$\mathbf{v}_Q = r\,\frac{d\theta}{dt}\,\mathbf{P}, \qquad \mathbf{a}_Q = -\left(\frac{d\theta}{dt}\right)^2 r\mathbf{R} + r\,\frac{d^2\theta}{dt^2}\,\mathbf{P},$$

(c) The Coriolis acceleration of P is

$$2\,\boldsymbol{\omega} \times \mathbf{v}' = 2\,\frac{d\theta}{dt}\,\frac{dr}{dt}\,\mathbf{P}.$$

$32.8 = \quad \bar{U} = \dfrac{dr}{dt}\,R + r\,\dfrac{d\theta}{dt}\,P$

$32.9 = \quad \bar{a} = \left[\dfrac{d^2 r}{dt^2} - r\left(\dfrac{d\theta}{dt}\right)^2\right] R + \left[r\,\dfrac{d^2\theta}{dt^2} + 2\,\dfrac{dr}{dt}\,\dfrac{d\theta}{dt}\right] P$

Chapter 4

Differential Invariants

36. Surfaces. *A surface is an aggregate of points whose coordinates are functions of two variables.* Thus the equations

(1) $$x = x(u, v), \qquad y = y(u, v), \qquad z = z(u, v)$$

represent a surface. The variables u, v are called *parameters* or *surface coordinates*; and each pair of values u, v within a prescribed region corresponds to a definite surface point. If x, y, z are functions of $t = \varphi(u, v)$, the equations (1) will represent a *curve.* In order to exclude this case, we shall require that the matrix

(2) $$\begin{pmatrix} x_u & y_u & z_u \\ x_v & y_v & z_v \end{pmatrix}$$

$x_u = \partial x / \partial u$

be *of rank two;* then at least one of its two-rowed determinants

(3) $$A = \frac{\partial(y, z)}{\partial(u, v)}, \qquad B = \frac{\partial(z, x)}{\partial(u, v)}, \qquad C = \frac{\partial(x, y)}{\partial(u, v)}$$

is not identically zero.† However the three determinants may all vanish for certain surface points. Such points are called *singular* in contrast to the *regular points* where at least one determinant is not zero.

If $\mathbf{r} = [x, y, z]$ is the position vector to the surface, equations (1) may be replaced by a single vector equation

(4) $$\mathbf{r} = \mathbf{r}(u, v);$$

† In the excluded case $x_u = x_t t_u$, $x_v = x_t t_v$, etc., and A, B, C vanish identically.

[handwritten top margin: Rank 2 → Surface; 1 → Curve]

and the matrix will be of rank two if

(5) $$\mathbf{r}_u \times \mathbf{r}_v = [A, B, C] \neq \mathbf{0}.$$

If we put $u = f(t)$, $v = g(t)$ in (2), we obtain a curve on the surface. The curves $v = b$, $u = a$ are called the *parametric curves* of the surface through the point $u = a$, $v = b$; their vector equations are

[handwritten left margin: not the same ≠ imp]

$$\mathbf{r} = \mathbf{r}(u, b), \qquad \mathbf{r} = \mathbf{r}(a, v).$$

[handwritten: v=b above first eq, u=a above]

Their tangent vectors are $\mathbf{r}_u$ and $\mathbf{r}_v$ and at any regular point $\mathbf{r}_u \times \mathbf{r}_v \neq \mathbf{0}$; that is, the tangents are not parallel and determine a normal vector $\mathbf{r}_u \times \mathbf{r}_v$ to the surface. Hence the surface has a unique normal at every regular point.

Example 1. The equations

(6) $$x = a \sin u \cos v, \qquad y = a \sin u \sin v, \qquad z = a \cos u$$

[handwritten: p 108]

represent a sphere of radius a about the origin. Referring to Fig. 42*b*, we see that $u = 0$, the colatitude measured from the $+z$-pole, while $v = \varphi$ is the longitude measured from the xz-plane. The parametric curves $u = a$, $v = b$ are parallels of latitude and meridians, respectively. The matrix (2) is now

$$\begin{pmatrix} a\cos u \cos v & a \cos u \sin v & -a \sin u \\ -a \sin u \sin v & a \sin u \cos v & 0 \end{pmatrix}$$

[handwritten column labels: x_u, y_u, z_u above top row; x_v, y_v, z_v below bottom row]

and hence

$$\mathbf{r}_u \times \mathbf{r}_v = a^2 \sin u \, [\sin u \cos v, \sin u \sin v, \cos u].$$

The vector in brackets is normal to the sphere and indeed a *unit normal:*

$$\mathbf{n} = [\sin u \cos v, \sin u \sin v, \cos u].$$

Since $\mathbf{r}_u \times \mathbf{r}_v = \mathbf{0}$ when $\sin u = 0$, the poles $u = 0$ and $u = \pi$ are singular points; these points however are not intrinsic singularities but are due to the parametric representation; in fact the unit normals at the poles are correctly given by $\mathbf{n}$.

At a regular point u_0, v_0 one of the Jacobians (3) is not zero. If $\partial(x, y)/\partial(u, v) \neq 0$, we may solve the first two equations of (1) for u and v in terms of x and y;† and, on substituting these values in the third equation, we obtain z as a function of x and y:

(7) $$z = f(x, y).$$

This equation also represents the surface which now has the parametric form

(7)′ $$x = u, \qquad y = v, \qquad z = f(u, v).$$

† *Advanced Calculus*, §85.

[handwritten bottom: $x = x(u, v)$, $y = y(u, v)$ → u, v then from $z(u, v)$ we obtain: $z = f(x, ...)$]

Finally a surface may be given by the equation

(8) $$F(x, y, z) = 0.$$

This equation may be solved for z in the neighborhood of any point for which $F_z \neq 0$; we then again obtain an equation of the form (7).   *[handwritten: $z = f(x, y)$]*
   Any three functions

(9) $$x = x(t), \qquad y = y(t), \qquad z = z(t)$$

that reduce (8) to an identity in t correspond to a surface curve having the equations (9). If we substitute from (9) in (8) and differentiate the resulting equation with respect to t, we obtain

(10) $$F_x x_t + F_y y_t + F_z z_t = 0.$$

Now $[x_t, y_t, z_t]$ represents a tangent vector to curve (9) at a point $P(t)$; and, since (10) holds for *all* surface curves through this point, the vector

(11) $$\nabla F = [F_x, F_y, F_z]$$

is normal to all surface curves through P and hence to the surface $F = 0$ itself. This vector, denoted by ∇F, is called the *gradient* of the function $F(x, y, z)$.
   If $Q(x, y, z)$ is any point on the tangent plane to the surface (8) at the point $R_0(x_0, y_0, z_0)$, the vector $\mathbf{q} - \mathbf{r}_0$ is perpendicular to ∇F at R_0; hence the equation of the tangent plane to the surface at R_0 is

(12) $$(\mathbf{q} - \mathbf{r}_0) \cdot (\nabla F)_0 = 0.$$

[handwritten: $\vec{q} - \vec{r_0} \perp \nabla F$ or]

Example 2. The plane
$$F = Ax + By + Cz + D = 0$$
is normal to $\nabla F = [A, B, C]$.

Example 3. The ellipsoid

(13) $$F = \frac{x^2}{a^2} + \frac{y^2}{b^2} + \frac{z^2}{c^2} - 1 = 0$$

[handwritten: $\vec{q} = x\,i + y\,j + z\,k$]
[handwritten: $\vec{r_0} = x_0\,i + y_0\,j + z_0\,k$]
[handwritten: $(\vec{q} - \vec{r_0}) = (x - x_0)i + (y - y_0)j + (z - z_0)k$]

has the gradient
$$\nabla F = 2[x/a^2, y/b^2, z/c^2].$$

The equation of a tangent plane at the point (x_0, y_0, z_0) is therefore

$$\frac{x_0}{a^2}(x - x_0) + \frac{y_0}{b^2}(y - y_0) + \frac{z_0}{c^2}(z - z_0) = 0;$$

or, since (x_0, y_0, z_0) satisfies (13),

$$\frac{x_0 x}{a^2} + \frac{y_0 y}{b^2} + \frac{z_0 z}{c^2} - 1 = 0.$$

#1. $z = f(x)$.

replace $f(x)$ by $f\left(\sqrt{x^2+y^2}\right)$

90   **Differential Invariants**   **§36**

PROBLEMS

1. If $u = r$, $v = \varphi$ are polar coordinates in the xy-plane, show that the *surface of revolution* obtained by revolving the curve $z = f(x)$, $y = 0$, about the z-axis has the parametric equations:

$$x = u \cos v, \qquad y = u \sin v, \qquad z = f(u).$$

$$\frac{\partial x}{\partial y} = \frac{\partial f/\partial y}{-\partial f/\partial x}$$

$u = a$

What are the parametric curves? Find the unit normal vector to the surface.

2. A straight line, which always cuts the z-axis at right angles, is revolved about and moved along this axis. The surface thus generated is called a *conoid*. If $u = r$, $v = \varphi$ are polar coordinates in the xy-plane, and the height of the line is given in terms of the angle turned, $z = f(v)$, show that the conoid has the parametric equations

$$x = u \cos v, \qquad y = u \sin v, \qquad z = f(v).$$

In particular, when dz/dv is constant, the conoid is a *right helicoid* (a spiral ramp):

$$x = u \cos v, \qquad y = u \sin v, \qquad z = av.$$

What are the parametric curves?

3. The parametric equations of a space curve Γ are

$$x = f(u), \qquad y = g(u), \qquad z = h(u).$$

What surfaces are represented by the equations and what meaning has v in each case:

(i) $x = f(u) + v \cos \alpha$, $y = g(u) + v \cos \beta$, $z = h(u) + v \cos \gamma$;
(ii) $x = v f(u)$, $y = v g(u)$, $z = v h(u)$?

What are the parametric curves $u = $ const?

4. Give parametric equations for the ellipsoid (13) patterned after equations (6) for the sphere.

5. Show that the equations

$$x = f(u) + av, \qquad y = g(u) + bv, \qquad z = h(u) + cv,$$

represent all cylinders whose rulings are parallel to the vector $[a, b, c]$. What are the parametric curves $u = $ const?

6. Show that the equations

$$x = v f(u) + a, \qquad y = v g(u) + b, \qquad z = v h(u) + c,$$

represent all cones whose vertices are at the point (a, b, c). What are the parametric curves $u = $ const?

7. Show that the shortest distance d from the point $R_1(x_1, y_1, z_1)$ to the plane $Ax + By + Cz + D = 0$ is

$$d = \frac{|Ax_1 + By_1 + Cz_1 + D|}{\sqrt{A^2 + B^2 + C^2}}. \qquad \text{[Cf. Ex. 2.]}$$

8. Show that the surface

$$x = u + v, \qquad y = u - v, \qquad z = 4u^2$$

is the parabolic cylinder $z = (x + y)^2$. Find the direction of its rulings.

$[1 \ -1 \ 0]$

$f(x,y) = (f\ a+\tau\cos\theta,\ b+\tau\sin\theta)$
$D_\tau f = (-f,\ a+\tau\cos\theta\ \cos\theta,\ b+\tau\sin\theta)\cos\theta\ \iota + f_\tau\ a+\tau\cos\theta,$
$\qquad\qquad b+\tau\sin\theta)\sin\theta$
$D_\theta f = s,(a,b)\cos\tau + f_r\ (a,b)\cos\beta$

37. Directional Derivative. A scalar or vector that is uniquely defined at every point of a region is said to be a *point function*. If the point $P(x, y, z)$ is given by the position vector $\mathbf{r} = \overrightarrow{OP}$, we denote a scalar point function by $f(\mathbf{r})$ or $f(x, y, z)$, a vector point function by $\mathbf{f}(\mathbf{r})$ or $\mathbf{f}(x, y, z)$.

Consider now a scalar point function $f(x, y, z)$ in neighborhood of a point P_0 where it is continuous and differentiable. A ray (or half-line) through P_0 in the direction of the unit vector

$$\mathbf{e} = [\cos\alpha,\ \cos\beta,\ \cos\gamma]$$

has the vector equation

$$\mathbf{r} = \mathbf{r}_0 + s\mathbf{e} \quad \text{where} \quad s = |PP_0| > 0.$$

$\vec{r} = r_0 + s\vec{e}$

Hence the parametric equations of the ray are

(1) $\quad x = x_0 + s\cos\alpha, \qquad y = y_0 + s\cos\beta, \qquad z = z_0 + s\cos\gamma.$

Along this ray $f(x, y, z)$ is a function of s alone whose right-hand derivative may be computed by the chain rule:

$$\frac{df}{ds} = \frac{\partial f}{\partial x}\frac{dx}{ds} + \frac{\partial f}{\partial y}\frac{dy}{ds} + \frac{\partial f}{\partial z}\frac{dz}{ds};$$

or, in view of equations (1),

(2) $\qquad \dfrac{df}{ds} = \cos\alpha\, f_x + \cos\beta\, f_y + \cos\gamma\, f_z.$†

If f_x, f_y, f_z are computed at the point (x_0, y_0, z_0), formula (2) gives the *directional derivative* of $f(x, y, z)$ at P_0 in the direction of $\mathbf{e}$.

Since the direction cosines of $\mathbf{e}$ are equal to $\mathbf{e} \cdot \mathbf{i}$, $\mathbf{e} \cdot \mathbf{j}$, $\mathbf{e} \cdot \mathbf{k}$, we may also write (2) in the form   *direction*   *gradient*

(3) $\qquad \dfrac{df}{ds} = \mathbf{e} \cdot (\mathbf{i} f_x + \mathbf{j} f_y + \mathbf{k} f_z),$

† For a function $f(x, y)$ of two variables the direction $\mathbf{e}$ in the xy-plane has the direction cosines

$$\cos\alpha, \qquad \cos\left(\frac{\pi}{2} - \alpha\right) = \sin\alpha, \qquad \cos\gamma = 0;$$

and

(2)′ $\qquad \dfrac{df}{ds} = \cos\alpha\, f_x + \sin\alpha\, f_y.$

in which the first factor indicates the direction of the derivative, while the second, the *gradient*

(4) $$\nabla f = \mathbf{i} f_x + \mathbf{j} f_y + \mathbf{k} f_z \qquad (36.11)$$

depends only upon the point where ∇f is computed. Thus the formula

(5) $$\frac{df}{ds} = \mathbf{e} \cdot \nabla f = |\nabla f| \cos (\nabla f, \mathbf{e})$$

sets up a one-to-one correspondence between directions $\mathbf{e}$ at a point and df/ds, the directional derivatives there. In effect, the *vector* ∇f replaces the infinity of *scalars* df/ds.

From (5) we see that at a given point P_0 the maximum value of df/ds is assumed when $\mathbf{e} = \mathbf{n}$, a unit vector in the direction of ∇f, and this maximum is $|\nabla f|$. Moreover ∇f at P_0 is normal to the level surface

(6) $$f(x, y, z) = \text{const} = f(x_0, y_0, z_0)$$

passing through P_0 (§36). Thus the *direction* of ∇f at P_0 is normal to the level surface (6) and pointing in the direction of increasing f; and its magnitude,

(7) $$|\nabla f| = \mathbf{n} \cdot \nabla f = \frac{df}{dn},$$

magnitude only !

is the derivative of f in this direction. Hence in terms of this *normal derivative* we have an expression for the gradient

(8) $$\nabla f = \mathbf{n} \frac{df}{dn}$$

entirely independent of the coordinate system. Since

(9) $$\nabla x = \mathbf{i}, \qquad \nabla y = \mathbf{j}, \qquad \nabla z = \mathbf{k},$$

the equations

(10) $$\nabla f = \nabla x\, f_x + \nabla y\, f_y + \nabla z\, f_z ,$$

(11) $$|\nabla f|^2 = f_x^2 + f_y^2 + f_z^2 ,$$

hold in any system of rectangular coordinates.

If we replace x, y, z by functions of other independent variables u, v, w, $f(x, y, z)$ becomes $F(u, v, w)$. Along the ray (1)

$$\frac{dF}{ds} = \frac{du}{ds}\frac{\partial F}{\partial u} + \frac{dv}{ds}\frac{\partial F}{\partial v} + \frac{dw}{ds}\frac{\partial F}{\partial w} ,$$

or in view of (5)

$$\mathbf{e} \cdot \nabla F = \mathbf{e} \cdot (\nabla u\, F_u + \nabla v\, F_v + \nabla w\, F_w).$$

But, since this holds for all vectors **e**,

(12) $$\nabla F = \nabla u\, F_u + \nabla v\, F_v + \nabla w\, F_w.$$

This expression for the gradient in *curvilinear coordinates u, v, w* obviously includes (10).

In particular, for a function $F(u)$ of u alone

(13) $$\nabla F(u) = \frac{dF}{du}\,\nabla u.$$

For example, if r denotes the distance from the origin,

(14) $$\nabla F(r) = \frac{dF}{dr}\,\frac{\mathbf{r}}{r}.$$ (Ex. 1).

Example 1. The polar distance

$$OP = r = \sqrt{x^2 + y^2 + z^2}$$

has the gradient

(15) $$\nabla r = [x/r,\ y/r,\ z/r] = \mathbf{r}/r,$$

the unit radial vector in the direction $\overrightarrow{OP}$. This result also follows from the intrinsic definition (8); for the level surfaces of r are spheres about the origin for which

$$\mathbf{n} = \frac{\mathbf{r}}{r}, \qquad \frac{dr}{dn} = \frac{dr}{dr} = 1.$$

[handwritten: $\nabla f = \bar{n}\,\frac{df}{dn}$; $\frac{df}{dn} = \bar{n}\cdot\nabla r = \frac{df}{dr} = \frac{\bar{r}}{r}\cdot\nabla r = 1$; $\frac{dr}{du} = \frac{dr}{dr} = 1$; but $\bar{n} = \frac{r}{r}$]

Example 2. If the point P has the plane polar coordinates r, φ, we have

(16) $$\nabla r = \mathbf{R}, \qquad \nabla\varphi = \mathbf{P}/r,$$

where **P** is the unit vector 90° ahead of **R** (§28). These results follow at once from (8). For example, the level curves of φ are rays through the origin for which

$$\mathbf{n} = \mathbf{P}, \qquad \frac{d\varphi}{dn} = \lim_{\Delta\varphi\to 0}\frac{\Delta\varphi}{r\sin\Delta\varphi} = \frac{1}{r}.$$

If $f(r, \varphi) = c$ is the equation of a curve in polar coordinates, a normal to the curve at any point is given by

(17) $$\nabla f(r, \varphi) = f_r\,\nabla r + f_\varphi\,\nabla\varphi = f_r\,\mathbf{R} + \frac{f_\varphi}{r}\,\mathbf{P}.$$

PROBLEMS

1. If $f(x, y) = x^2 - 2xy + y^2$, find
(a) ∇f at $(2, 3)$;
(b) df/ds at $(2, 3)$ along a ray inclined $+45°$ to the x-axis;
(c) the direction and magnitude of df/ds at $(2, 3)$ when its value is greatest.

2. If $f(x, y, z) = xy + yz + zx$, find
(a) ∇f at $(1, 1, 3)$;
(b) df/ds at $(1, 1, 3)$ in the direction of $[1, 1, 1]$;
(c) the normal derivative df/dn at $(1, 1, 3)$;
(d) the equations of the tangent plane and normal line to the surface $xy + yz + zx = 7$ at $(1, 1, 3)$.

3. If $f(r, \varphi) = r - 2a \sin \varphi$, find ∇f at the point (r, φ). What is the magnitude of the normal derivative at (r, θ)?

4. If $u(x, y)$ and $v(x, y)$ are functions that satisfy the equations $u_x = v_y, \ u_y = -v_x$ show that

(a) $\nabla u = \nabla v \times \mathbf{k}, \ \nabla v = \mathbf{k} \times \nabla u$.

(b)   At any point (x, y), $du/ds = dv/ds'$ where s' is a ray 90° in advance of s.

5. If $r = \sqrt{x^2 + y^2 + z^2}$, show that

$$\nabla r^2 = 2\mathbf{r}, \qquad \nabla(1/r) = -\mathbf{r}/r^3, \qquad \nabla \log r = \mathbf{r}/r^2, \qquad \nabla(\mathbf{a} \cdot \mathbf{r}) = \mathbf{a}.$$

6. Show that the systems of equilateral hyperbolas $x^2 - y^2 = a$, $xy = b$ cut at right angles.

[The normal to the curve $f(x, y) = c$ is parallel to ∇f.]

7. Show that the systems of cardioids $r = a(1 - \cos \varphi)$, $r = b(1 + \cos \varphi)$ cut at right angles. [Cf. (16).]

8. Show that the curve $f(r_1, r_2) = c$ in bipolar coordinates has a normal parallel to $f_{r_1}\mathbf{R}_1 + f_{r_2}\mathbf{R}_2$.

Show that the systems of confocal ellipses and hyperbolas $r_1 + r_2 = a$, $r_1 - r_2 = b$ cut at right angles.

9. Prove that the systems of coaxal circles $r_1/r_2 = a$, $\varphi_2 - \varphi_1 = b$ cut at right angles.

38. Gradient of a Vector. A vector point function $\mathbf{f}(\mathbf{r})$ is given by three scalar point functions f_1, f_2, f_3 which form its rectangular components:

$$(1) \qquad\qquad \mathbf{f}(\mathbf{r}) = \mathbf{i}f_1 + \mathbf{j}f_2 + \mathbf{k}f_3.$$

If these scalar functions are differentiable, we say that $\mathbf{f}(\mathbf{r})$ is differentiable.

If $\mathbf{f}(\mathbf{r})$ is differentiable, we may compute its directional derivative at P_0 in the direction $\mathbf{e}$ just as in §37:

$$(2) \qquad\qquad \frac{d\mathbf{f}}{ds} = \cos \alpha \, \mathbf{f}_x + \cos \beta \, \mathbf{f}_y + \cos \gamma \, \mathbf{f}_z.$$

If we replace the direction cosines by $\mathbf{e} \cdot \mathbf{i}$, $\mathbf{e} \cdot \mathbf{j}$, $\mathbf{e} \cdot \mathbf{k}$, we may write symbolically

$$(3) \qquad\qquad \frac{d\mathbf{f}}{ds} = \mathbf{e} \cdot (\mathbf{i}\mathbf{f}_x + \mathbf{j}\mathbf{f}_y + \mathbf{k}\mathbf{f}_z).$$

Here the quantity in parenthesis has the same form as the gradient of a scalar. But since $\mathbf{f}$ is a *vector*, the *gradient*

$$(4) \qquad\qquad \nabla \mathbf{f} = \mathbf{i}\mathbf{f}_x + \mathbf{j}\mathbf{f}_y + \mathbf{k}\mathbf{f}_z$$

has as yet no meaning; for it consists of the sum of three ordered pairs of vectors. An expression of this sort is called a *dyadic*, whereas the ordered vector pairs are called *dyads*. We could now develop an algebra of dyadics by defining equivalence, addition, and multiplication;† but

† See *Vector and Tensor Analysis*, Chapter IV, for a systematic development of dyadic algebra.

for our purpose this is unnecessary. We shall merely regard $\nabla\mathbf{f}$ defined by (4) as an *operator* that sets up a one-to-one correspondence between directions $\mathbf{e}$ at a point and $d\mathbf{f}/ds$, the directional derivatives there:

$$(5) \qquad \frac{d\mathbf{f}}{ds} = \mathbf{e} \cdot \nabla\mathbf{f}.$$

In effect, the *dyadic* $\nabla\mathbf{f}$ replaces an infinity of vectors $d\mathbf{f}/ds$.

We shall call any "sum" of dyads a *dyadic*: thus the dyadic

$$\mathbf{P} = \mathbf{a}_1\mathbf{b}_1 + \mathbf{a}_2\mathbf{b}_2 + \cdots + \mathbf{a}_n\mathbf{b}_n$$

represents a general dyadic in which the vectors $\mathbf{a}_i$ are *antecedents*, $\mathbf{b}_i$ *consequents*. The dyadic

$$\mathbf{P}_c = \mathbf{b}_1\mathbf{a}_1 + \mathbf{b}_2\mathbf{a}_2 + \cdots + \mathbf{b}_n\mathbf{a}_n$$

is called the *conjugate* of $\mathbf{P}$; and, if (with equality defined as below)

$$\mathbf{P} = \mathbf{P}_c, \qquad \mathbf{P} \text{ is } symmetric,$$

$$\mathbf{P} = -\mathbf{P}_c, \qquad \mathbf{P} \text{ is } skew.$$

Symmetric and skew dyadics are especially important since any dyadic $\mathbf{P}$ can be expressed as a sum of a symmetric and a skew dyadic in exactly one way, namely

$$(6) \qquad \mathbf{P} = \frac{\mathbf{P} + \mathbf{P}_c}{2} + \frac{\mathbf{P} - \mathbf{P}_c}{2}.$$

The proof follows from $\mathbf{P}_{cc} = \mathbf{P}$ and is left to the reader. ✓ *see bot of p 94*

When vectors are cross-multiplied into a dyadic $\mathbf{P} = \sum \mathbf{a}_i\mathbf{b}_i$ new dyadics are formed; thus we define

$$(7) \qquad \mathbf{r} \times \mathbf{P} = \sum (\mathbf{r} \times \mathbf{a}_i)\mathbf{b}_i, \qquad \mathbf{P} \times \mathbf{r} = \sum \mathbf{a}_i(\mathbf{b}_i \times \mathbf{r}).$$

DEFINITION. *Two dyadics are said to be equal when both transform an arbitrary vector in exactly the same way*:

$$\mathbf{P} = \mathbf{Q} \qquad \text{when and only when} \qquad \mathbf{u} \cdot \mathbf{P} = \mathbf{u} \cdot \mathbf{Q}$$

for any vector $\mathbf{u}$.

From this definition we easily deduce the

THEOREM. *If* $\mathbf{e}_i \cdot \mathbf{P} = \mathbf{e}_i \cdot \mathbf{Q}$ *for three noncoplanar vectors* $\mathbf{e}_1, \mathbf{e}_2, \mathbf{e}_3,$ *then* $\mathbf{P} = \mathbf{Q}$.

Proof. As in §10 we can express any vector $\mathbf{u}$ in the form $\mathbf{u} = u^1\mathbf{e}_1 + u^2\mathbf{e}_2 + u^3\mathbf{e}_3$; hence

$$\mathbf{u} \cdot \mathbf{P} = \sum_{i=1}^{3} u^i\mathbf{e}_i \cdot \mathbf{P} = \sum_{i=1}^{3} u^i\mathbf{e}_i \cdot \mathbf{Q} = \mathbf{u} \cdot \mathbf{Q}.$$

When **f** is the position vector $\mathbf{r} = x\mathbf{i} + y\mathbf{j} + z\mathbf{k}$, $\mathbf{r}_x = \mathbf{i}$, $\mathbf{r}_y = \mathbf{j}$, $\mathbf{r}_z = \mathbf{k}$, and, from (4),

$$(8)\qquad\qquad \nabla\mathbf{r} = \mathbf{ii} + \mathbf{jj} + \mathbf{kk} = \mathbf{I}.$$

The dyadic **I** is called the *idemfactor* (Latin *idem* = same) because it transforms any vector **u** into itself:

$$(9)\qquad\qquad \mathbf{u}\cdot\mathbf{I} = \mathbf{I}\cdot\mathbf{u} = \mathbf{u}\qquad \text{for every } \mathbf{u};$$

for from (15.10)

$$(10)\qquad \mathbf{u} = \mathbf{u}\cdot\mathbf{ii} + \mathbf{u}\cdot\mathbf{jj} + \mathbf{u}\cdot\mathbf{kk} = \mathbf{ii}\cdot\mathbf{u} + \mathbf{jj}\cdot\mathbf{u} + \mathbf{kk}\cdot\mathbf{u}.$$

Moreover, since $u^i = \mathbf{u}\cdot\mathbf{e}^i$, we have from (16.1)

$$(11)\qquad\qquad \mathbf{u} = \sum_{i=1}^{3}\mathbf{u}\cdot\mathbf{e}^i\mathbf{e}_i = \sum_{i=1}^{3}\mathbf{e}_i\mathbf{e}^i\cdot\mathbf{u}.$$

We thus obtain the more general form of **I**:

$$(12)\qquad \mathbf{I} = \mathbf{e}^1\mathbf{e}_1 + \mathbf{e}^2\mathbf{e}_2 + \mathbf{e}^3\mathbf{e}_3 = \mathbf{e}_1\mathbf{e}^1 + \mathbf{e}_2\mathbf{e}^2 + \mathbf{e}_3\mathbf{e}^3.$$

Finally, to justify the use of the plus sign between dyads, we define the dyadic sum $\mathbf{P} + \mathbf{Q}$ by

$$(13)\qquad \mathbf{u}\cdot(\mathbf{P}+\mathbf{Q}) = \mathbf{u}\cdot\mathbf{P} + \mathbf{u}\cdot\mathbf{Q}\qquad \text{for every } \mathbf{u}.$$

Thus, to add two dyadics, we merely add the dyads of one to those of the other.

The zero dyadic **O** has the property

$$(14)\qquad\qquad\qquad \mathbf{P} + \mathbf{O} = \mathbf{P};$$

and, from (13), we have also

$$(15)\qquad\qquad \mathbf{u}\cdot\mathbf{O} = 0\qquad \text{for every } \mathbf{u}.$$

Example. The dyadic $\mathbf{a}\times\mathbf{I} = \mathbf{I}\times\mathbf{a}$; for

$$\mathbf{u}\cdot(\mathbf{a}\times\mathbf{I}) = \mathbf{u}\cdot(\mathbf{a}\times\mathbf{i})\mathbf{i} + (\mathbf{a}\times\mathbf{j})\mathbf{j} + (\mathbf{a}\times\mathbf{k})\mathbf{k}$$
$$= (\mathbf{u}\times\mathbf{a})\cdot(\mathbf{ii}+\mathbf{jj}+\mathbf{kk}) = \mathbf{u}\times\mathbf{a};$$
$$\mathbf{u}\cdot(\mathbf{I}\times\mathbf{a}) = \mathbf{u}\cdot(\mathbf{ii}\times\mathbf{a}+\mathbf{jj}\times\mathbf{a}+\mathbf{kk}\times\mathbf{a})$$
$$= (\mathbf{u}\cdot\mathbf{ii}+\mathbf{u}\cdot\mathbf{jj}+\mathbf{u}\cdot\mathbf{kk})\times\mathbf{a} = \mathbf{u}\times\mathbf{a}.$$

39. Invariants of a Dyadic. By definition the dyadic equation $\mathbf{P}=\mathbf{Q}$ is equivalent to the vector equations

$$(1)\qquad\qquad \mathbf{u}\cdot\mathbf{P} = \mathbf{u}\cdot\mathbf{Q}\qquad \text{for every } \mathbf{u}.$$

Hence it is also equivalent to the scalar equations

(2) $\mathbf{u} \cdot \mathbf{P} \cdot \mathbf{v} = \mathbf{u} \cdot \mathbf{Q} \cdot \mathbf{v}$ for any $\mathbf{u}$, $\mathbf{v}$,

or to the vector equations

(3) $\mathbf{P} \cdot \mathbf{v} = \mathbf{Q} \cdot \mathbf{v}$ for every $\mathbf{v}$.

In these equations $\mathbf{u}$ is used as a *prefactor*, $\mathbf{v}$ as a *postfactor*.

From (1) and (3) we have the dyadic distributive laws:

(4)(5) $(\mathbf{a} + \mathbf{b})\mathbf{c} = \mathbf{ac} + \mathbf{bc}$, $\mathbf{a}(\mathbf{b} + \mathbf{c}) = \mathbf{ab} + \mathbf{ac}$.

Thus (4) follows at once from

$$\mathbf{u} \cdot (\mathbf{a} + \mathbf{b})\mathbf{c} = \mathbf{u} \cdot (\mathbf{ac} + \mathbf{bc}).$$

Using these laws, we may express a dyadic $\mathbf{P} = \sum \mathbf{a}_i \mathbf{b}_i$ in various forms by substituting vector sums for $\mathbf{a}_i$, $\mathbf{b}_i$, and expanding or collecting terms. In all these changes, however, there are certain quantities formed from the vectors of the dyadic which remain the same. Among these *invariants* of $\mathbf{P}$, the most important are the scalar and the vector

(6)(7) $P_s = \sum \mathbf{a}_i \cdot \mathbf{b}_i,$ $\mathbf{p} = \sum \mathbf{a}_i \times \mathbf{b}_i$

obtained by placing a dot or a cross between the vectors of each dyadic in $\mathbf{P}$.

THEOREM 1. *The dyadic* $\mathbf{P} = \sum \mathbf{a}_i \mathbf{b}_i$ *has the scalar invariant* $P_s = \sum \mathbf{a}_i \cdot \mathbf{b}_i$ *and the vector invariant* $\mathbf{p} = \sum \mathbf{a}_i \times \mathbf{b}_i$.

Proof. Let $\mathbf{P} = \mathbf{Q}$. From (10.13)

$$\mathbf{u} \cdot \mathbf{v} = u_1 v_1 + u_2 v_2 + u_3 v_3$$

$$= \mathbf{i} \cdot (\mathbf{uv}) \cdot \mathbf{i} + \mathbf{j} \cdot (\mathbf{uv}) \cdot \mathbf{j} + \mathbf{k} \cdot (\mathbf{uv}) \cdot \mathbf{k};$$

hence

$$P_s = \mathbf{i} \cdot \mathbf{P} \cdot \mathbf{i} + \mathbf{j} \cdot \mathbf{P} \cdot \mathbf{j} + \mathbf{k} \cdot \mathbf{P} \cdot \mathbf{k}, \qquad Q_s = \mathbf{i} \cdot \mathbf{Q} \cdot \mathbf{i} + \mathbf{j} \cdot \mathbf{Q} \cdot \mathbf{j} + \mathbf{k} \cdot \mathbf{Q} \cdot \mathbf{k}.$$

Since the corresponding terms in these sums are equal by (2), $P_s = Q_s$.

Again, from (11.8)

$$(\mathbf{u} \times \mathbf{v})_1 = u_2 v_3 - u_3 v_2 = \mathbf{j} \cdot (\mathbf{uv}) \cdot \mathbf{k} - \mathbf{k} \cdot (\mathbf{uv}) \cdot \mathbf{j};$$

hence the first components of $\mathbf{p}$ and $\mathbf{q}$ are

$$p_1 = \mathbf{j} \cdot \mathbf{P} \cdot \mathbf{k} - \mathbf{k} \cdot \mathbf{P} \cdot \mathbf{j}, \qquad q_1 = \mathbf{j} \cdot \mathbf{Q} \cdot \mathbf{k} - \mathbf{k} \cdot \mathbf{Q} \cdot \mathbf{j}.$$

Since the corresponding terms on the right are equal by (2), $p_1 = q_1$; similarly $p_2 = q_2$, $p_3 = q_3$, and hence $\mathbf{p} = \mathbf{q}$.

THEOREM 2. *The scalar and vector invariants of the sum of two dyadics are the sums of their respective invariants.*

Proof. If $\mathbf{R} = \mathbf{P} + \mathbf{Q}$, it is obvious that

$$R_s = P_s + Q_s, \qquad \mathbf{r} = \mathbf{p} + \mathbf{q}.$$

It is this property that gives these invariants their special importance in geometry and physics.

Example. From (38.8) we see that the invariants of $\mathbf{I}$ are

$$\mathbf{i} \cdot \mathbf{i} + \mathbf{j} \cdot \mathbf{j} + \mathbf{k} \cdot \mathbf{k} = 3, \qquad \mathbf{i} \times \mathbf{i} + \mathbf{j} \times \mathbf{j} + \mathbf{k} \times \mathbf{k} = 0.$$

Hence, from (38.12), we deduce that

$$\mathbf{e}^1 \cdot \mathbf{e}_1 + \mathbf{e}^2 \cdot \mathbf{e}_2 + \mathbf{e}^3 \cdot \mathbf{e}_3 = 3 \qquad \mathbf{e}^1 \times \mathbf{e}_1 + \mathbf{e}^2 \times \mathbf{e}_2 + \mathbf{e}^3 \times \mathbf{e}_3 = 0$$

PROBLEMS

1. If $\mathbf{e}_i \cdot \mathbf{P} = \mathbf{f}_i$ $(i = 1, 2, 3)$, prove that $\mathbf{P} = \mathbf{e}^1\mathbf{f}_1 + \mathbf{e}^2\mathbf{f}_2 + \mathbf{e}^3\mathbf{f}_3$.

2. If $\mathbf{P} \cdot \mathbf{e}_i = \mathbf{g}_i$ $(i = 1, 2, 3)$, prove that $\mathbf{P} = \mathbf{g}_1\mathbf{e}^1 + \mathbf{g}_2\mathbf{e}^2 + \mathbf{g}_3\mathbf{e}^3$.

3. If $\mathbf{a}$, $\mathbf{b}$, $\mathbf{c}$ are arbitrary noncoplanar vectors, show that any dyadic may be expressed as the sum of three dyads having $\mathbf{a}$, $\mathbf{b}$, $\mathbf{c}$ either as antecedents or as consequents.

4. Prove that $\mathbf{a} \times \mathbf{I}$ is a skew dyadic.

5. Find the invariants of $\mathbf{a} \times \mathbf{I}$.

6. Prove that $\mathbf{ab} - \mathbf{ba} = -\tfrac{1}{2}\mathbf{I} \times (\mathbf{a} \times \mathbf{b})$.

7. If the dyadic $\mathbf{P}$ is skew and has the vector invariant $\mathbf{p}$, show that $\mathbf{P} = -\tfrac{1}{2}\mathbf{I} \times \mathbf{p}$. Show that $\mathbf{P}$ transforms all vectors into vectors perpendicular to $\mathbf{p}$.

8. Show that the vector invariant of any symmetric dyadic is zero.

9. Show that the scalar invariant of any skew dyadic is zero.

10. The dyadic product $\mathbf{P} \cdot \mathbf{Q}$ is defined by the equation

(8) $$(\mathbf{P} \cdot \mathbf{Q}) \cdot \mathbf{u} = \mathbf{P} \cdot (\mathbf{Q} \cdot \mathbf{u}) \qquad \text{for every } \mathbf{u}.$$

From this definition show that dyadic multiplication is

Associative: $$(\mathbf{P} \cdot \mathbf{Q}) \cdot \mathbf{R} = \mathbf{P} \cdot (\mathbf{Q} \cdot \mathbf{R});$$

Distributive: $$(\mathbf{P} + \mathbf{Q}) \cdot \mathbf{R} = \mathbf{P} \cdot \mathbf{R} + \mathbf{Q} \cdot \mathbf{R};$$

but not in general commutative: $\mathbf{P} \cdot \mathbf{Q} \neq \mathbf{Q} \cdot \mathbf{P}$.

[*Vector and Tensor Analysis*, §65.]

11. From the definition (8) deduce the dyad product:

(9) $$(\mathbf{ab}) \cdot (\mathbf{cd}) = (\mathbf{b} \cdot \mathbf{c})\,\mathbf{ad}.$$

12. Use (9) to prove that

(10) $$(\mathbf{P} \cdot \mathbf{Q})_c = \mathbf{Q}_c \cdot \mathbf{P}_c.$$

13. From (8) and (10) show that

(11) $$\mathbf{u} \cdot (\mathbf{P} \cdot \mathbf{Q}) = (\mathbf{u} \cdot \mathbf{P}) \cdot \mathbf{Q} \qquad \text{for every } \mathbf{u}.$$

14. The idemfactor I is often called the *unit dyadic*. Justify this term by proving that

(12) $P \cdot I = I \cdot P = P.$

15. Prove that, in *all* cases,

$$a\,b \times c + b\,c \times a + c\,a \times b = [abc]I.$$

16. If $P^n = P \cdot P \cdots$ to n factors, prove that

$$I \times k = ji - ij, \qquad (I \times k)^2 = -ii - jj,$$
$$(I \times k)^3 = ij - ji, \qquad (I \times k)^4 = ii + jj.$$

40. Divergence and Rotation.   The gradient ∇f (or grad f) of a vector point function is a dyadic whose invariants are of the utmost importance in geometry and mathematical physics.

The scalar invariant, formed by dot-multiplying the dyad vectors of ∇f, is called the *divergence* of f and is written $\nabla \cdot f$ or div f.

The vector invariant, formed by cross-multiplying the dyad vectors of ∇f, is called the *rotation* or *curl* of f and is written $\nabla \times f$, rot f, or curl f.†

In terms of rectangular coordinates we therefore have the defining equations:

(1) $\nabla f = \mathrm{grad}\ f = i\,f_x + j\,f_y + k\,f_z,$

(2) $\nabla \cdot f = \mathrm{div}\ f = i \cdot f_x + j \cdot f_y + k \cdot f_z,$

(3) $\nabla \times f = \mathrm{rot}\ f = i \times f_x + j \times f_y + k \times f_z.$

If f is resolved into its rectangular components

$$f = f_1 i + f_2 j + f_3 k,$$

f_1, f_2, f_3 are scalar functions of $x,\ y,\ z$, and ∇f assumes the nine-term form:

$$D_x f_1\ ii + D_x f_2\ ij + D_x f_3\ ik +$$

(4) $\nabla f = D_y f_1\ ji + D_y f_2\ jj + D_y f_3\ jk +$

$$D_z f_1\ ki + D_z f_2\ kj + D_z f_3\ kk,$$

where $D_x = \partial/\partial x$, etc.   This form is often abbreviated into the matrix,

(4)′ $\nabla f = \begin{pmatrix} D_x f_1 & D_x f_2 & D_x f_3 \\ D_y f_1 & D_y f_2 & D_y f_3 \\ D_z f_1 & D_z f_2 & D_z f_3 \end{pmatrix},$

† *Curl* is favored by the British and American authors, *rotation* by continental Europeans.   In the interests of a uniform notation (for the language of mathematics is universal) we write rot f in this book although we may speak of "curl."

in which the nine *unit dyads* **ii**, **ij**, $\cdots$, **kk** are omitted.†   By dotting and crossing between the vectors of (4), the invariants become

(5)   *dotting* $\operatorname{div} \mathbf{f} = \dfrac{\partial f_1}{\partial x} + \dfrac{\partial f_2}{\partial y} + \dfrac{\partial f_3}{\partial z}$,

(6)   *Crossing* $\operatorname{rot} \mathbf{f} = \left(\dfrac{\partial f_3}{\partial y} - \dfrac{\partial f_2}{\partial z}\right)\mathbf{i} + \left(\dfrac{\partial f_1}{\partial z} - \dfrac{\partial f_3}{\partial x}\right)\mathbf{j} + \left(\dfrac{\partial f_2}{\partial x} - \dfrac{\partial f_1}{\partial y}\right)\mathbf{k}.$

The last is easily remembered in the determinant form (11.9):

(7)   *rot f* $= \nabla \times \mathbf{f} = \begin{vmatrix} \mathbf{i} & \mathbf{j} & \mathbf{k} \\ \partial/\partial x & \partial/\partial y & \partial/\partial z \\ f_1 & f_2 & f_3 \end{vmatrix}.$

$r_x = i \quad r_y = j \quad r_z = k$

For the position vector $\mathbf{r} = x\mathbf{i} + y\mathbf{j} + z\mathbf{k}$ we have

$$\nabla \mathbf{r} = \mathbf{i}\mathbf{r}_x + \mathbf{j}\mathbf{r}_y + \mathbf{k}\mathbf{r}_z = \mathbf{ii} + \mathbf{jj} + \mathbf{kk}$$

the *idemfactor*; hence

(8) $\nabla \mathbf{r} = \mathbf{I}, \quad \operatorname{div} \mathbf{r} = 3, \quad \operatorname{rot} \mathbf{r} = \mathbf{0}.$

When $\mathbf{f} = \nabla\varphi$, the gradient of a scalar $\varphi(x, y, z)$, we have

$$f_1 = \frac{\partial\varphi}{\partial x}, \quad f_2 = \frac{\partial\varphi}{\partial y}, \quad f_3 = \frac{\partial\varphi}{\partial z}.$$

With these components (5) and (6) give

(9) $\operatorname{div} \nabla\varphi = \dfrac{\partial^2\varphi}{\partial x^2} + \dfrac{\partial^2\varphi}{\partial y^2} + \dfrac{\partial^2\varphi}{\partial z^2}$;

(10) $\operatorname{rot} \nabla\varphi = \mathbf{0}.$

In (9) the differential operator $\operatorname{div} \nabla$ or $\nabla \cdot \nabla$ is called the *Laplacian* and often is written

$$\nabla^2 = \frac{\partial^2}{\partial x^2} + \frac{\partial^2}{\partial y^2} + \frac{\partial^2}{\partial z^2}.$$

The proof of (10) depends on the equality of the mixed second derivatives of φ (as $\varphi_{xy} = \varphi_{yx}$); this is always the case when the derivatives in question are continuous.‡

  † When dyadics are written in matrix form, their algebra is the same as matric algebra. See *Vector and Tensor Analysis*, §78. Note that the idemfactor **I** becomes the unit matrix, the zero dyadic the zero matrix.

  ‡ *Advanced Calculus*, p. 163.

When $\mathbf{f} = \text{rot } \mathbf{g}$, the rotation of a vector $\mathbf{g}(x, y, z)$,

$$f_1 = \frac{\partial g_3}{\partial y} - \frac{\partial g_2}{\partial z}, \qquad f_2 = \frac{\partial g_1}{\partial z} - \frac{\partial g_3}{\partial x}, \qquad f_3 = \frac{\partial g_2}{\partial x} - \frac{\partial g_1}{\partial y}.$$

In this case (5) and (6) give

(11) $\text{div rot } \mathbf{g} = 0,$

(12) $\text{rot rot } \mathbf{g} = \nabla \text{ div } \mathbf{g} - \nabla^2 \mathbf{g}.$

The proofs are straightforward and depend upon the equality of mixed second derivatives. In (12) for example, the first component of rot rot $\mathbf{g}$ is

$$\frac{\partial}{\partial y}\left(\frac{\partial g_2}{\partial x} - \frac{\partial g_1}{\partial y}\right) - \frac{\partial}{\partial z}\left(\frac{\partial g_1}{\partial z} - \frac{\partial g_3}{\partial x}\right) =$$

$$\frac{\partial}{\partial x}\left(\frac{\partial g_1}{\partial x} + \frac{\partial g_2}{\partial y} + \frac{\partial g_3}{\partial z}\right) - \nabla^2 g_1 = \frac{\partial}{\partial x} \text{ div } \mathbf{g} - \nabla^2 g_1.$$

The four identities (9) through (12) are of the first importance. When written as

(9) $\nabla \cdot \nabla \varphi = \nabla^2 \varphi,$

(10) $\nabla \times \nabla \varphi = \mathbf{0},$

(11) $\nabla \cdot \nabla \times \mathbf{g} = 0,$

(12) $\nabla \times (\nabla \times \mathbf{g}) = \nabla(\nabla \cdot \mathbf{g}) - \nabla^2 \mathbf{g},$

they may be remembered by treating ∇ formally as a vector. In (10), $\nabla \times \nabla = \mathbf{0}$; in (11) ∇ enters twice in the box product; and in (12) the expansion theorem (12,1) gives the correct result. Thus in symbolic form, these basic formulas are easier to remember than to forget!

Example 1. The gradient of the vector function

$$\mathbf{f} = z\mathbf{i} + x\mathbf{j} + y\mathbf{k}$$

is the dyadic

$$\nabla \mathbf{f} = \mathbf{ij} + \mathbf{jk} + \mathbf{ki} \tag{1};$$

or, in matrix form (4)′,

$$\nabla \mathbf{f} = \begin{pmatrix} 0 & 1 & 0 \\ 0 & 0 & 1 \\ 1 & 0 & 0 \end{pmatrix}$$

Hence

$$\text{div } \mathbf{f} = \mathbf{i} \cdot \mathbf{j} + \mathbf{j} \cdot \mathbf{k} + \mathbf{k} \cdot \mathbf{i} = 0, \tag{2},$$

$$\text{rot } \mathbf{f} = \mathbf{i} \times \mathbf{j} + \mathbf{j} \times \mathbf{k} + \mathbf{k} \times \mathbf{i} = \mathbf{k} + \mathbf{i} + \mathbf{j} \tag{3};$$

or we may compute div $\mathbf{f}$ from (5), rot $\mathbf{f}$ from (6). Moreover the scalar function

$$|\mathbf{f}| = (z^2 + x^2 + y^2)^{1/2}.$$

has the gradient

$$\nabla |\mathbf{f}| = \frac{x\mathbf{i} + y\mathbf{j} + z\mathbf{k}}{(x^2 + y^2 + z^2)^{1/2}} = \frac{\mathbf{r}}{r}. \tag{37.4}.$$

Example 2. The velocity at any point P of a rigid body is given by (35.1)

$$\mathbf{v} = \mathbf{v}_A + \boldsymbol{\omega} \times \mathbf{r} \qquad (\mathbf{r} = \overrightarrow{AP}).$$

At any given instant t, $\mathbf{v}$ is a vector point function; and from (3)

$$\text{rot } \mathbf{v} = \text{rot } (\boldsymbol{\omega} \times \mathbf{r})$$

$$= \mathbf{i} \times \left(\boldsymbol{\omega} \times \frac{\partial \mathbf{r}}{\partial x} \right) + \text{cycl}$$

$$= \mathbf{i} \times (\boldsymbol{\omega} \times \mathbf{i}) + \text{cycl}$$

$$= \boldsymbol{\omega} - \omega_1 \mathbf{i} + \boldsymbol{\omega} - \omega_2 \mathbf{j} + \boldsymbol{\omega} - \omega_3 \mathbf{k}$$

$$= 3\boldsymbol{\omega} - \boldsymbol{\omega} = 2\boldsymbol{\omega}.$$

At any instant the velocity distribution $\mathbf{v}$ *in a rigid body has a rotation equal to twice its instantaneous angular velocity* $\boldsymbol{\omega}$.

41. Product Formulas. First note that

(1) $$\qquad\qquad \text{div } (\mathbf{f} + \mathbf{g}) = \text{div } \mathbf{f} + \text{div } \mathbf{g},$$

(2) $$\qquad\qquad \text{rot } (\mathbf{f} + \mathbf{g}) = \text{rot } \mathbf{f} + \text{rot } \mathbf{g}.$$

We next apply the defining equations (40.1–3) to various products of functions.

If λ is a scalar, $\mathbf{f}$ a vector point function, we have

(3) $$\qquad\qquad \nabla(\lambda \mathbf{f}) = (\nabla \lambda)\mathbf{f} \quad + \lambda \nabla \mathbf{f},$$

(4) $$\qquad\qquad \text{div } (\lambda \mathbf{f}) = (\nabla \lambda) \cdot \mathbf{f} + \lambda \text{ div } \mathbf{f},$$

(5) $$\qquad\qquad \text{rot } (\lambda \mathbf{f}) = (\nabla \lambda) \times \mathbf{f} + \lambda \text{ rot } \mathbf{f}.$$

From (40.1) we have

$$\nabla(\lambda \mathbf{f}) = \mathbf{i}(\lambda_x \mathbf{f} + \lambda \mathbf{f}_x) + \text{cycl}$$

$$= (\mathbf{i}\lambda_x + \mathbf{j}\lambda_y + \mathbf{k}\lambda_z)\mathbf{f} + \lambda(\mathbf{i}\mathbf{f}_x + \mathbf{j}\mathbf{f}_y + \mathbf{k}\mathbf{f}_z),$$

which is (3). This yields (4) and (5) by dotting and crossing between dyad vectors.

If **f** and **g** are vector point functions,

(6) $\qquad$ div $(\mathbf{f} \times \mathbf{g}) = \mathbf{g} \cdot \text{rot } \mathbf{f} - \mathbf{f} \cdot \text{rot } \mathbf{g},$

(7) $\qquad$ rot $(\mathbf{f} \times \mathbf{g}) = \mathbf{g} \cdot \nabla \mathbf{f} \quad - \mathbf{f} \cdot \nabla \mathbf{g} + \mathbf{f} \text{ div } \mathbf{g} - \mathbf{g} \text{ div } \mathbf{f}.$

We give the proof of (7): from (40.3),

$$\text{rot } (\mathbf{f} \times \mathbf{g}) = \mathbf{i} \times (\mathbf{f}_x \times \mathbf{g} + \mathbf{f} \times \mathbf{g}_x) \ + \text{cycl}$$

$$= (\mathbf{g} \cdot \mathbf{i}) \, \mathbf{f}_x \ - (\mathbf{i} \cdot \mathbf{f}_x) \, \mathbf{g} + (\mathbf{i} \cdot \mathbf{g}_x) \, \mathbf{f} - (\mathbf{f} \cdot \mathbf{i}) \, \mathbf{g}_x + \text{cycl}$$

$$= \mathbf{g} \cdot \nabla \mathbf{f} \quad - (\text{div } \mathbf{f}) \, \mathbf{g} + (\text{div } \mathbf{g}) \, \mathbf{f} - \mathbf{f} \cdot \nabla \mathbf{g}.$$

We next prove that

(8) $\qquad\qquad\qquad (\nabla \mathbf{f}) \cdot \mathbf{g} - \mathbf{g} \cdot (\nabla \mathbf{f}) = \mathbf{g} \times \text{rot } \mathbf{f};$

the left member equals

$$\mathbf{i}(\mathbf{f}_x \cdot \mathbf{g}) - (\mathbf{g} \cdot \mathbf{i})\mathbf{f}_x + \text{cycl} = \mathbf{g} \times (\mathbf{i} \times \mathbf{f}_x) + \text{cycl} = \mathbf{g} \times \text{rot } \mathbf{f}.$$

We can now show that

(9) $\qquad$ $\nabla(\mathbf{f} \cdot \mathbf{g}) = \mathbf{g} \cdot \nabla \mathbf{f} + \mathbf{g} \times \text{rot } \mathbf{f} + \mathbf{f} \cdot \nabla \mathbf{g} + \mathbf{f} \times \text{rot } \mathbf{g};$

for, from (40.1),

$$\nabla(\mathbf{f} \cdot \mathbf{g}) = \mathbf{i}\,(\mathbf{f}_x \cdot \mathbf{g} + \mathbf{g}_x \cdot \mathbf{f}) + \text{cycl} = (\nabla \mathbf{f}) \cdot \mathbf{g} + (\nabla \mathbf{g}) \cdot \mathbf{f},$$

which, in view of (8), gives (9).

Example 1. *The function $1/r$ is a solution of Laplace's equation:*

(10) $\qquad\qquad\qquad\qquad$ $\nabla^2 \dfrac{1}{r} = \text{div } \nabla \dfrac{1}{r} = 0.$

For, from (37.14),

$$\nabla \frac{1}{r} = -\frac{1}{r^2} \nabla r = -\frac{\mathbf{r}}{r^3} \, ;$$

and, from (4),

$$\text{div } \nabla \frac{1}{r} = - \left(\frac{1}{r^3} \text{ div } \mathbf{r} + \mathbf{r} \cdot \nabla \frac{1}{r^3} \right) = -\frac{3}{r^3} - \mathbf{r} \cdot \left(\frac{-3}{r^4} \frac{\mathbf{r}}{r} \right) = 0.$$

Example 2. If u and v are scalar functions,

(11) $\qquad\qquad\qquad\qquad$ div $(\nabla u \times \nabla v) = 0.$

Since rot $\nabla u = $ rot $\nabla v = 0$, this follows at once from (6).

PROBLEMS

1. Find the gradient of the vectors

$$\mathbf{f} = [x - y, \, y - z, \, z - x],$$

$$\mathbf{g} = [x^2 + yz, \, y^2 + zx, \, z^2 + xy],$$

$$\mathbf{h} = [yz^2, \, zx^2, \, xy^2],$$

in matrix form, and find their divergence and rotation.

2. If $r = \sqrt{x^2 + y^2 + z^2}$, find

(a) ∇r^2 and $\nabla^2 r^2$;   (b) ∇r^{-1} and $\nabla^2 r^{-1}$.

3. If $\mathbf{a}$ is a constant vector, prove that $\nabla(\mathbf{r} \times \mathbf{a}) = \mathbf{I} \times \mathbf{a}$.

4. If u is a scalar point function, prove that $\operatorname{rot}(f(u)\,\nabla u) = \mathbf{0}$. Hence show that $\operatorname{rot}(f(r)\,\mathbf{r}) = \mathbf{0}$.

5. If $\mathbf{R}$, $\mathbf{P}$ are the unit vectors of §28 in the xy-plane and $r = \sqrt{x^2 + y^2}$, show that

$$\operatorname{div}\mathbf{R} = \frac{1}{r}, \qquad \operatorname{rot}\mathbf{R} = 0; \qquad \operatorname{div}\mathbf{P} = 0, \qquad \operatorname{rot}\mathbf{P} = \frac{\mathbf{k}}{r}.$$

6. If $r = \sqrt{x^2 + y^2 + z^2}$, prove that

$$\nabla^2 f(r) = f''(r) + \frac{2f'(r)}{r}.$$

7. If $\nabla^2 f(r) = 0$, find $f(r)$.

8. If $\mathbf{r}/r$ is the unit radial vector in space, prove that

$$\operatorname{div}\frac{\mathbf{r}}{r} = \frac{2}{r}, \qquad \operatorname{rot}\frac{\mathbf{r}}{r} = \mathbf{0}.$$

9. If $\mathbf{a}$ is a constant vector, prove that

$$\nabla(\mathbf{a} \cdot \mathbf{r}) = \mathbf{a}, \qquad \operatorname{div}(\mathbf{a} \times \mathbf{r}) = 0, \qquad \operatorname{rot}(\mathbf{a} \times \mathbf{r}) = 2\mathbf{a}.$$

10. If $\mathbf{e}$ is a unit vector, prove that

$$\operatorname{div}(\mathbf{e} \cdot \mathbf{r})\,\mathbf{e} = 1, \qquad \operatorname{rot}(\mathbf{e} \cdot \mathbf{r})\,\mathbf{e} = \mathbf{0};$$

$$\operatorname{div}[(\mathbf{e} \times \mathbf{r}) \times \mathbf{e}] = 2, \qquad \operatorname{rot}[(\mathbf{e} \times \mathbf{r}) \times \mathbf{e}] = \mathbf{0}.$$

42. Curvilinear Coordinates. Let us change from rectangular coordinates (x, y, z) to curvilinear coordinates (u, v, w) by means of the equations

(1) $x = F(u, v, w), \qquad y = G(u, v, w), \qquad z = H(u, v, w),$

where F, G, H have continuous first partial derivatives in a certain region in which their Jacobian is not zero. The functions, therefore, are not connected by any functional relation. Since the Jacobian is continuous, its sign cannot change in the region; and, to be explicit, we shall suppose that the Jacobian

$$(2) \qquad J = \frac{\partial(x, y, z)}{\partial(u, v, w)} = \mathbf{r}_u \times \mathbf{r}_v \cdot \mathbf{r}_w > 0.$$

This involves no loss in generality; for, if the Jacobian were negative, an interchange of v and w (for example) would make it positive.

Under these hypotheses the equations (1) have a unique inverse in some neighborhood I_0 of any point (x_0, y_0, z_0) of the region:

$$(3) \qquad u = f(x, y, z), \qquad v = g(x, y, z), \qquad w = h(x, y, z);$$

and f, g, h also have continuous first partial derivatives.† In the neighborhood I_0 the correspondence $(x, y, z) \leftrightarrow (u, v, w)$ is one-to-one, so that a point $P(x, y, z)$ may also be specified by the three numbers (u, v, w) given by (3).

When (u_0, v_0, w_0) are given, P_0 is the point of intersection of the three surfaces

$$f(x, y, z) = u_0, \qquad g(x, y, z) = v_0, \qquad h(x, y, z) = w_0.$$

These will intersect in three curves, the *coordinate curves*, along which only one of the quantities u, v, w can vary. For this reason, u, v, w are called *curvilinear coordinates*, in distinction to the rectangular coordinates x, y, z, for which the coordinate curves are straight lines.

Consider now any vector point function $\mathbf{f}(u, v, w)$; its derivative in the direction $\mathbf{e}$ is

$$\frac{d\mathbf{f}}{ds} = \frac{\partial \mathbf{f}}{\partial u}\frac{du}{ds} + \frac{\partial \mathbf{f}}{\partial v}\frac{dv}{ds} + \frac{\partial \mathbf{f}}{\partial w}\frac{dw}{ds}.$$

Since $d\mathbf{f}/ds = \mathbf{e} \cdot \nabla \mathbf{f}$, $du/ds = \mathbf{e} \cdot \nabla u$, we have

$$\mathbf{e} \cdot \nabla \mathbf{f} = \mathbf{e} \cdot (\nabla u\, \mathbf{f}_u + \nabla v\, \mathbf{f}_v + \nabla w\, \mathbf{f}_w)$$

for all vectors $\mathbf{e}$. Hence (§38, Def.)

$$(4) \qquad \nabla \mathbf{f} = \nabla u\, \mathbf{f}_u + \nabla v\, \mathbf{f}_v + \nabla w\, \mathbf{f}_w,$$

$$(5) \qquad \nabla \cdot \mathbf{f} = \nabla u \cdot \mathbf{f}_u + \nabla v \cdot \mathbf{f}_v + \nabla w \cdot \mathbf{f}_w,$$

$$(6) \qquad \nabla \times \mathbf{f} = \nabla u \times \mathbf{f}_u + \nabla v \times \mathbf{f}_v + \nabla w \times \mathbf{f}_w,$$

give the gradient, divergence, and rotation of a vector point function in general curvilinear coordinates.

† For the theorems involved here see *Advanced Calculus*, §§87–89.

When the position vector $\mathbf{r}$ is regarded as a function of x, y, z, we have $\nabla \mathbf{r} = \mathbf{I}$ (40.8); but, when $\mathbf{r}$ is regarded as a function of u, v, w, $\nabla \mathbf{r}$ is given by (4); hence

$$(7) \qquad \mathbf{I} = \nabla u\, \mathbf{r}_u + \nabla v\, \mathbf{r}_v + \nabla w\, \mathbf{r}_w.$$

From this equation we can conclude that:

The vector triads ∇u, ∇v, ∇w and $\mathbf{r}_u$, $\mathbf{r}_v$, $\mathbf{r}_w$ form reciprocal sets.†

Proof. Write $\mathbf{e}_1 = \nabla u$, $\mathbf{e}_2 = \nabla v$, $\mathbf{e}_3 = \nabla w$, and let $\mathbf{e}^1$, $\mathbf{e}^2$, $\mathbf{e}^3$ denote the reciprocal set. Then, on dot-multiplying (7) by $\mathbf{e}^1$, $\mathbf{e}^2$, $\mathbf{e}^3$ as prefactors, we find that $\mathbf{e}^1 = \mathbf{r}_u$, $\mathbf{e}^2 = \mathbf{r}_v$, $\mathbf{e}^3 = \mathbf{r}_w$.

The vectors $\mathbf{r}_u$ are tangent to the u-curves, the curves along which v and w are constant. Thus at any point $P(u, v, w)$, $\mathbf{r}_u$, $\mathbf{r}_v$, $\mathbf{r}_w$ are tangent to the three coordinate curves meeting there. Moreover from the properties of reciprocal sets:

$$(8) \qquad \nabla u = \frac{\mathbf{r}_v \times \mathbf{r}_w}{J}, \qquad \nabla v = \frac{\mathbf{r}_w \times \mathbf{r}_u}{J}, \qquad \nabla w = \frac{\mathbf{r}_u \times \mathbf{r}_v}{J},$$

$$(9) \qquad \nabla u \times \nabla v \cdot \nabla w = \frac{\partial(u, v, w)}{\partial(x, y, z)} = \frac{1}{J}.$$

$J = $ Box product

In computing the invariants of ∇f it is usually more convenient to eliminate ∇u, ∇v, ∇w from the above formulas by means of equations (8). Thus from (5) we obtain

$$(10) \qquad \nabla \cdot \mathbf{f} = \frac{1}{J}\left(\mathbf{r}_v \times \mathbf{r}_w \cdot \mathbf{f}_u + \mathbf{r}_w \times \mathbf{r}_u \cdot \mathbf{f}_v + \mathbf{r}_u \times \mathbf{r}_v \cdot \mathbf{f}_w\right),$$

or, in view of the identity,

$$(\mathbf{r}_v \times \mathbf{r}_w)_u + (\mathbf{r}_w \times \mathbf{r}_u)_v + (\mathbf{r}_u \times \mathbf{r}_v)_w = \mathbf{0},$$

$$(11) \qquad J \operatorname{div} \mathbf{f} = (\mathbf{r}_v \times \mathbf{r}_w \cdot \mathbf{f})_u + (\mathbf{r}_w \times \mathbf{r}_u \cdot \mathbf{f})_v + (\mathbf{r}_u \times \mathbf{r}_v \cdot \mathbf{f})_w.$$

In the important case when all coordinate curves cut at right angles, the coordinates are said to be *orthogonal*; then

$$(12) \qquad \mathbf{r}_v \cdot \mathbf{r}_w = \mathbf{r}_w \cdot \mathbf{r}_u = \mathbf{r}_u \cdot \mathbf{r}_v = 0.$$

† The nine equations $\nabla u \cdot \mathbf{r}_u = 1$, $\nabla u \cdot \mathbf{r}_v = 0$, $\cdots$ also follow from the chain rule: for example

$$u_x x_u + u_y y_u + u_z z_u = u_u = 1, \qquad u_x x_v + u_y y_v + u_z z_v = u_v = 0.$$

We choose the notation so that

(13) $\mathbf{r}_u = U\mathbf{a}, \qquad \mathbf{r}_v = V\mathbf{b}, \qquad \mathbf{r}_w = W\mathbf{c},$

where $\mathbf{a}$, $\mathbf{b}$, $\mathbf{c}$ are a dextral set of (variable) unit vectors and U, V, W are all positive; then $J = UVW$. Now (11) becomes

(14) div $\mathbf{f} = \dfrac{1}{UVW} \left[\dfrac{\partial}{\partial u} \left(\dfrac{VW}{U} \mathbf{r}_u \cdot \mathbf{f} \right) + \dfrac{\partial}{\partial v} \left(\dfrac{WU}{V} \mathbf{r}_v \cdot \mathbf{f} \right) + \dfrac{\partial}{\partial w} \left(\dfrac{UV}{W} \mathbf{r}_w \cdot \mathbf{f} \right) \right].$

When we replace $\mathbf{f}$ by the gradient of a scalar

(15) $\nabla g = \nabla u\, g_u + \nabla v\, g_v + \nabla w\, g_w,$ (37.12)

we obtain the important formula for the Laplacian of a scalar function in orthogonal coordinates:

(16) $\nabla^2 g = \dfrac{1}{UVW} \left[\dfrac{\partial}{\partial u} \left(\dfrac{VW}{U} g_u \right) + \dfrac{\partial}{\partial v} \left(\dfrac{WU}{V} g_v \right) + \dfrac{\partial}{\partial w} \left(\dfrac{UV}{W} g_w \right) \right].$

When the curvilinear coordinates are given by equations (1), we may compute U, V, W from equations of the type

(17) $U = |\mathbf{r}_u| = |x_u\mathbf{i} + y_u\mathbf{j} + z_u\mathbf{k}| = \sqrt{x_u{}^2 + y_u{}^2 + z_u{}^2}.$

Example 1. Cylindrical Coordinates. The point $P(x, y, z)$ projects into the point $Q(x, y, 0)$ in the xy-plane. If ρ, φ are polar coordinates of Q in the xy-plane, $u = \rho$, $v = \varphi$, $w = z$ are called the cylindrical co-ordinates of P (Fig. 42a). They are related to the rectangular coordinates by the equations

(18) $x = \rho \cos \varphi, \qquad y = \rho \sin \varphi, \qquad z = z.$

The level surfaces $\rho = a$, $\varphi = b$, $z = c$ are cylinders about the z-axis, planes through the z-axis, and planes perpendicular to the z-axis. The coordinate curves, for ρ, are rays per-pendicular to the z-axis; for φ, horizontal circles centered on the z-axis; for z, lines parallel to the z-axis.

From $\mathbf{r} = [x, y, z]$ we have

$\mathbf{r}_\rho = [\cos \varphi, \sin \varphi, 0], \qquad U = 1;$
$\mathbf{r}_\varphi = [-\rho \sin \varphi, \rho \cos \varphi, 0], \qquad V = \rho;$
$\mathbf{r}_z = [0, 0, 1], \qquad W = 1.$

Since these vectors are mutually perpendicular and $J = UVW = \rho > 0$, cylindrical coordi-nates form an orthogonal system which is dextral in the order ρ, φ, z.

From (16) the Laplacian

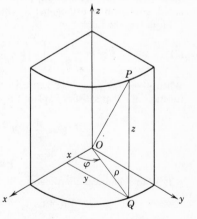

Fig. 42a. Cylindrical coordinates: ρ, φ, z.

(19) $\nabla^2 g = \dfrac{1}{\rho} \dfrac{\partial}{\partial \rho} (\rho g_\rho) + \dfrac{1}{\rho^2} g_{\varphi\varphi} + g_{zz}.$

When $g = \log \rho$, $\rho g_\rho = 1$; hence $\log \rho$ is a particular solution of Laplace's equation $\nabla^2 g = 0$.

Example 2. Spherical Coordinates. The spherical coordinates of a point $P(x, y, z)$ are its distance $r = OP$ from the origin, the angle θ between OP and the z-axis, and the dihedral angle φ between the xz-plane and the plane zOP (Fig. 42b). They are related to the rectangular coordinates by the equations:

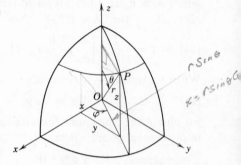

Fig. 42b. Spherical coordinates: r, θ, φ.

$$
\text{(20)} \qquad
\begin{aligned}
x &= r \sin \theta \cos \varphi, \\
y &= r \sin \theta \sin \varphi, \\
z &= r \cos \theta.
\end{aligned}
$$

The level surfaces $r = a$, $\theta = b$, $\varphi = c$ are spheres about O, cones about the z-axis with vertex at O, and planes through the z-axis. The coordinate curves, for r, are rays from the origin; for θ, vertical circles centered at the origin; for φ, horizontal circles centered on the z-axis.

From $\mathbf{r} = [x, y, z]$ we have

$$
\begin{aligned}
\mathbf{r}_r &= [\sin \theta \cos \varphi, \sin \theta \sin \varphi, \cos \theta], & U &= 1; \\
\mathbf{r}_\theta &= [r \cos \theta \cos \varphi, r \cos \theta \sin \varphi, -r \sin \theta], & V &= r; \\
\mathbf{r}_\varphi &= [-r \sin \theta \sin \varphi, r \sin \theta \cos \varphi, 0], & W &= r \sin \theta.
\end{aligned}
$$

Since these vectors are mutually perpendicular and $J = UVW = r^2 \sin \theta > 0$, spherical coordinates form an orthogonal system which is dextral in the order r, θ, φ.

From (16) the Laplacian

$$
\text{(21)} \qquad \nabla^2 g = \frac{1}{r^2 \sin \theta} \left[\sin \theta \, \frac{\partial}{\partial r} (r^2 g_r) + \frac{\partial}{\partial \theta} (\sin \theta \, g_\theta) + \frac{1}{\sin \theta} g_{\varphi\varphi} \right].
$$

When $g = 1/r$, $r^2 g_r = -1$; hence $1/r$ satisfies Laplace's equation. The most general function of r that satisfies Laplace's equation is the general solution

$$
g = \frac{A}{r} + B \quad \text{of} \quad \frac{d}{dr} \left(r^2 \frac{dg}{dr} \right) = 0.
$$

PROBLEMS

1. With cylindrical coordinates ρ, φ, z, show that

$$
\nabla \rho = \mathbf{r}_\rho, \qquad \nabla \varphi = \mathbf{r}_\varphi \rho^2, \qquad \nabla z = \mathbf{r}_z.
$$

2. With spherical coordinates r, θ, φ, show that

$$
\nabla r = \mathbf{r}_r, \qquad \nabla \theta = \mathbf{r}_\theta / r^2, \qquad \nabla \varphi = \mathbf{r}_\varphi / r^2 \sin^2 \theta.
$$

3. Deduce the result of Prob. 41.6 from (21).

4. Prove that the equations

$$
x = a_1 u + a_2 v + a_3 w, \qquad y = b_1 u + b_2 v + b_3 w, \qquad z = c_1 u + c_2 v + c_3 w
$$

represent a change from one set of rectangular coordinates x, y, z into another u, v, w when the vectors $\mathbf{r}_u$, $\mathbf{r}_v$, $\mathbf{r}_w$ form a self-reciprocal set.

[The identity $x^2 + y^2 + z^2 = u^2 + v^2 + w^2$ implies the self-reciprocity of $\mathbf{r}_u$, $\mathbf{r}_v$, $\mathbf{r}_w$; for it shows that $a_i a_j + b_i b_j + c_i c_j = \delta_{ij}$ and hence $\mathbf{r}_u$, $\mathbf{r}_v$, $\mathbf{r}_w$ are a set of orthogonal unit vectors.]

5. If u, v, w are curvilinear coordinates, prove the operational identities:

$$\nabla = \nabla u \frac{\partial}{\partial u} + \nabla v \frac{\partial}{\partial v} + \nabla w \frac{\partial}{\partial w} \ ;$$

$$\mathbf{r}_u \cdot \nabla = \frac{\partial}{\partial u} \ ; \qquad (\mathbf{r}_u \times \mathbf{r}_v) \times \nabla = \mathbf{r}_v \frac{\partial}{\partial u} - \mathbf{r}_u \frac{\partial}{\partial v} \ ;$$

$$[\mathbf{r}_u \mathbf{r}_v \mathbf{r}_w] \nabla = \mathbf{r}_v \times \mathbf{r}_w \frac{\partial}{\partial u} + \mathbf{r}_w \times \mathbf{r}_u \frac{\partial}{\partial v} + \mathbf{r}_u \times \mathbf{r}_v \frac{\partial}{\partial w} \ .$$

6. Deduce the formula for rot $\mathbf{f}$ in curvilinear coordinates
(*a*) analogous to (42.11):
$$J \operatorname{rot} \mathbf{f} = \{(\mathbf{r}_v \times \mathbf{r}_w) \times \mathbf{f}\}_u + \text{cycl};$$

(*b*) analogous to (40.7):

$$J \operatorname{rot} \mathbf{f} = \begin{vmatrix} \mathbf{r}_u & \mathbf{r}_v & \mathbf{r}_w \\ \partial/\partial u & \partial/\partial v & \partial/\partial w \\ \mathbf{r}_u \cdot \mathbf{f} & \mathbf{r}_v \cdot \mathbf{f} & \mathbf{r}_w \cdot \mathbf{f} \end{vmatrix} .$$

7. If $\mathbf{f}(u, v)$ is a function defined on the surface $\mathbf{r} = \mathbf{r}(u, v)$ and $\mathbf{e}$ a unit vector in the tangent plane at the point (u, v), prove that the directional derivative of $\mathbf{f}(u, v)$ along all surface curves tangent to $\mathbf{e}$ is given by

$$\frac{d\mathbf{f}}{ds} = \mathbf{e} \cdot (\mathbf{a}\,\mathbf{f}_u + \mathbf{b}\,\mathbf{f}_v)$$

where $\mathbf{a}$, $\mathbf{b}$, $\mathbf{n}$ is the set reciprocal to $\mathbf{r}_u$, $\mathbf{r}_v$, $\mathbf{n}$.

[The unit normal $\mathbf{n}$ has the direction of $\mathbf{r}_u \times \mathbf{r}_v$; *Vector and Tensor Analysis*, §95.]

8. On the surface $\mathbf{r} = \mathbf{r}(u, v)$ the *surface gradient, divergence*, and *rotation* of a function $\mathbf{f}(u, v)$ are defined as

$$\operatorname{Grad} \mathbf{f} = \mathbf{a}\,\mathbf{f}_u + \mathbf{b}\,\mathbf{f}_v,$$
$$\operatorname{Div} \mathbf{f} = \mathbf{a} \cdot \mathbf{f}_u + \mathbf{b} \cdot \mathbf{f}_v,$$
$$\operatorname{Rot} \mathbf{f} = \mathbf{a} \times \mathbf{f}_u + \mathbf{b} \times \mathbf{f}_v.$$

Prove that

$$\operatorname{Div} \mathbf{r} = 2, \qquad \operatorname{Rot} \mathbf{r} = 0, \qquad \operatorname{Rot} \mathbf{n} = 0.$$

[*Vector and Tensor Analysis*, §96.]

Chapter 5 _____

Integral Theorems

43. Line Integrals. Let the functions $P(x, y, z)$, $Q(x, y, z)$, $R(x, y, z)$ be defined at all points of a smooth curve Γ given by the parametric equations

(1) $\qquad x = x(t), \qquad y = y(t), \qquad z = z(t) \qquad (t_1 \leq t \leq t_2).$

Then the line integral over Γ,

$$\int_\Gamma P\,dx + Q\,dy + R\,dz$$

is computed as the Riemann integral between $t = t_1$ and $t = t_2$ by substituting from equations (1) in the integrand. If P, Q, R become $P(t)$, $Q(t)$, $R(t)$, the integral above becomes

(2) $\qquad \displaystyle\int_\Gamma P\,dx + Q\,dy + R\,dz = \int_{t_1}^{t_2} [P(t)\,x'(t) + Q(t)\,y'(t) + R(t)\,z'(t)]\,dt.$

If the functions $P(t)$, $Q(t)$, $R(t)$ are integrable and the curve Γ is smooth (§26), the integral certainly exists. If Γ is merely *piecewise smooth*, (2) holds over each smooth arc and hence, by addition, over the entire curve. The finite discontinuities of $x'(t)$, $y'(t)$, $z'(t)$ do not prejudice the existence of the integral. Thus Γ may be any broken line, for example a *step line* consisting of two adjacent sides of a rectangle. Moreover Γ may be a closed curve or polygon which does not cross itself; in this case

$$\oint_\Gamma P\,dx + Q\,dy + R\,dz$$

denotes the circuit integral about Γ in the positive sense. For a plane curve which encloses a region $\mathscr{R}$, *the positive sense is one that leaves the*

110

region to the left. Thus the positive sense on a simple closed curve is counterclockwise.

If we regard P, Q, R as the components of a vector point function

$$\mathbf{f} = [P, Q, R],$$

and write the equation of the curve in vector form

$$\mathbf{r} = \mathbf{i}\, x(t) + \mathbf{j}\, y(t) + \mathbf{k}\, z(t) = \mathbf{r}(t), \qquad (t_1 \leq t \leq t_2),$$

the integral (2) assumes the compact form

$$(3) \qquad \int_{\mathbf{r}_1}^{\mathbf{r}_2} \mathbf{f} \cdot d\mathbf{r} = \int_{t_1}^{t_2} \mathbf{f}(t) \cdot \frac{d\mathbf{r}}{dt}\, dt,$$

which applies equally well to two or three dimensions.

The value of a line integral is independent of the parametric representation of the curve. This follows from the general theorem on the change of variable in integrals.† With the arc s along the curve as parameter, $d\mathbf{r}/ds = \mathbf{T}$ (28.4), and the line integral becomes

$$(4) \qquad \int_{\Gamma} \mathbf{f} \cdot \frac{d\mathbf{r}}{ds}\, ds = \int_{s_1}^{s_2} \mathbf{f} \cdot \mathbf{T}\, ds,$$

the integral of the tangential component of $\mathbf{f}$ along the curve. If $\mathbf{f}$ is everywhere normal to Γ, the line integral is zero.

Example 1. Compute $I = \int x\, dy - y\, dx$ from $(0, 0)$ to $(1, 1)$ over the
(i)   straight line $y = x$;
(ii)   step path $y = 0$, $x = 1$ ($\lrcorner$);
(iii) step path $x = 0$, $y = 1$ ($\ulcorner$);
(iv) parabola $y = x^2$;
(v)   circle $x = \cos t$, $y = 1 + \sin t$ $(-\tfrac{1}{2}\pi \leq t \leq 0)$.
(vi) Integrate also around the square $(0, 0) - (1, 0) - (1, 1) - (0, 1) - (0, 0)$.

Solutions.

(i) $I = \displaystyle\int_0^1 (x - x)\, dx = 0$;

(ii) $I = 0 + \displaystyle\int_0^1 dy = 1$;

(iii) $I = 0 - \displaystyle\int_0^1 dx = -1$;

(iv) $I = \displaystyle\int_0^1 (2x^2 - x^2)\, dx = \dfrac{1}{3}$;

(v) $I = \displaystyle\int_{-\pi/2}^0 [\cos^2 t + (1 + \sin t) \sin t]\, dt = \dfrac{\pi}{2} - 1$.

(vi) $I = 0 + \displaystyle\int_0^1 dy - \int_1^0 dx + 0 = 2$.

† *Advanced Calculus*, §123.

Example 2. The line integral over a curve Γ in Ex. 1 has a simple interpretation. If we change to polar coordinates,

$$x = r \cos \varphi, \qquad y = r \sin \varphi$$

$$dx = -r \sin \varphi \, d\varphi + \cos \varphi \, dr, \qquad dy = r \cos \varphi \, d\varphi + \sin \varphi \, dr,$$

we find that

$$I = \int_{(x_1,y_1)}^{(x_2,y_2)} x \, dy - y \, dx = \int_{\varphi_1}^{\varphi_2} r^2 \, d\varphi = 2A$$

where $\tan \varphi_1 = y_1/x_1$, $\tan \varphi_2 = y_2/x_2$, and A is the area of the sector OP_1P_2 subtended by Γ at the origin (Fig. 43). We may now express A as a *circuit integral*

$$(5) \quad A = \frac{1}{2} \int_{\varphi_1}^{\varphi_2} r^2 \, d\varphi = \frac{1}{2} \oint x \, dy - y \, dx$$

taken over the complete boundary of the sector; for the radial lines, $\varphi = \varphi_1$ and $\varphi = \varphi_2$, contribute nothing. The area A is positive or negative according as the circuit is counterclockwise or clockwise.

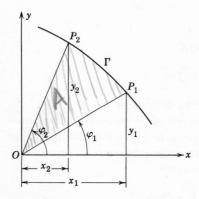

Fig. 43. Area of a sector.

All the results of Ex. 1 are now readily verified.

Example 3. Compute $\oint y^2 \, dx - x^2 \, dy$ about the triangle whose vertices are $(1, 0)$, $(0, 1)$, $(-1, 0)$.

Beginning the circuit at $(1, 0)$, the sides of the triangle are segments of the lines

$$x + y = 1, \qquad y - x = 1, \qquad y = 0;$$

hence the circuit integral equals

$$\int_1^0 [(1 - x)^2 + x^2] \, dx + \int_0^{-1} [(1 + x)^2 - x^2] \, dx = -\frac{2}{3}.$$

Example 4. Compute $\oint (y^2 \, dx - x^2 \, dy)$ about the circle $x = \cos t, y = 1 + \sin t$.

The integral taken counterclockwise equals

$$-\int_0^{2\pi} [(1 + \sin t)^2 \sin t + \cos^3 t] \, dt = -2\pi.$$

Example 5. Compute the line integral

$$I = \int y \, dx + z \, dy + x \, dz$$

(a) over the broken line $(0, 0, 0) - (1, 0, 0) - (1, 1, 0) - (1, 1, 1)$;

(b) over the broken line $(0, 0, 0) - (0, 1, 0) - (1, 1, 0) - (1, 1, 1)$;

(c) over the line $x = y = z = t \ (0 \leq t \leq 1)$;

(d) over the twisted cubic $x = t, y = t^2, z = t^3 \ (0 \leq t \leq 1)$.

Solutions.

(a) $I = 0 + 0 + \displaystyle\int_0^1 dz = 1$;

(b) $I = 0 + \displaystyle\int_0^1 dx + \int_0^1 dz = 2$;

(c) $I = \displaystyle\int_0^1 3t\, dt = \frac{3}{2}$;

(d) $I = \displaystyle\int_0^1 (t^2 + 2t^4 + 3t^2)dt = \frac{1}{3} + \frac{2}{5} + \frac{3}{4} = \frac{89}{60}$.

PROBLEMS

1. Compute the line integral,
$$\int_{(0,0)}^{(1,1)} (x^2 + y)\, dx + (2x + y)\, dy,$$
over the five paths given in Ex. 43.1.

2. Compute the circuit integral in Ex. 43.3 over
(a) the circle $x = x_0 + r \cos t,\ y = y_0 + r \sin t$;
(b) the ellipse $x = a \cos t,\ y = b \sin t$;
c) the square included by the lines $x = 0,\ y = 0,\ x = 1,\ y = 1$.

3. Compute $\displaystyle\oint \left(\frac{dx}{y} + \frac{dy}{x} \right)$ over the triangle included by the lines $y = 1,\ x = 4,\ y = x$.

4. Compute the line integral
$$\int_{(1,0)}^{(2,1)} \frac{1 + y^2}{x^3}\, dx - \frac{1 + x^2}{x^2} y\, dy$$

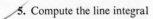

(a) over the step path $(1, 0) - (2, 0) - (2, 1)$;
(b) over the step path $(1, 0) - (1, 1) - (2, 1)$;
(c) over the line $y = x - 1$.

5. Compute the line integral
$$\int_{(1.2)}^{(3,4)} x^2 y\, dx + y^3\, dy$$

(a) over the step path $(1, 2) - (3, 2) - (3, 4)$;
(b) over the step path $(1, 2) - (1, 4) - (3, 4)$;
(c) over the line $x - y + 1 = 0$.

6. Compute $\displaystyle\int y\, dx - x\, dy + dz$ over one turn of the helix
$$x = 2 \cos t,\ y = 2 \sin t,\ z = 3t.$$

44. Line Integrals Independent of the Path.   We now inquire under what circumstances the line integral
$$\int_{\mathbf{r}_1}^{\mathbf{r}_2} \mathbf{f} \cdot d\mathbf{r} = \int_{t_1}^{t_2} \mathbf{f} \cdot \frac{d\mathbf{r}}{dt}\, dt,$$

taken between the points P_1 and P_2, is independent of the curve $\mathbf{r} = \mathbf{r}(t)$ joining the points. We consider only regular oriented curves, namely curves that are piecewise smooth, without double points,† and directed from P_1 to P_2.

We note that, if $\int \mathbf{f} \cdot d\mathbf{r}$ is independent of the path in a region $\mathscr{R}$, then $\oint \mathbf{f} \cdot d\mathbf{r} = 0$ for all closed curves in the region. For, if $P_1AP_2BP_1$ is a closed curve

$$\oint \mathbf{f} \cdot d\mathbf{r} = \int_{P_1AP_2} + \int_{P_2BP_1} \mathbf{f} \cdot d\mathbf{r} = \int_{P_1AP_2} - \int_{P_1BP_2} \mathbf{f} \cdot d\mathbf{r};$$

hence, if $\int_{\mathbf{r}_1}^{\mathbf{r}_2} \mathbf{f} \cdot d\mathbf{r}$ is independent of the path, $\oint \mathbf{f} \cdot d\mathbf{r} = 0$. Conversely, if $\oint \mathbf{f} \cdot d\mathbf{r} = 0$ over all closed curves of $\mathscr{R}, \int \mathbf{f} \cdot d\mathbf{r}$ is the same over any two paths from P_1 to P_2 that do not cross. But, even if the curves cross, the corresponding line integrals are equal; for both equal the integral over a third curve from P_1 to P_2 which cuts neither.‡

THEOREM 1. *If the continuous vector function $\mathbf{f}(\mathbf{r})$ is the gradient ∇F of a single-valued scalar point function in a region $\mathscr{R}$, the line integral $\int_{\mathbf{r}_1}^{\mathbf{r}_2} \mathbf{f} \cdot d\mathbf{r}$ has the same value over all regular curves in $\mathscr{R}$ directed from P_1 to P_2; and*

(1) $$\int_{\mathbf{r}_1}^{\mathbf{r}_2} \mathbf{f} \cdot d\mathbf{r} = \int_{\mathbf{r}_1}^{\mathbf{r}_2} d\mathbf{r} \cdot \nabla F = F(\mathbf{r}_2) - F(\mathbf{r}_1).$$

Proof. Let $\mathbf{f} = [P, Q, R] = \nabla F$; then

$$\mathbf{f} \cdot \frac{d\mathbf{r}}{dt} = \left(P\frac{dx}{dt} + Q\frac{dy}{dt} + R\frac{dz}{dt} \right)$$

$$= \frac{\partial F}{\partial x}\frac{dx}{dt} + \frac{\partial F}{\partial y}\frac{dy}{dt} + \frac{\partial F}{\partial z}\frac{dz}{dt} = \frac{dF}{dt}$$

by the chain rule; hence

$$\int_{\mathbf{r}_1}^{\mathbf{r}_2} \mathbf{f} \cdot d\mathbf{r} = \int_{t_1}^{t_2} \frac{dF}{dt} dt = F(x, y, z)\Big|_{t_1}^{t_2} = F(\mathbf{r}_2) - F(\mathbf{r}_1).$$

† Points at which a curve crosses itself or is tangent to itself are *double points* of the curve.

‡ For *plane* regions, this argument is fallacious, for a third curve which cuts neither may not exist. If the given curves cross but a *finite* number of times the proof follows by considering each loop separately. But for an infinite number of crossings the proof is more difficult.

Example 1.   Since

$$r^2 = x^2 + y^2 + z^2, \qquad \nabla r^2 = 2[x, y, z] = 2\mathbf{r},$$

$$\int_{\mathbf{r}_1}^{\mathbf{r}_2} \mathbf{r} \cdot d\mathbf{r} = \int_{\mathbf{r}_1}^{\mathbf{r}_2} d\mathbf{r} \cdot \nabla \frac{1}{2} r^2 = \frac{1}{2} r_2{}^2 - \frac{1}{2} r_1{}^2.$$

$\bar{f} = \nabla\varphi$

$(\nabla \times \bar{f} = 0)$

We next prove the converse of Theorem 1.

THEOREM 2.   *If* $\mathbf{f}(\mathbf{r}) = [P, Q, R]$ *is a continuous vector function in a region* $\mathscr{R}$ *in which* $\int \mathbf{f} \cdot d\mathbf{r}$ *has the same value over all regular curves directed between the same end points, then in* $\mathscr{R}$ $\mathbf{f}$ *is the gradient of the function*

(2) $$F(\mathbf{r}) = \int_{\mathbf{r}_0}^{\mathbf{r}} \mathbf{f} \cdot d\mathbf{r}.$$

Proof.   With a fixed lower limit, the integral (2) is a function $F(x, y, z)$ of the upper limit (x, y, z); for the path of integration is immaterial. Now, if we compute $F(x + h, y, z)$ over a curve from (x_0, y_0, z_0) to (x, y, z) and thence to $(x + h, y, z)$ over a straight segment, we have

$$F(x + h, y, z) - F(x, y, z) = \int_{(x,y,z)}^{(x+h,y,z)} P \, dx + Q \, dy + R \, dz$$

$x = x$

$\frac{dx}{dt} = 1$

$y = y$

$dy/dt = 0$

$z = z$

$\frac{dz}{dt} = 0$

$$= \int_x^{x+h} P(t, y, z) \, dt$$

$$= h \, P(\xi, y, z), \qquad x < \xi < x + h,$$

by the mean value theorem for integrals.†   Therefore

$$\frac{\partial F}{\partial x} = \lim_{h \to 0} \frac{h \, P(\xi, y, z)}{h} = \lim_{\xi \to x} P(\xi, y, z) = P(x, y, z)$$

since $P(x, y, z)$ is continuous.   In similar fashion we show that

$$\frac{\partial F}{\partial y} = Q(x, y, z), \qquad \frac{\partial F}{\partial z} = R(x, y, z),$$

and hence

$$\mathbf{f} = [P, Q, R] = [\partial F/\partial x, \partial F/\partial y, \partial F/\partial z] = \nabla F.$$

In brief, these theorems state that the line integral $\int \mathbf{f} \cdot d\mathbf{r}$ is independent of the path when and only when $\mathbf{f} = \nabla F$ a gradient vector, or (what is the same thing) $\mathbf{f} \cdot d\mathbf{r} = dF$, a perfect differential.   In order to use this test we must learn how to *recognize* a gradient vector.   This will be our next task.

† *Advanced Calculus*, §121.

Example 2. If we compute the line integral

$$I = \int_{(1,2)}^{(3,4)} (x + y^2)\, dx + 2xy\, dy$$

over two step paths from $(1, 2)$ to $(3, 4)$ and also over the line joining these points, we find in each case that $I = 48$. This suggests that I is independent of the path. To verify this we observe that

$$x\, dx + y^2\, dx + x(2y\, dy) = d(\tfrac{1}{2}x^2 + xy^2);$$

hence, if $F = \tfrac{1}{2}x^2 + xy^2$,

$$[x + y^2, 2xy] = [F_x, F_y] = \nabla F,$$

and

$$I = F(3, 4) - F(1, 2) = 52\tfrac{1}{2} - 4\tfrac{1}{2} = 48.$$

Example 3. If $\mathbf{f} = -\mathbf{r}/r^3$,

$$\mathbf{f} = -\frac{1}{r^2} \nabla r = \frac{d}{dr}\left(\frac{1}{r}\right) \nabla r = \nabla \frac{1}{r}\cdot$$

Therefore, over any path from P_1 to P_2 that does not pass through the origin,

$$\int_{\mathbf{r}_1}^{\mathbf{r}_2} \mathbf{f} \cdot d\mathbf{r} = \int_{\mathbf{r}_1}^{\mathbf{r}_2} d\mathbf{r} \cdot \nabla \frac{1}{r} = \frac{1}{r_2} - \frac{1}{r_1}\cdot$$

45. Irrotational Vectors. A vector function $\mathbf{f(r)}$ is said to be *irrotational* in a region if rot $\mathbf{f} = \mathbf{0}$ there. We have seen in §40 that, if the scalar function $\varphi(\mathbf{r})$ has continuous second partial derivatives in a region, its gradient $\nabla \varphi$ is irrotational:

(1)   rot $\nabla \varphi = \mathbf{0}$ (40.10).

This raises the question: Can every vector $\mathbf{f}$ that is irrotational in a region be expressed as a gradient vector? The answer is *yes* provided the region is *simply connected* in the sense of the following

DEFINITION. A closed curve is called *reducible* in a region if it can be shrunk continuously to a point within the region. A region in which all regular closed curves are reducible is called *simply connected*.

Thus a plane region bounded by a single regular closed curve is simply connected; but the region between two concentric circles is not. In three dimensions, the region inside a sphere or rectangular prism is simply connected. The same is true of the region between two concentric spheres. But the region within a torus is not simply connected; for all closed curves that encircle its axis are irreducible.

If $\mathbf{f} = [P, Q, R]$,

(2)   rot $\mathbf{f} = \begin{vmatrix} \mathbf{i} & \mathbf{j} & \mathbf{k} \\ \partial/\partial x & \partial/\partial y & \partial/\partial z \\ P & Q & R \end{vmatrix}$;

hence, rot $\mathbf{f} = \mathbf{0}$ implies

$$(3) \qquad\qquad R_y = Q_z, \qquad P_z = R_x, \qquad Q_x = P_y.$$

When $R = 0$, $\mathbf{f}$ is a plane vector and rot $\mathbf{f} = \mathbf{0}$ implies $Q_x = P_y$.

We consider the plane case first and for a simple rectangular region.

THEOREM 1. *If the plane vector* $\mathbf{f} = [P, Q, 0]$ *has continuous first partial derivatives in a rectangle and*

$$\text{rot } \mathbf{f} = [0, 0, Q_x - P_y] = 0,$$

$\mathbf{f} = \nabla f$

then $\mathbf{f} = \nabla F$, *a gradient vector.*

Proof. Define $F(x, y)$ by the line integral

$$\int \mathbf{f} \cdot d\mathbf{r} = \int P(x, y) \, dx + Q(x, y) \, dy$$

taken over the step path $(x_0, y_0) - (x, y_0) - (x, y)$:

$$F(x, y) = \int_{x_0}^{x} P(t, y_0) \, dt + \int_{y_0}^{y} Q(x, t) \, dt.$$

Now from the rules for differentiating an integral,† we have

$$F_y = Q(x, y), \qquad F_x = P(x, y_0) + \int_{y_0}^{y} Q_x(x, t) \, dt.$$

By hypothesis $Q_x(x, t) = P_t(x, t)$; hence

$$F_x = P(x, y_0) + P(x, t) \Big|_{t=y_0}^{t=y} = P(x, y).$$

We thus have

$$\mathbf{f} = [P, Q] = [F_x, F_y] = \nabla F.$$

Theorem 44.1 now shows that $\displaystyle\int \mathbf{f} \cdot d\mathbf{r}$ is independent of the path; hence

$$(4) \qquad\qquad F(x, y) = \int_{(x_0, y_0)}^{(x, y)} P \, dx + Q \, dy$$

over *any* path in the rectangle from (x_0, y_0) to (x, y).

For example, the step path $(x_0, y_0) - (x_0, y) - (x, y)$ yields

$$(5) \qquad\qquad F(x, y) = \int_{x_0}^{x} P(x, y) \, dx + \int_{y_0}^{y} Q(x_0, y) \, dy$$

where the integrals are written in reverse order.

† *Advanced Calculus*, §119, §133.

In three dimensions we have the corresponding

THEOREM 2. *If the vector* $\mathbf{f} = [P, Q, R]$ *has continuous first partial derivatives in a rectangular prism and*

$$\text{rot } \mathbf{f} = [R_y - Q_z, P_z - R_x, Q_x - P_y] = 0,$$

then $\mathbf{f} = \nabla F$, *a gradient vector.*

Proof. Define $F(x, y, z)$ by the line integral,

$$\int \mathbf{f} \cdot d\mathbf{r} = \int P \, dx + Q \, dy + R \, dz,$$

taken over the step path $(x_0, y_0, z_0) - (x, y_0, z_0) - (x, y, z_0) - (x, y, z)$. Then

$$F(x, y, z) = \int_{x_0}^{x} P(t, y_0, z_0) \, dt + \int_{y_0}^{y} Q(x, t, z_0) \, dt + \int_{z_0}^{z} R(x, y, t) \, dt, \quad \checkmark$$

and we find $F_z = R(x, y, z)$, $F_y = Q(x, y, z)$ as before. Moreover

$$F_x = P(x, y_0, z_0) + \int_{y_0}^{y} Q_x(x, t, z_0) \, dt + \int_{z_0}^{z} R_x(x, y, t) \, dt$$

$$= P(x, y_0, z_0) + \int_{y_0}^{y} P_t(x, t, z_0) \, dt + \int_{z_0}^{z} P_t(x, y, t) \, dt$$

$$= P(x, y_0, z_0) + P(x, t \ z_0)\Big|_{t=y_0}^{t=y} + P(x, y, t)\Big|_{t=z_0}^{t=z}$$

$$= P(x, y, z).$$

Therefore $\mathbf{f} = [P, Q, R] = \nabla F$; $\int \mathbf{f} \cdot d\mathbf{r}$ is independent of the path and

$$(6) \qquad F(x, y, z) = \int_{(x_0, y_0, z_0)}^{(x, y, z)} P \, dx + Q \, dy + R \, dz$$

over *any* path in the rectangular prism from (x_0, y_0, z_0) to (x, y, z).

For example, the step path $(x_0, y_0, z_0) - (x_0, y_0, z) - (x_0, y, z) - (x, y, z)$ yields

$$(7) \quad F(x, y, z) = \int_{x_0}^{x} P(x, y, z) \, dx + \int_{y_0}^{y} Q(x_0, y, z) \, dy + \int_{z_0}^{z} R(x_0, y_0, z) \, dz,$$

where the integrals are written in reverse order.

Formulas (5) and (7) are easily remembered. Both give a function F which vanishes at $\mathbf{r}_0$. Changing the initial point $\mathbf{r}_0$ merely alters F by a

$$(5) \quad F(x, y) = \int_{x_0}^{x} P(x, y) \, dx + \int_{y_0}^{y} Q(x_0, y) \, dy$$

constant.   In practice $\mathbf{r}_0$ is chosen to simplify the integrals as much as possible.   If the region in which rot $\mathbf{f} = 0$ includes the origin, this point is usually a good choice.

In mathematical physics it is customary to express an irrotational vector $\mathbf{f}$ as the *negative* of a gradient.   Thus, if rot $\mathbf{f} = 0$ in a simply connected region,

(8) $$\mathbf{f} = -\nabla\varphi,$$

and φ is called the (scalar) *potential* of $\mathbf{f}$.

Example 1.   When

$$\mathbf{f} = [2x^2 + 6xy,\ 3x^2 - y^2,\ 0] \qquad \text{rot } \mathbf{f} = 0.$$

Integrating over the step path $(0, 0) - (x, 0) - (x, y)$, we get

$$F(x, y) = \int_0^x 2x^2\,dx + \int_0^y (3x^2 - y^2)\,dy = \frac{2}{3}x^3 + 3x^2y - \frac{1}{3}y^3,$$

and, over $(0, 0) - (0, y) - (x, y)$,

$$F(x, y) = \int_0^x (2x^2 + 6xy)\,dx - \int_0^y y^2\,dy = \frac{2}{3}x^3 + 3x^2y - \frac{1}{3}y^3,$$

where the integrals are written in reverse order. *(with respect to path)*
We can now compute the line integral between any two points:

$$\int_{\mathbf{r}_1}^{\mathbf{r}_2} \mathbf{f} \cdot d\mathbf{r} = F(x_2, y_2) - F(x_1, y_1).$$

Example 2.   When

$$\mathbf{f} = [2xz,\ 2yz^2,\ x^2 + 2y^2z - 1], \qquad \text{rot } \mathbf{f} = 0.$$

Integrating over the step path $(0, 0, 0) - (x, 0, 0) - (x, y, 0) - (x, y, z)$, we get

$$F(x, y, z) = 0 + 0 + \int_0^z (x^2 + 2y^2z - 1)\,dz = x^2z + y^2z^2 - z;$$

and, over the step path $(0, 0, 0) - (0, 0, z) - (0, y, z) - (x, y, z)$,

$$F(x, y, z) = \int_0^x 2xz\,dx + \int_0^y 2yz^2\,dy - \int_0^z dz = x^2z + y^2z^2 - z,$$

where the integrals are written in reverse order.

Although step paths usually give the simplest calculation for $F(x, y, z)$, a straight segment joining (x_0, y_0, z_0) to (x, y, z) is sometimes preferable.

If $\mathbf{f}(\mathbf{r})$ is continuous when $\mathbf{r} = 0$, we can integrate along the radial line from 0 to $\mathbf{r}$. The points of this line have position vectors $t\mathbf{r}$ $(0 \leq t \leq 1)$, and hence

$$(9) \qquad F(\mathbf{r}) = \int_0^1 \mathbf{f}(t\mathbf{r}) \cdot d(t\mathbf{r}) = \mathbf{r} \cdot \int_0^1 \mathbf{f}(t\mathbf{r}) \, dt.$$

In particular when $\mathbf{f} = [P, Q, R]$ is homogeneous of degree n, $\mathbf{f}(t\mathbf{r}) = t^n \mathbf{f}(\mathbf{r})$ and (9) becomes

$$(10) \qquad F(\mathbf{r}) = \frac{\mathbf{r} \cdot \mathbf{f}(\mathbf{r})}{n+1} = \frac{xP + yQ + zR}{n+1}, \qquad n > -1.$$

If $n < -1$, we may integrate from $t = \infty$ to $t = 1$ and again obtain (10).

Example 3. In Ex. 1, $\mathbf{f}$ is homogeneous of degree 2; hence from (10)

$$F(x, y) = \tfrac{1}{3}[x(2x^2 + 6xy) + y(3x^2 - y^2)]$$
$$= \tfrac{2}{3}x^3 + 3x^2y - \tfrac{1}{3}y^3.$$

Example 4. In Ex. 2, $\mathbf{f}$ is not homogeneous, but (9) is applicable. Thus

$$F(x, y, z) = [x, y, z] \cdot \int_0^1 [2xzt^2, 2yz^2t^3, x^2t^2 + 2y^2zt^3 - 1] \, dt$$

$$= [x, y, z] \cdot [\tfrac{2}{3}xz, \tfrac{1}{2}yz^2, \tfrac{1}{3}x^2 + \tfrac{1}{2}y^2z - 1]$$

$$= x^2z + y^2z^2 - z.$$

Example 5. The vector $\mathbf{f} = r^{n-1}\,\mathbf{r}$ is a gradient vector; for $\mathbf{r}/r = \nabla r$ (37.15), and

$$\mathbf{f} = r^n \nabla r = \begin{cases} \nabla \dfrac{r^{n+1}}{n+1}, & n \neq -1, \\[2ex] \nabla \log r, & n = -1. \end{cases}$$

The function F may also be found from (10) if $n \neq -1$.

46. Simply Connected Regions. When rot $\mathbf{f} = 0$ in a rectangular region, we were able to construct a function $F(\mathbf{r}) = \int_{\mathbf{r}_0}^{\mathbf{r}} \mathbf{f} \cdot d\mathbf{r}$ by integrating over a step path from P_0 to an arbitrary point P of the region. This construction cannot be used for simply connected regions in general; for, starting from P_0, we may not be able to reach P with a step path that lies in the region. To overcome this difficulty requires a rather detailed argument which we shall only sketch in outline.†

Consider a variable polygon $\Gamma(t)$ in the region whose vertices are

† Cf. Courant, *Differential and Integral Calculus*, Blackie, vol. 2, p. 357.

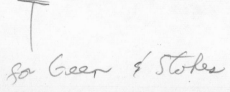

given by position vectors $\mathbf{r}_1(t)$, $\mathbf{r}_2(t)$, $\cdots$, $\mathbf{r}_k(t)$ which are continuous functions of the time t such that $\Gamma(t)$ shrinks to a point as t varies from 0 to 1. If we can show that the circuit integral

$$(1) \qquad\qquad I(t) = \oint_{\Gamma(t)} \mathbf{f} \cdot d\mathbf{r} = \text{const}$$

while $\Gamma(t)$ shrinks to a point, the constant must be zero. Since the original polygon given by $\mathbf{r}_1(0)$, $\mathbf{r}_2(0)$, $\cdots$, $\mathbf{r}_k(0)$ is arbitrary, this means that $\oint \mathbf{f} \cdot d\mathbf{r} = 0$ over any closed polygon in the region. Hence $\int_{\mathbf{r}_0}^{\mathbf{r}} \mathbf{f} \cdot d\mathbf{r}$ is the same for all polygonal paths between $\mathbf{r}_0$ and $\mathbf{r}$ and defines a function $F(\mathbf{r})$. We can now show as in §45 that $\mathbf{f} = \nabla F$ and that the line integral has the same value over all regular curves between the same end points.

Thus the proof hinges on (1). To establish this result consider two polygons $\Gamma(t)$ and $\Gamma(t')$ where $0 \leq t < t' \leq 1$. Choose n points A_1, A_2, $\cdots$, A_n on $\Gamma(t)$, so that each pair $A_i A_{i+1}$ lies in a rectangle R (or rectangular prism) inside our region. As $t \to t'$, let $A_i \to B_i$ on $\Gamma(t')$ (Fig. 46a). Now choose $t' - t$ so small that $B_i B_{i+1}$ also lies in R_i ($i = 1, 2, \cdots, n$). When rot $\mathbf{f} = 0$, the circuit integral over the quad-rangle $A_i A_{i+1} B_{i+1} B_i A_i$ is zero by Theorem 1 or 2 of §45; and, if we add all such circuit integrals, we have

$$I(t) - I(t') = 0.$$

Thus (1) is established.

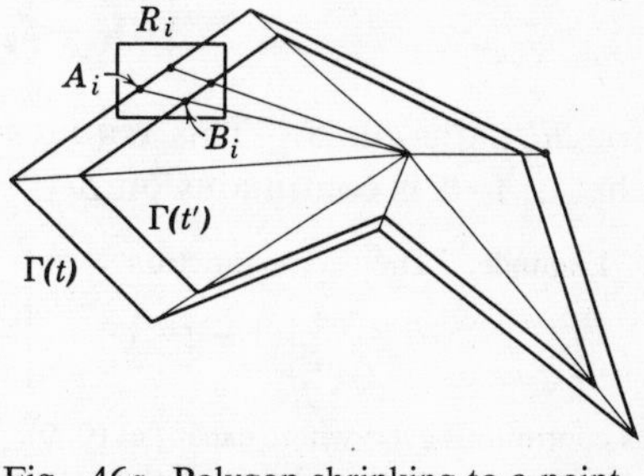

Our final result is stated in the

Fig. 46a. Polygon shrinking to a point.

THEOREM. *If the vector function* $\mathbf{f}(\mathbf{r})$ *has continuous first partial derivatives in a simply connected region, the line integral* $\int \mathbf{f} \cdot d\mathbf{r}$ *taken over any curve inside the region will be independent of the path when and only when* rot $\mathbf{f} = 0$.

Proof. We have just shown that in a simply connected region rot $\mathbf{f} = 0$ implies that $\int \mathbf{f} \cdot d\mathbf{r}$ is independent of the path. Conversely, if $\int \mathbf{f} \cdot d\mathbf{r}$ is independent of the path, $\mathbf{f}$ is a gradient vector (Theorem 44.2), and hence rot $\mathbf{f} = 0$.

If $\mathbf{f}$ satisfies the conditions of the theorem in a simply connected region

V except on a surface S where $\mathbf{f}$ has finite discontinuities, we still have $\oint \mathbf{f} \cdot d\mathbf{r} = 0$ over all closed curves in V if *the tangential component of* $\mathbf{f}$ *is continuous on* S.

Proof. Let S divide V into two parts, V_1 and V_2, and $PAQB$ be a closed curve cutting S at A and B (Fig. 46b). Then, if AB is a regular curve on S,

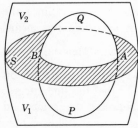

$$\oint_{ABPA} \mathbf{f}_1 \cdot d\mathbf{r} = \int_{AB} \mathbf{f}_1 \cdot d\mathbf{r} + \int_{BPA} \mathbf{f} \cdot d\mathbf{r} = 0,$$

$$\oint_{BAQB} \mathbf{f}_2 \cdot d\mathbf{r} = \int_{BA} \mathbf{f}_2 \cdot d\mathbf{r} + \int_{AQB} \mathbf{f} \cdot d\mathbf{r} = 0,$$

and, on addition,

$$\int_{AB} (\mathbf{f}_1 - \mathbf{f}_2) \cdot d\mathbf{r} + \oint_{BPAQB} \mathbf{f} \cdot d\mathbf{r} = 0.$$

Fig. 46b. Surface of discontinuity.

Hence $\oint \mathbf{f} \cdot d\mathbf{r} = 0$ for all closed paths in V when and only when the line integral

$$\int (\mathbf{f}_1 - \mathbf{f}_2) \cdot \mathbf{T} \, ds = 0$$

for *all* paths on S. This requires that $\mathbf{f}_1 \cdot \mathbf{T} = \mathbf{f}_2 \cdot \mathbf{T}$ at all points of S; that is, $\mathbf{f} \cdot \mathbf{T}$ is continuous on S.

Example. The vector function

$$\mathbf{f} = [P, Q] = \left[-\frac{y}{x^2 + y^2}, \frac{x}{x^2 + y^2} \right]$$

is continuous everywhere except at $(0, 0)$. In the region R consisting of the entire plane outside of a small circle about the origin, $\mathbf{f}, \mathbf{f}_x, \mathbf{f}_y$ are all continuous; moreover

$$Q_x = P_y = \frac{y^2 - x^2}{(x^2 + y^2)^2} \quad \text{and} \quad \text{rot } \mathbf{f} = 0 \quad \text{in } R.$$

Thus $\oint \mathbf{f} \cdot d\mathbf{r} = 0$ about any curve of R that does not encircle the origin; for such a curve can be embedded in a simply connected subregion of R. But, for any curve about the origin,

$$\int \mathbf{f} \cdot d\mathbf{r} = \oint \frac{x \, dy - y \, dx}{x^2 + y^2} = \int_0^{2\pi} d\varphi = 2\pi$$

on putting $x = r \cos \varphi$, $y = r \sin \varphi$; such a curve cannot be embedded in a simply connected subregion of R. Thus, in the doubly connected region R, $\int \mathbf{f} \cdot d\mathbf{r}$ is *not* independent of the path even though rot $\mathbf{f} = 0$ everywhere in R.

PROBLEMS

1. Express

$$\mathbf{f} = [2x^2 + 6xy, 3x^2 - y^2, 0]$$

as ∇F, and compute $\displaystyle\int_{(0,1)}^{(2,3)} \mathbf{f} \cdot d\mathbf{r}.$

2. If the integral

$$\int_{(0,1)}^{(x,y)} \left(\frac{2x}{y} - 3\right) dx + \left(4 - \frac{x^2}{y^2}\right) dy$$

defines a function $F(x, y)$ when $y > 0$, find it.

3. Express

$$\mathbf{f} = [2xyz^3, x^2z^3, 3x^2yz^2]$$

as ∇F, and compute $\displaystyle\int_{(1,2,-1)}^{(2,3,1)} \mathbf{f} \cdot d\mathbf{r}.$

4. Compute

$$\int_{(a,b)}^{(x,y)} \frac{x\, dx + y\, dy}{x^2 + y^2}$$

over any path that avoids the origin.   When (x, y) is (a, b), find the value of the circuit integral.   Is your answer correct if the circuit encloses the origin?

5. If the vector

$$\mathbf{f} = \begin{cases} x\mathbf{i} + y\mathbf{j} + z\mathbf{k}, & z \geq 0, \\ x\mathbf{i} + y\mathbf{j} - z\mathbf{k}, & z < 0, \end{cases}$$

prove that $\displaystyle\oint \mathbf{f} \cdot d\mathbf{r} = 0$ over any closed curve.

Compute $\displaystyle\int_{(1,2,-3)}^{(2,3,4)} \mathbf{f} \cdot d\mathbf{r}.$

6. Show that the vector

$$\mathbf{f} = \begin{cases} \mathbf{r}, & r \leq a, \\ -a^3 \nabla \dfrac{1}{r}, & r > a, \end{cases}$$

is continuous and irrotational throughout space.   Find a *continuous* function $F(r)$ such that $\mathbf{f} = \nabla F$.

Compute $\displaystyle\int_0^\infty \mathbf{f} \cdot d\mathbf{r}$ over any path.

47. Green's Theorem in the Plane. Let $\mathscr{R}$ be a closed region that is bounded by one or more simple closed curves. Then the *positive sense* on the boundary is the one that leaves $\mathscr{R}$ to the left. Thus, for the region within a closed curve C (Fig. 47a), the positive sense over C is counter-clockwise; but, for the region interior to C_1, exterior to C_2 and C_3 (Fig. 47c), the positive sense is counterclockwise for the outer boundary, clockwise for the inner boundaries.

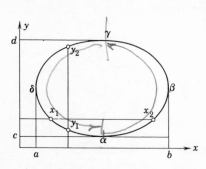

Fig. 47a. Region bounded by a simple closed curve.

GREEN'S THEOREM. *Let $\mathscr{R}$ be a closed region bounded by one or more closed regular† curves and capable of dissection into subregions whose boundaries are cut in at most two points by parallels to the axes. Then, if $P(x, y)$, $Q(x, y)$, P_y, Q_x are continuous in $\mathscr{R}$,*

$$(1) \qquad \iint_R \left(\frac{\partial Q}{\partial x} - \frac{\partial P}{\partial y} \right) dx\, dy = \oint P\, dx + Q\, dy,$$

where the circuit integral is taken over the boundary of $\mathscr{R}$ in the positive sense.

Proof.   Suppose first that $\mathscr{R}$ is bounded by single closed curve C which is cut in at most two points by any line parallel to the axes (Fig. 47a).

We first compute the double integral $\iint Q_x\, dx\, dy$ as a repeated integral,‡ integrating first with respect to x between the curves $x = x_1(y)$ and $x = x_2(y)$, and then with respect to y between the parallels $y = c$ and $y = d$, which limit the curve below and above:

$$\iint \frac{\partial Q}{\partial x}\, dx\, dy = \int_c^d dy \int_{x_1(y)}^{x_2(y)} \frac{\partial Q}{\partial x}\, dx$$

$$= \int_c^d [Q(x_2, y) - Q(x_1, y)]\, dy$$

$$= \int_c^d Q(x_2, y)\, dy + \int_d^c Q(x_1, y)\, dy,$$

where the integrals are taken over the arcs $\alpha\beta\gamma$ and $\gamma\delta\alpha$, respectively; hence

$$(2) \qquad \iint_R \frac{\partial Q}{\partial x}\, dx\, dy = \oint_C Q(x, y)\, dy.$$

---

† A *regular curve* is piecewise smooth and without double points.
‡ *Advanced Calculus*, §159.

We next compute $\displaystyle\iint \frac{\partial P}{\partial y}\, dx\, dy$ as a repeated integral, integrating first with respect to y between the curves $y = y_1(x)$ and $y = y_2(x)$, and then with respect to x between the parallels $x = a$ and $y = b$, which limit the curve to the left and right:

$$\iint \frac{\partial P}{\partial y}\, dx\, dy = \int_a^b dx \int_{y_1(x)}^{y_2(x)} \frac{\partial P}{\partial y}\, dy$$

$$= \int_a^b [P(x, y_2) - P(x, y_1)]\, dx$$

$$= -\int_a^b P(x, y_1)\, dx - \int_b^a P(x, y_2)\, dx,$$

where the integrals are taken over the arcs $\delta\alpha\beta$ and $\beta\gamma\delta$, respectively; hence

(3) $$-\iint_R \frac{\partial P}{\partial y}\, dx\, dy = \oint_C P(x, y)\, dx.$$

On adding (2) and (3) we get (1).

We may now extend equation (3) to regions that may be dissected into a finite number of subregions having the property stated in the theorem. For each subregion equation (3) is valid; and, when these equations are added, the double integrals combine into an integral over the entire region; but the line integrals over the internal boundaries cancel, since each is tra-

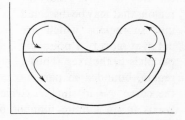

Fig. 47b. Dissected region.

versed twice but in opposite directions, leaving only the circuit integral over the external boundary (Fig. 47b).

A region $\mathcal{R}$ bounded by a single closed curve is *simply connected* (§46); for any closed curve in $\mathcal{R}$ can be continuously contracted into a point within the region. But, if the boundary of $\mathcal{R}$ consists of two or more closed curves (Fig. 47c), it is *multiply connected*; for a closed curve about C_2 or C_3 cannot be contracted to a point without crossing C_2 or C_3. But the region $\mathcal{R}$ of Fig. 47c can be made simply connected by two cross cuts, aa' and bb', joining C_1 to C_2 and C_3; and, if we pass around the new boundary as shown by the arrows (each cross cut being traversed twice), the entire circuit is made in the positive sense.

We can now apply Green's theorem (1) to region of Fig. 47c made simply connected with cross cuts. In the left member the double integral covers the region interior to C_1 and exterior to C_2 and C_3. In the right member the line integral comprises circuits in the positive sense over

C_1, C_2 and C_3; for the cross-cut integrals cancel as they are traversed twice and in opposite senses.

An internal boundary of a region may consist of a single point P_0 which must be excluded from $\mathscr{R}$ to meet the continuity requirements of Green's theorem. Such a *punctured* region is multiply connected; for a curve about P_0 cannot be contracted to a point within the region without crossing P_0. If the region consists of the entire plane punctured at P_0, a cross cut from P_0 to infinity will make it simply connected; for all closed curves not crossing the cut may be contracted to a point.

It can be shown by a rather intricate argument that *Green's theorem holds for any region bounded by curves that are piecewise smooth*. This does not follow from the argument just given; for this is only valid for regions that may be dissected into subregions which are cut in at most two points by parallels to the axes. Thus a region, bounded in part by

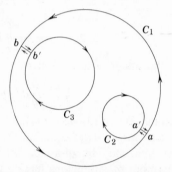

Fig. 47*c*. Multiply connected region made simply connected by cross cuts.

the curve $y = x^2 \sin(1/x)$ (which is smooth when $x > 0$), is cut by the x-axis in an infinite number of points and could not be dissected as postulated above. Nevertheless Green's theorem holds good even with such eccentric regional boundaries. The proof depends on a limiting process.

Green's theorem is also valid when $P(x, y)$ and $Q(x, y)$ are replaced by vector functions

$$\mathbf{P}(x, y) = \mathbf{i}\,P_1(x, y) + \mathbf{j}\,P_2(x, y) + \mathbf{k}\,P_3(x, y),$$

$$\mathbf{Q}(x, y) = \mathbf{i}\,Q_1(x, y) + \mathbf{j}\,Q_2(x, y) + \mathbf{k}\,Q_3(x, y),$$

whose components $P_i(x, y)$, $Q_i(x, y)$ satisfy the stated requirements. To show this we need only apply the theorem to the three pairs of functions $P_i(x, y)$, $Q_i(x, y)$, multiply the equations by $\mathbf{i}$, $\mathbf{j}$, $\mathbf{k}$ respectively, and add them.

We note, finally, that Green's theorem holds when P and Q are dyadics. The integrals of dyadics require no new definitions; for any dyadic $\mathbf{P} = \sum \mathbf{a}_i \mathbf{b}_i$ can be reduced to the form

$$\mathbf{P} = \mathbf{i}\mathbf{p}_1 + \mathbf{j}\mathbf{p}_2 + \mathbf{k}\mathbf{p}_3$$

by expressing each antecedent $\mathbf{a}_i$ in the form (8.1), expanding into a sum

p ·96 ?

$$\oint P\,dx + Q\,dy = \iint_R \left(\frac{\partial Q}{\partial x} - \frac{\partial P}{\partial y}\right) dx\,dy$$

of dyads, and then collecting the terms in **i, j, k** by means of the distributive laws (39.4–5). Thus, when **P** and **Q** are dyadics (such that **P, Q, P**$_y$, **Q**$_x$ are continuous in R)

$$\iint_R \left(\frac{\partial \mathbf{Q}}{\partial x} - \frac{\partial \mathbf{P}}{\partial y}\right) dx\,dy = \mathbf{i} \iint \left(\frac{\partial q_1}{\partial x} - \frac{\partial p_1}{\partial y}\right) dx\,dy + \text{cycl}$$

$$= \mathbf{i} \oint (\mathbf{p}_1\,dx + \mathbf{q}_1\,dy) + \text{cycl}$$

and hence

(4) $$\iint \left(\frac{\partial \mathbf{Q}}{\partial x} - \frac{\partial \mathbf{P}}{\partial y}\right) dx\,dy = \oint \mathbf{P}\,dx + \mathbf{Q}\,dy.$$

Example 1. When $Q = x/2,\ P = -y/2,\ Q_x - P_y = 1$; hence from Green's theorem

(5) $$\frac{1}{2}\oint x\,dy - y\,dx = \iint dx\,dy = A,$$

$$\oint x\,dy - y\,dx = 2A$$

the area enclosed by the curve (43.5).
On putting $Q = x, P = 0$ or $Q = 0, P = -y$, we have also

(6) $$A = \oint x\,dy = -\oint y\,dx.$$

Example 2. With $Q = x^2,\ P = -y^2,\ Q_x - P_y = 2(x + y)$; hence from Green's theorem

(7) $$\oint x^2\,dy - y^2\,dx = 2\iint (x + y)\,dx\,dy = 2A(x^* + y^*),$$

where (x^*, y^*) is the centroid of the area enclosed by the curve.
We may use (7) to check the results in Ex. 43.3–4.
For the triangle of Ex. 43.3, $A = 1,\ x^* = 0,\ y^* = \frac{1}{3}$; hence the circuit integral equals $-\frac{2}{3}$.
For the circle of Ex. 43.4, $A = \pi,\ x^* = 0,\ y^* = 1$; hence the circuit integral equals -2π.

Example 3. If the closed curve C of Fig. 47a is revolved about the x-axis, the volume generated is

$$V_x = \pi \int_a^b (y_2{}^2 - y_1{}^2)\,dx = -\pi \int_a^b y_1{}^2\,dx - \pi \int_b^a y_2{}^2\,dx = -\pi \oint y^2\,dx.$$

If C is revolved about the y-axis, the volume generated is

$$V_y = \pi \int_c^d (x_2{}^2 - x_1{}^2)\,dy = \pi \int_c^d x_2{}^2\,dy + \pi \int_d^c x_1{}^2\,dy = \pi \oint x^2\,dy.$$

If we apply Green's theorem to these circuit integrals we find

$$V_x = 2\pi \int y\,dx\,dy = 2\pi y^* A, \qquad V_y = 2\pi \int x\,dx\,dy = 2\pi x^* A,$$

where (x^*, y^*) is the centroid of the area A enclosed by C.
These results are known as the theorem of Pappus.

PROBLEMS

1. Solve Prob. 43.2 by Green's theorem.

2. Solve Prob. 43.3 by Green's theorem.

3. Find the area of a sector of the ellipse $x = a \cos t$, $y = b \sin t$ from $t = 0$ to $t = \varphi$.

4. Find the area of a sector of the hyperbola $x = a \cosh t$, $y = b \sinh t$ from $t = 0$ to $t = \varphi$.

5. Find the area of the loop of the *folium of Descartes*:

$$x = \frac{3at}{1 + t^3}, \qquad y = \frac{3at^2}{1 + t^3}.$$

6. The epicycloid formed by a circle of radius b rolling over a circle of radius a has the parametric equations

$$x = (a + b) \cos k\theta - b \cos (1 + k)\theta,$$
$$y = (a + b) \sin k\theta - b \sin (1 + k)\theta,$$

where $k = b/a$ and θ is the angle through which the moving circle turns. Show that the area of one arch of the epicycloid exterior to the fixed circle is

$$A = 3\pi b^2 + 2\pi b^3/a.$$
$$[x \, dy - y \, dx = b(1 + k)(1 + 2k)(1 - \cos \theta) \, d\theta.]$$

7. Show that the vector area (§11) within a closed curve traversed counterclockwise is

$$A\mathbf{k} = \frac{1}{2} \oint \mathbf{r} \times d\mathbf{r}.$$

Hence show that a polygon in the xy-plane whose vertices have the position vectors $\mathbf{r}_1, \mathbf{r}_2, \cdots, \mathbf{r}_n$ has the vector area

$$A\mathbf{k} = \tfrac{1}{2}(\mathbf{r}_1 \times \mathbf{r}_2 + \mathbf{r}_2 \times \mathbf{r}_3 + \cdots + \mathbf{r}_n \times \mathbf{r}_1).$$

8. Show that the area within a closed curve in the xy-plane has the moments of inertia

$$I_x = \oint xy^2 \, dy, \qquad I_y = -\oint x^2y \, dx, \qquad I_z = \oint xy^2 \, dy - x^2y \, dx,$$

about the axes of coordinates.

Find I_x, I_y, I_z for the ellipse $x = a \cos t$, $y = b \sin t$.

9. Prove that

$$\frac{1}{3} \oint x^3 \, dy - y^3 \, dx = I_z,$$

the moment of inertia about the z-axis of the enclosed area.

Find I_z for the rectangle whose vertices are $x = \pm a$, $y = \pm b$.

10. Compute

$$\oint (2x - y) \, dx + (x + 3y) \, dy$$

over the ellipse $x = 2 \cos t$, $y = \sin t$, and verify by Green's theorem.

11. Compute $\iint x^2 \, dx \, dy$ over the area inside the square $(0, 0) - (4, 0) - (4, 4) - (0, 4) - (0, 0)$ and outside of the rectangle $(1, 1) - (2, 1) - (2, 3) - (1, 3) - (1, 1)$. Verify by transforming the integral into a line integral over the entire boundary.

12. Compute $\frac{1}{2} \oint x \, dy - y \, dx$ over the boundary given in Prob. 11. Verify your answer.

13. Find the area between the parabolas $4y = x^2$, $4x = y^2$ by circuit integration.

14. Compute $\oint (xy - x^2) \, dx + x^2 y \, dy$ over the triangle bounded by the lines $y = 0$, $x = 1$, $y = x$, and verify by Green's theorem.

48. Vector Forms of Green's Theorem. Green's theorem admits of two vector interpretations.

1. Let us put

$$\mathbf{f} = [P, Q, 0], \qquad \text{rot } \mathbf{f} = [0, 0, Q_x - P_y].$$

Since the unit tangent vector to the boundary of $\mathscr{R}$ is

$$\mathbf{T} = [dx/ds, dy/ds, 0] \tag{28.4},$$

equation (47.1) becomes

$$\iint_R \mathbf{k} \cdot \text{rot } \mathbf{f} \, dA = \oint \mathbf{f} \cdot \mathbf{T} \, ds, \tag{1}$$

where $dA = dx \, dy$ is the element of area. We shall see that (1) is a special case of Stokes' theorem (§50).

The integral of the tangential component of a vector about a curve is called its *circulation*. Thus equation (1) states:

The circulation of a vector about a plane curve is equal to the integral of the normal component of its rotation over the enclosed area. The sense of circulation and the normal form a right-handed screw.

2. Let us put

$$\mathbf{f} = [Q, -P, 0], \qquad \text{div } \mathbf{f} = Q_x - P_y.$$

Since the unit exterior normal vector to the boundary is

$$\mathbf{n} = \mathbf{T} \times \mathbf{k} = [dy/ds, -dx/ds, 0],$$

equation (47.1) becomes

$$\iint_R \text{div } \mathbf{f} \, dA = \oint \mathbf{f} \cdot \mathbf{n} \, ds. \tag{2}$$

We shall see that (2) is the plane version of the divergence theorem (§52).

The integral of the outward normal component of a vector about a curve is called its *normal flux*. Thus equation (2) states:

The normal flux of a vector across a closed plane curve is equal to the integral of its divergence over the enclosed area.

Thus, if we apply (1) and (2) to the position vector $\mathbf{r} = [x, y, 0]$ in the xy-plane, we obtain

$$0 = \oint \mathbf{r} \cdot \mathbf{T}\, ds, \qquad 2A = \oint \mathbf{r} \cdot \mathbf{n}\, ds.$$

Green's theorem in form (1) affords a simple proof of the

THEOREM. *If* $\mathbf{f}$ *is a plane vector with continuous first partial derivatives in a region* $\mathscr{R}$,

$$(3) \qquad \operatorname{rot} \mathbf{f} = 0 \quad \text{implies} \quad \oint \mathbf{f} \cdot d\mathbf{r} = 0$$

over all regular closed curves in the region; and, conversely,

$$(4) \qquad \oint \mathbf{f} \cdot d\mathbf{r} = 0 \quad \text{implies} \quad \operatorname{rot} \mathbf{f} = \mathbf{0},$$

provided the region can be dissected into subregions whose boundaries are cut in at most two points by parallels to the axes.

Proof. When $\operatorname{rot} \mathbf{f} = 0$ throughout $\mathscr{R}$, (1) shows that $\oint \mathbf{f} \cdot d\mathbf{r} = 0$ over all regular closed curves in $\mathscr{R}$.

Conversely, if $\oint \mathbf{f} \cdot d\mathbf{r} = 0$ over all regular closed curves, then

$$\operatorname{rot} \mathbf{f} = (Q_x - P_y)\, \mathbf{k} = \mathbf{0} \qquad \text{in } \mathscr{R}.$$

For, if the *continuous* function $Q_x - P_y \neq 0$ at any interior point (x_0, y_0) of the region, we can always find a circle about (x_0, y_0) in which $Q_x - P_y$ keeps the same sign.† On integrating over its boundary we have $\oint \mathbf{f} \cdot d\mathbf{r} \neq 0$ from (1) contrary to hypothesis. Thus $Q_x - P_y = 0$ at all interior points, and, by continuity, also on the boundary. But $Q_x - P_y = 0$ implies $\operatorname{rot} \mathbf{f} = \mathbf{0}$.

49. Surface Integrals. The parametric equations of a surface S,

$$(1) \qquad x = x(u, v), \qquad y = y(u, v), \qquad z = z(u, v),$$

may be combined into a single vector equation

$$(2) \qquad \mathbf{r} = x\mathbf{i} + y\mathbf{j} + z\mathbf{k} = \mathbf{r}(u, v).$$

† *Advanced Calculus*, §74.

The *parametric curves* on the surface,

$$v = \text{const} \quad \text{(the } u\text{-curves)},$$

$$u = \text{const} \quad \text{(the } v\text{-curves)},$$

have tangent vectors $\mathbf{r}_u$ and $\mathbf{r}_v$, respectively, and at a *regular point* of the surface (§36) the normal vector $\mathbf{r}_u \times \mathbf{r}_v \neq \mathbf{0}$. The lengths of the vectors $\mathbf{r}_u \, du$, $\mathbf{r}_v \, dv$ are the elements of arc on the parametric curves; and the vector area of the parallelogram they form,

$$(3) \qquad\qquad d\mathbf{S} = \mathbf{r}_u \times \mathbf{r}_v \, du \, dv,$$

is called the *vector element of area* on the surface. Its magnitude

$$(4) \qquad\qquad dS = |\mathbf{r}_u \times \mathbf{r}_v| \, du \, dv$$

is the *scalar element of area*. If we regard the parameters u, v as rectangular coordinates in the uv-plane, any region S' of this plane corresponds to a portion of the surface whose area is *defined* as the double integral

$$(5) \qquad\qquad S = \int\int_{S'} |\mathbf{r}_u \times \mathbf{r}_v| \, du \, dv.$$

It can be shown that the surface area thus computed is independent of the choice of rectangular axes x, y, z and also of the choice of parameters u, v.† Moreover dS reduces to $dx \, dy$ on the xy-plane: $x = u$, $y = v$, $z = 0$; for

$$\mathbf{r}_u = \mathbf{i}, \qquad \mathbf{r}_v = \mathbf{j}, \qquad \mathbf{r}_u \times \mathbf{r}_v = \mathbf{k}, \qquad dS = du \, dv = dx \, dy.$$

The quantity $|\mathbf{r}_u \times \mathbf{r}_v|$ may be expressed in terms of the *fundamental quantities* for the surface, namely,

$$(6) \qquad E = \mathbf{r}_u \cdot \mathbf{r}_u, \qquad F = \mathbf{r}_u \cdot \mathbf{r}_v, \qquad G = \mathbf{r}_v \cdot \mathbf{r}_v.$$

From (14.2),

$$(\mathbf{r}_u \times \mathbf{r}_v) \cdot (\mathbf{r}_u \times \mathbf{r}_v) = (\mathbf{r}_u \cdot \mathbf{r}_u)(\mathbf{r}_v \cdot \mathbf{r}_v) - (\mathbf{r}_u \cdot \mathbf{r}_v)^2 = EG - F^2,$$

and hence

$$(7) \qquad\qquad |\mathbf{r}_u \times \mathbf{r}_v| = \sqrt{EG - F^2}.$$

On a *bilateral* (two-sided) surface it is possible to distinguish one side from the other—by painting the sides with different colors for example.‡

---

† *Advanced Calculus*, §164.

‡ A Möbius strip, materialized by giving a strip of paper one twist and pasting its ends together, is a *unilateral surface*. If we attempt to paint one side we paint it all over; for it only *has* one side.

On a bilateral surface $\mathbf{r} = \mathbf{r}(u, v)$, the positive side is the side toward which the normal $\mathbf{r}_u \times \mathbf{r}_v$ points. If $\mathbf{f}(\mathbf{r})$ is any vector function defined over the surface, the integral

$$(8) \qquad \int\int_S \mathbf{f} \cdot d\mathbf{S} = \int\int_{S'} \mathbf{f} \cdot \mathbf{r}_u \times \mathbf{r}_v \, du \, dv$$

is called a *surface integral over the positive side of S*. On putting

$$(9) \qquad d\mathbf{S} = \mathbf{n} \, dS$$

where $\mathbf{n}$ is a *unit* normal in the direction of $\mathbf{r}_u \times \mathbf{r}_v$, we may also write (8) in the form

$$(10) \qquad \int\int_S \mathbf{f} \cdot \mathbf{n} \, dS = \int\int_{S'} \mathbf{f} \cdot \mathbf{n} \sqrt{EG - F^2} \, du \, dv,$$

[handwritten: $|r_u \times r_v| = \sqrt{EG - F^2}$]

where $\mathbf{f} \cdot \mathbf{n}$ is the normal component of $\mathbf{f}$ over the surface.

Compare now the line integral

$$\int \mathbf{f} \cdot d\mathbf{r} = \int \mathbf{f} \cdot \mathbf{T} \, ds$$

with the surface integral

$$\int\int \mathbf{f} \cdot d\mathbf{S} = \int\int \mathbf{f} \cdot \mathbf{n} \, dS;$$

the former integrates *tangential* components of a vector over a curve, the latter integrates *normal* components of a vector over a surface.

50. Stokes' Theorem. Consider a bilateral surface that is *piecewise smooth*. Such a surface consists of portions S having an equation $\mathbf{r} = \mathbf{r}(u, v)$ and over which the normal vector $\mathbf{r}_u \times \mathbf{r}_v$ is continuous; furthermore, we assume that $\mathbf{r}_{uv} = \mathbf{r}_{vu}$.† The positive side of S is the side toward which $\mathbf{r}_u \times \mathbf{r}_v$ points; and a person, erect on the *positive* side, will have S to his left when he traverses its boundary in the *positive sense*.

The vector form of Green's theorem,

$$\int\int \mathbf{k} \cdot \mathrm{rot}\, \mathbf{f} \, dA = \oint \mathbf{f} \cdot d\mathbf{r}, \qquad (48.1)$$

which converts the surface integral of rot $\mathbf{f}$ over a plane region into the circuit integral of $\mathbf{f}$ over its boundary, may be generalized to apply to curved surfaces; we need only replace the vector element of area,

$$\mathbf{k} \, dA = \mathbf{r}_x \times \mathbf{r}_y \, dx \, dy \quad \text{by} \quad \mathbf{n} \, dS = \mathbf{r}_u \times \mathbf{r}_v \, du \, dv,$$

where $\mathbf{n}$ is a unit normal in the direction of $\mathbf{r}_u \times \mathbf{r}_v$.

† This is certainly the case when the functions in (49.1) have continuous second partial derivatives. *Advanced Calculus*, §82.

[handwritten notes at bottom:]

$$ds = |r_u \times r_v| \, du \, dv$$

$$\text{but } n = \frac{r_u \times r_v}{|r_u \times r_v|} \qquad n \, ds = d\bar{s} = (r_u \times r_v) \, du \, dv$$

dy dx [handwritten]

STOKES' THEOREM. *Let S be a surface consisting of portions that are piecewise smooth and bounded by regular closed curves. Then, if the vector function* **f(r)** *has a continuous gradient* ∇**f** *over S, the surface integral of* rot **f** *over S is equal to the circuit integral of* **f** *over its boundary C in the positive sense:*

(1)
$$\iint_S \mathbf{n} \cdot \text{rot } \mathbf{f} \, dS = \oint_C \mathbf{f} \cdot d\mathbf{r}.$$

Proof. It will suffice to prove (1) for a smooth portion of the surface over which $\mathbf{r}_{uv} = \mathbf{r}_{vu}$; for, if such equations for all the smooth portions are added, we obtain (1). Note that in adding the circuit integrals all internal boundaries are traversed twice and in opposite directions so that the corresponding line integrals cancel.

We may therefore assume that S is smooth and bounded by a regular closed curve C. Let S' be the region of the uv-plane which contains all

if one is continuous [handwritten]
& the other exists [handwritten]
they are equal [handwritten]

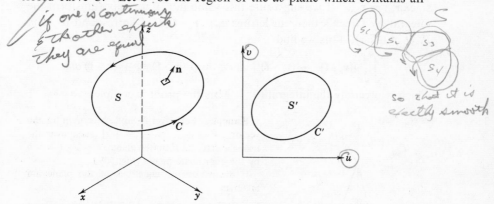

Sc *Sᴸ* *S3* [handwritten]
S4 [handwritten]
So that it is [handwritten]
exactly smooth [handwritten]

Fig. 50*a*. Surface S mapped on a plane region S'.

parameter values u, v corresponding to points of S (Fig. 50*a*). Moreover, we suppose that S is so restricted that the correspondence $(u, v) \leftrightarrow (x, y, z)$ is one-to-one. If we put

$$\mathbf{n} \, dS = \mathbf{dS} = \mathbf{r}_u \times \mathbf{r}_v \, du \, dv,$$

the surface integral in (1) becomes

(2)
$$\iint_{S'} (\mathbf{r}_u \times \mathbf{r}_v) \cdot \text{rot } \mathbf{f} \, du \, dv$$

taken over the region S' of the uv-plane. The curve C forming the boundary of S maps into a curve C', the boundary of S'; and the circuit integral in (1) may be computed as a circuit integral over C':

(3)
$$\oint_{C'} \mathbf{f} \cdot (\mathbf{r}_u \, du + \mathbf{r}_v \, dv).$$

Stokes [handwritten]
Green [handwritten]
Courant [handwritten]

We now apply Green's theorem in the uv-plane to show that the integrals (2) and (3) are equal.

On making use of formula (14.2),

$$(\mathbf{a} \times \mathbf{b}) \cdot (\mathbf{c} \times \mathbf{d}) = (\mathbf{a} \cdot \mathbf{c})(\mathbf{b} \cdot \mathbf{d}) - (\mathbf{a} \cdot \mathbf{d})(\mathbf{b} \cdot \mathbf{c}),$$

we find that

$$(\mathbf{r}_u \times \mathbf{r}_v) \cdot \operatorname{rot} \mathbf{f} = (\mathbf{r}_u \times \mathbf{r}_v) \cdot (\mathbf{i} \times \mathbf{f}_x + \mathbf{j} \times \mathbf{f}_y + \mathbf{k} \times \mathbf{f}_z)$$
$$= x_u\, \mathbf{r}_v \cdot \mathbf{f}_x - x_v\, \mathbf{r}_u \cdot \mathbf{f}_x +$$
$$y_u\, \mathbf{r}_v \cdot \mathbf{f}_y - y_v\, \mathbf{r}_u \cdot \mathbf{f}_y +$$
$$z_u\, \mathbf{r}_v \cdot \mathbf{f}_z - z_v\, \mathbf{r}_u \cdot \mathbf{f}_z,$$

and hence, from the chain rule,

(4) $(\mathbf{r}_u \times \mathbf{r}_v) \cdot \operatorname{rot} \mathbf{f} = \mathbf{r}_v \cdot \mathbf{f}_u - \mathbf{r}_u \cdot \mathbf{f}_v = (\mathbf{r}_v \cdot \mathbf{f})_u - (\mathbf{r}_u \cdot \mathbf{f})_v,$

since $\mathbf{r}_{vu} = \mathbf{r}_{uv}$. If we substitute this value in (2), we may transform the integral by Green's theorem letting u, v, $\mathbf{r}_u \cdot \mathbf{f}$, $\mathbf{r}_v \cdot \mathbf{f}$ correspond to x, y, P, Q in (47.1); thus we find

$$\int\int_{S'} [(\mathbf{r}_v \cdot \mathbf{f})_u - (\mathbf{r}_u \cdot \mathbf{f})_v]\, du\, dv = \oint_{C'} (\mathbf{r}_u \cdot \mathbf{f})\, du + (\mathbf{r}_v \cdot \mathbf{f})\, dv,$$

which is precisely the integral (3). Thus the proof is complete.

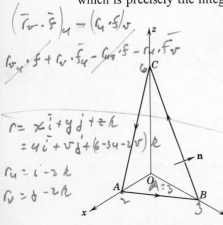

Fig. 50b. Circuit integral computed by Stokes' theorem.

Example. Let us verify Stokes' theorem for the vector $\mathbf{f} = [x + y,\ 2x - z,\ y + z]$ taken over the triangle ABC cut from the plane $3x + 2y + z = 6$ by the coordinate planes (Fig. 50b).

If the parametric equations of the plane are taken as

$$x = u, \qquad y = v, \qquad z = 6 - 3u - 2v,$$

its positive normal $\mathbf{n}$ has the direction of

$$\mathbf{r}_u \times \mathbf{r}_v = [1, 0, -3] \times [0, 1, -2] = [3, 2, 1],$$

and the vector element of area is

$$\mathbf{n}\, dS = \mathbf{r}_u \times \mathbf{r}_v\, du\, dv = [3, 2, 1]\, dx\, dy.$$

Since $\operatorname{rot} \mathbf{f} = [2, 0, 1]$,

$$\int\int_{ABC} \mathbf{n} \cdot \operatorname{rot} \mathbf{f}\, dS = 7 \int\int_{AOB} dx\, dy = 7 \cdot 3 = 21;$$

for the area of the triangle AOB (the projection of ABC on the xy-plane) is 3.

Corresponding to the direction of $\mathbf{n}$, the positive sense of circuit is ABC. The circuit integral,

$$\oint_{ABC} (x + y)\, dx + (2x - z)\, dy + (y + z)\, dz,$$

is the sum of the line integrals over AB, BC, CA which prove to be 1, 36, −16, respectively. Thus the theorem is verified $(21 = 1 + 36 - 16)$.

PROBLEMS

1. Verify Stokes' theorem for $\mathbf{f} = [2y + z, x - z, y - x]$ taken over the triangle ABC cut from the plane $x + y + z = 1$ by the coordinate planes.

[If $A(1, 0, 0)$, $B(0, 1, 0)$, $C(0, 0, 1)$, the line integrals over AB, BC, CA, are $-\frac{1}{2}, 1, 1$; hence $\oint \mathbf{f} \cdot dr = \frac{3}{2}$ over ABC.]

2. Verify Stokes' theorem for the vector $\mathbf{f} = [z, x, y]$ taken over the half of the sphere $x^2 + y^2 + z^2 = a^2$ lying above the xy-plane.

$$\left[\oint \mathbf{f} \cdot dr \text{ around the circle } x^2 + y^2 = a^2 \text{ reduces to } \oint x \, dy = \pi a^2. \right]$$

3. Compute $\oint \mathbf{f} \cdot d\mathbf{r}$ around the circle $(x - 1)^2 + y^2 = 1$, $z = 3$ when $\mathbf{f} = [-y, x, 2]$.

4. If $u(x, y, z)$, $v(x, y, z)$ have continuous gradients, show that

$$\iint_S \mathbf{n} \cdot \nabla u \times \nabla v \, dS = \oint_C u \, dv,$$

where S is a portion of a surface bounded by a closed curve C.

5. When $u = \rho^2/2$, $v = \varphi$ in Prob. 4, show that

$$\iint_S \mathbf{k} \cdot \mathbf{n} \, dS = \frac{1}{2} \oint_C \rho^2 \, d\varphi.$$

[See Ex. 37.2; ρ, φ are the cylindrical coordinates of Ex. 42.1.]

51. Generalized Stokes' Theorem. With the same conditions on the function $\mathbf{f}(\mathbf{r})$ and the surface, we can prove the more general transformation

$$(1) \qquad\qquad \iint_S d\mathbf{S} \times \nabla \mathbf{f} = \oint_C d\mathbf{r}\, \mathbf{f}$$

between the integrals of dyadics. In the surface integral, the vector $d\mathbf{S} = (\mathbf{r}_u \times \mathbf{r}_v) \, du \, dv$ is cross-multiplied into the vectors of $\nabla \mathbf{f}$ on the left: thus

$$(\mathbf{r}_u \times \mathbf{r}_v) \times (\mathbf{i} \mathbf{f}_x + \mathbf{j} \mathbf{f}_y + \mathbf{k} \mathbf{f}_z) = (\mathbf{r}_u \times \mathbf{r}_v) \times \mathbf{i} \mathbf{f}_x + \text{cycl.}$$

If we now make use of the formula

$$(\mathbf{a} \times \mathbf{b}) \times \mathbf{c} = (\mathbf{a} \cdot \mathbf{c})\mathbf{b} - (\mathbf{b} \cdot \mathbf{c})\mathbf{a}, \qquad\qquad (12.1)$$

we find that

$$\begin{aligned}
(2) \quad (\overset{a}{\mathbf{r}_u} \times \overset{b}{\mathbf{r}_v}) \times \overset{c}{\nabla \mathbf{f}} &= (\mathbf{r}_u \times \mathbf{r}_v) \times (\mathbf{i} \mathbf{f}_x + \mathbf{j} \mathbf{f}_y + \mathbf{k} \mathbf{f}_z) \\
&= (x_u \mathbf{r}_v - x_v \mathbf{r}_u)\mathbf{f}_x + (y_u \mathbf{r}_v - y_v \mathbf{r}_u)\mathbf{f}_y + (z_u \mathbf{r}_v - z_v \mathbf{r}_u)\mathbf{f}_z \\
&= \mathbf{r}_v(x_u \mathbf{f}_x + y_u \mathbf{f}_y + z_u \mathbf{f}_z) - \mathbf{r}_u(x_v \mathbf{f}_x + y_v \mathbf{f}_y + z_v \mathbf{f}_z) \\
&= \mathbf{r}_v \mathbf{f}_u - \mathbf{r}_u \mathbf{f}_v \\
&= (\mathbf{r}_v \mathbf{f})_u - (\mathbf{r}_u \mathbf{f})_v.
\end{aligned}$$

Hence, on applying Green's theorem (47.4) in which $\mathbf{P}$ and $\mathbf{Q}$ are dyadics, we have

$$\int\int_S d\mathbf{S} \times \nabla\mathbf{f} = \int\int_{S'} [(\mathbf{r}_v\,\mathbf{f})_u - (\mathbf{r}_u\,\mathbf{f})_v]\,du\,dv$$

$$= \oint_{C'} \mathbf{r}_u\,\mathbf{f}\,du + \mathbf{r}_v\,\mathbf{f}\,dv$$

$$= \oint_{C'} (\mathbf{r}_u\,du + \mathbf{r}_v\,dv)\mathbf{f}$$

$$= \oint_C d\mathbf{r}\,\mathbf{f}$$

as stated in (1). In this equation the *order* of the vectors is essential.

The dyadic equation (1) gives two others on taking scalar and vector invariants (§39). Since dot and cross multiplication is distributive with respect to addition, either invariant of a dyadic integral is equal to integral of the invariant. Thus both scalar and vector invariants of the dyadic integrals in (1) may be taken *under the integral sign*.

On taking the scalar invariant, the integrand of the surface integral (apart from $du\,dv$) becomes

$$(\mathbf{r}_u \times \mathbf{r}_v) \times \mathbf{i} \cdot \mathbf{f}_x + \text{cycl} = (\mathbf{r}_u \times \mathbf{r}_v) \cdot (\mathbf{i} \times \mathbf{f}_x + \text{cycl})$$

$$= (\mathbf{r}_u \times \mathbf{r}_v) \cdot \operatorname{rot} \mathbf{f};$$

and the circuit integral becomes $\oint d\mathbf{r} \cdot \mathbf{f}$. Thus, in view of (50.2), we again obtain Stokes' theorem.

On taking the vector invariant, the integrand of the surface integral becomes

$$[(\mathbf{r}_u \times \mathbf{r}_v) \times \mathbf{i}] \times \mathbf{f}_x + \text{cycl} = (\mathbf{i}\mathbf{f}_x + \text{cycl}) \cdot (\mathbf{r}_u \times \mathbf{r}_v) - (\mathbf{r}_u \times \mathbf{r}_v)(\mathbf{i} \cdot \mathbf{f}_x + \text{cycl})$$

$$= \nabla\mathbf{f} \cdot (\mathbf{r}_u \times \mathbf{r}_v) - (\mathbf{r}_u \times \mathbf{r}_v) \operatorname{div} \mathbf{f};$$

and the circuit integral becomes $\oint d\mathbf{r} \times \mathbf{f}$. Thus, on writing $\mathbf{r}_u \times \mathbf{r}_v\,du\,dv = \mathbf{n}\,dS$, we obtain the new theorem:

$$(3) \qquad \int\int_S \{(\nabla\mathbf{f}) \cdot \mathbf{n} - \mathbf{n} \operatorname{div} \mathbf{f}\}\,dS = \oint_C d\mathbf{r} \times \mathbf{f}.$$

For example, if $\mathbf{f} = \mathbf{r}$, the position vector to the surface, $\nabla\mathbf{r} = \mathbf{I}$, $\operatorname{div} \mathbf{r} = 3$ from (40.8), and (3) becomes

$$(4) \qquad \int\int_S \mathbf{n}\,dS = \frac{1}{2} \oint_C \mathbf{r} \times d\mathbf{r}.$$

This expresses the vector area of a surface as a circuit integral about its boundary. Thus over the upper half H of a hemisphere of radius a, $\mathbf{r} = a\mathbf{R}$, $d\mathbf{r} = a\mathbf{P} \, d\theta$, and its vector area

$$\int\int_H \mathbf{n} \, dS = \frac{1}{2} a^2 \int_0^{2\pi} \mathbf{R} \times \mathbf{P} \, d\theta = \pi a^2 \mathbf{k}.$$

PROBLEMS

1. If the closed curve C encloses a portion S of a surface, show that

$$\int_S \mathbf{n} \times \mathbf{r} \, dS = \frac{1}{2} \oint_C r^2 \, d\mathbf{r}.$$

2. If $\mathbf{f} = \mathbf{i}\, u(x, y) + \mathbf{j}\, v(x, y)$, prove that

$$\oint_C \mathbf{f} \times \, d\mathbf{r} = \mathbf{k} \int_A \operatorname{div} \mathbf{f} \, dA,$$

where C is a closed curve in the xy-plane enclosing the region A.

3. Prove that the vector area of a closed surface is zero.

52. Divergence Theorem. A basic transformation of volume to surface integrals is given by the

DIVERGENCE THEOREM (GAUSS). *If the vector function $\mathbf{f}(\mathbf{r})$ has continuous first partial derivatives in the region V bounded by a closed surface S over which the unit external normal $\mathbf{n}$ is sectionally continuous, then the volume integral of $\operatorname{div} \mathbf{f}$ within S is equal to the external surface integral of $\mathbf{f}$ over S:*

$$(1) \qquad \int\int\int_V \operatorname{div} \mathbf{f} \, dV = \int\int_S \mathbf{n} \cdot \mathbf{f} \, dS.$$

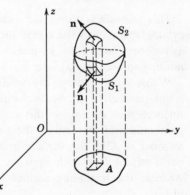

Fig. 52a. Region bounded by a closed surface.

Proof. Since

$$\operatorname{div} \mathbf{f} = \mathbf{i} \cdot \mathbf{f}_x + \mathbf{j} \cdot \mathbf{f}_y + \mathbf{k} \cdot \mathbf{f}_z \quad (40.2),$$

the volume integral of $\operatorname{div} \mathbf{f}$ is the sum of three integrals. In order to compute the integral of $\mathbf{k} \cdot \mathbf{f}_z$, we first consider a surface S which is cut in at most two points by a line parallel to the z-axis (Fig. 52a); denote them by (x, y, z_1) and (x, y, z_2) where $z_1 < z_2$. Then S has a lower portion S_1 consisting of the points (x, y, z_1) and an upper portion S_2 consisting of the points (x, y, z_2). The points for which $z_1 = z_2$ form a closed curve separating S_1 from S_2. Now, if S_1 and S_2 project into an area A of the xy-plane,

$$(2) \quad \iiint_V \frac{\partial \mathbf{f}}{\partial z}\, dx\, dy\, dz = \iint_A dx\, dy \int_{z_1(x,y)}^{z_2(x,y)} \frac{\partial \mathbf{f}}{\partial z}\, dz$$

$$= \iint_A \mathbf{f}(x, y, z_2)\, dx\, dy - \iint_A \mathbf{f}(x, y, z_1)\, dx\, dy.$$

If we regard x, y as the parameters u, v on the surfaces S_1 and S_2, the vector element of surface is $\mathbf{r}_x \times \mathbf{r}_y\, dx\, dy$ (49.3). Now from

$$\mathbf{r} = \mathbf{i}x + \mathbf{j}y + \mathbf{k}z(x, y), \qquad \mathbf{r}_x = \mathbf{i} + \mathbf{k}z_x, \qquad \mathbf{r}_y = \mathbf{j} + \mathbf{k}z_y,$$

$$\mathbf{r}_x \times \mathbf{r}_y = \mathbf{k} - \mathbf{i}z_x - \mathbf{j}z_y.$$

Over S_2, $z = z_2(x, y)$, and the vector $\mathbf{r}_x \times \mathbf{r}_y$ has the direction of the external normal $\mathbf{n}$; but, over S_1, $z = z_1(x, y)$, and $\mathbf{r}_x \times \mathbf{r}_y$ has the direction of the internal normal $-\mathbf{n}$. Hence, if $\mathbf{n}\, dS$ denotes the *external* vector element of area on S,

$$\mathbf{n}\, dS = \pm(\mathbf{k} - \mathbf{i}z_x - \mathbf{j}z_y)\, dx\, dy, \qquad \mathbf{n} \cdot \mathbf{k}\, dS = \pm dx\, dy,$$

where the plus sign applies to S_2, the minus to S_1. The two integrals over A may now be combined into a single integral over S, and we may write

$$(3) \quad \iiint_V \mathbf{f}_z\, dx\, dy\, dz = \iint_S \mathbf{n} \cdot \mathbf{k}\, \mathbf{f}(x, y, z)\, dS.$$

This formula is also valid when S is bounded laterally by a part of a cylinder parallel to the z-axis and separating S_1 from S_2. For (2) holds as before; and, in (3), $\mathbf{k} \cdot \mathbf{n} = 0$ over the cylinder, so that it contributes nothing to the integral over S.

We now may remove the condition that S is cut in only two points by a line parallel to the z-axis. For, if we divide V into parts bounded by surfaces that do satisfy this condition and apply formula (3) to each point and add the results, the volume integrals will combine to the left member of (3); the surface integrals over the boundaries between the parts cancel (for each appears twice but with opposed values of $\mathbf{n}$), whereas the remaining surface integrals combine to the right member of (3).

Finally we may extend (3) to regions bounded by two or more closed surfaces, that is, regions with cavities in them, by this same process of subdivision. Additional surfaces must be introduced so that the parts of V are all bounded by a single closed surface, and the surface integrals over these will cancel in pairs as before.

When x, y, z form a dextral system of axes, the same is true of y, z, x and z, x, y. Hence, if in (3) we make cyclic interchanges in x, y, z, we obtain the corresponding formulas:

$$(4) \qquad \iiint_V \mathbf{f}_x \, dx \, dy \, dz = \iint_S \mathbf{n} \cdot \mathbf{i} \, \mathbf{f}(x, y, z) \, dS,$$

$$(5) \qquad \iiint \mathbf{f}_y \, dx \, dy \, dz = \iint_S \mathbf{n} \cdot \mathbf{j} \, \mathbf{f}(x, y, z) \, dS.$$

Now dot-multiply (3), (4), (5) by $\mathbf{k}$, $\mathbf{i}$, $\mathbf{j}$, respectively, and add the resulting equations. Then the volume integral becomes

$$\iiint (\mathbf{i} \cdot \mathbf{f}_x + \mathbf{j} \cdot \mathbf{f}_y + \mathbf{k} \cdot \mathbf{f}_z) \, dx \, dy \, dz = \iiint \operatorname{div} \mathbf{f} \, dV;$$

$$\overline{\mathbf{f}_x} = \dot{e} \, \frac{\partial \mathbf{f}_i}{\partial x}$$

and the surface integral

$$\iint \mathbf{n} \cdot (\mathbf{i}(\mathbf{i} \cdot \mathbf{f}) + \mathbf{j}(\mathbf{j} \cdot \mathbf{f}) + \mathbf{k}(\mathbf{k} \cdot \mathbf{f})) \, dS = \iint \mathbf{n} \cdot \mathbf{f} \, dS.$$

This proves formula (1).

Volume and surface integrals are often denoted by a single integral sign when the differential dV or dS indicates their character. Moreover $\oint \cdots dS$ is used to denote integration over a *closed* surface. In this notation the divergence theorem becomes

$$(1)' \qquad \int_V \operatorname{div} \mathbf{f} \, dV = \oint_S \mathbf{n} \cdot \mathbf{f} \, dS.$$

With suitable conditions on $\mathbf{f}$, the divergence theorem applies to an *infinite region* V_∞ outside of a closed surface S.

THEOREM 2. *With the same conditions on $\mathbf{f}$ and S as before, we have*

$$(6) \qquad \int_{V_\infty} \operatorname{div} \mathbf{f} \, dV = \oint_S \mathbf{n} \cdot \mathbf{f} \, dS$$

provided

$$(7) \qquad \lim_{r \to \infty} r^2 \mathbf{f} \to \mathbf{0} \quad uniformly,$$

where r is the distance from any fixed point P, and the unit normal $\mathbf{n}$, external to the region V_∞, points toward the interior of S.

Proof. Let $\sum$ be a sphere about P large enough to enclose S completely. Then the divergence theorem applied to the region V between S and $\sum$ gives

$$\int_V \operatorname{div} \mathbf{f}\, dV = \oint_S \mathbf{n} \cdot \mathbf{f}\, dS + \oint_\Sigma \mathbf{n} \cdot \mathbf{f}\, dS,$$

$\mathbf{n}$ being an external normal with respect to the region V. The uniform approach of $r^2\mathbf{f}$ to zero means that

$$r^2|\mathbf{f}| < \varepsilon \qquad \text{when} \qquad r > R,$$

a suitably large value. If the radius r of $\sum$ is now chosen $> R$, we have

$$\left| \oint_\Sigma \mathbf{n} \cdot \mathbf{f}\, dS \right| \leq \oint_\Sigma |\mathbf{f}|\, dS < \frac{\varepsilon}{r^2} \oint_\Sigma dS = 4\pi\varepsilon,$$

and hence the surface integral over $\sum$ approaches zero as $r \to \infty$. At the same time $V \to V_\infty$, and the theorem is proved.

Example 1. When $\mathbf{f} = \mathbf{r}$, $\operatorname{div} \mathbf{r} = 3$; then from (1)

$$V = \frac{1}{3} \int_S \mathbf{n} \cdot \mathbf{r}\, dS = \frac{1}{3} \oint_S p\, dS,$$

$$f = \overline{n} \cdot \overline{r}$$

where p is the perpendicular from O on the tangent plane to S at the end point of $\mathbf{r}$. Thus the volume within S is expressed as a surface integral over S.

For a *cone* of base B, altitude h, take O at the vertex. Then $p = 0$ over the lateral surface, $p = h$ over the base, and $V = \frac{1}{3}Bh$.

For a *sphere* of radius a, take O at the center. Then $p = a$ and $V = \frac{1}{3}aS = \frac{4}{3}\pi a^3$.

Example 2. Solid Angle. The rays from a point O through the points of a closed curve generate a cone; and the surface of a unit sphere about O intercepted by this cone is called the *solid* angle Ω of the cone.

Let us apply the divergence theorem to the vector

$$\mathbf{f} = -\nabla\frac{1}{r} = \frac{\mathbf{r}}{r^3}$$

in the region interior to a cone of solid angle Ω which is limited externally by a surface S, internally by a portion σ of a small sphere of radius a about O (Fig. 52b). Within this region $\mathbf{f}$ has continuous first partial derivatives, and from Ex. 41.1.

$$\operatorname{div} \mathbf{f} = -\nabla^2\frac{1}{r} = 0, \quad \text{and hence} \quad \oint \mathbf{n} \cdot \mathbf{f}\, dS = 0.$$

Over the small sphere the external normal $\mathbf{n} = -\mathbf{r}/a$; while over the conical surface $\mathbf{n} \cdot \mathbf{r} = 0$; hence,

$$\oint \mathbf{n} \cdot \mathbf{f}\, dS = \int_S \frac{\mathbf{n} \cdot \mathbf{r}}{r^3}\, dS - \int_\sigma \frac{\mathbf{r}}{a} \cdot \frac{\mathbf{r}}{a^3}\, dS = \int_S \frac{\mathbf{n} \cdot \mathbf{r}}{r^3}\, dS - \frac{\sigma}{a^2} = 0.$$

But, since $\sigma/a^2 = \Omega/1^2$, we have

(8)
$$\Omega = \int_S \frac{\mathbf{n} \cdot \mathbf{r}}{r^3} \, dS = -\int_S \mathbf{n} \cdot \nabla \left(\frac{1}{r}\right) dS.$$

If S is closed surface, we have

(9)
$$-\oint_S \mathbf{n} \cdot \nabla \left(\frac{1}{r}\right) dS = \begin{cases} 4\pi, & O \text{ inside of } S, \\ 0, & O \text{ outside of } S. \end{cases}$$

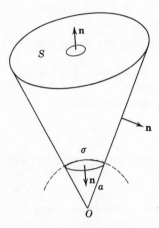

Fig. 52*b*. Solid angle.

When O is outside of S, $\mathbf{f}$ has continuous partial derivatives throughout its interior, and (9) follows at once from (1). In this case the elements of solid angle $d\Omega = \mathbf{n} \cdot \mathbf{r} \, dS/r^3$ corresponding to the same conical element cancel in pairs.

Example 3. If div $\mathbf{f} = 0$ in a region V, the normal flux of $\mathbf{f}$ is zero over any closed surface which satisfies the requirements of the divergence theorem:

(10)
$$\oint \mathbf{n} \cdot \mathbf{f} \, dS = 0 \qquad \text{if} \qquad \text{div } \mathbf{f} = 0.$$

Suppose now that div $\mathbf{f} = 0$ in a simply connected region V except on a surface S dividing S in two parts V_1 and V_2 and on which $\mathbf{f}$ has finite discontinuities. We can then show by an argument, which parallels that given at the end of §46, that $\oint \mathbf{n} \cdot \mathbf{f} \, dS = 0$ over all closed surfaces in V if *the normal component of* $\mathbf{f}$ *is continuous on* S.

PROBLEMS

1. Verify the divergence theorem for the vector $\mathbf{f} = x^2\mathbf{i} + y^2\mathbf{j} + z^2\mathbf{k}$ taken over the cube $0 \leq x, y, z \leq 1$.

2. Find $\int \mathbf{f} \cdot \mathbf{n} \, dS$ for the vector $\mathbf{f} = x\mathbf{i} - y\mathbf{j} + 2z\mathbf{k}$ over the sphere $x^2 + y^2 + (z - 1)^2 = 1$.

3. Find a vector $\mathbf{f} = g(r)\mathbf{r}$ such that div $\mathbf{f} = r^m \ (m > -3)$. Prove that

$$\int r^m \, dV = \frac{1}{m+3} \oint r^m \, \mathbf{r} \cdot \mathbf{n} \, dS.$$

4. The vector $\mathbf{f} = k\nabla(1/r)$, where r is the distance from a point O, represents an attraction which varies as $1/r^2$ (inverse square law). If S is a closed surface about O, prove that

$$\oint_S \mathbf{f} \cdot \mathbf{n} \, dS = -4\pi k.$$

5. If $\mathbf{f} = \nabla\varphi$ and div $\mathbf{f} = 0$, show that div $(\varphi\mathbf{f}) = |\mathbf{f}|^2$ and hence

$$\int_V |\mathbf{f}|^2 \, dV = \oint_S \varphi \, \mathbf{f} \cdot \mathbf{n} \, dS,$$

where V is the region within the closed surface S.

6. Prove that, when $m > -1$,

$$\int_V r^{m-1} \mathbf{r} \, dV = \frac{1}{m+1} \oint_S r^{m+1} \mathbf{n} \, dS.$$

[Apply (53.3).]

7. If $\mathbf{f} = [x^2 - z^2, \ 2xy, \ y^2 + z]$, find $\oint \mathbf{f} \cdot \mathbf{n} \, dS$ over

(a)   the surface of a cube bounded by the six planes $x = y = z = 0, \ x = y = z = 1$.
(b)   the surface bounded by the cylinder $y^2 + z^2 = 4$ and the planes $x = 0, \ x = 2$.

8. The vector

$$\mathbf{f} = \begin{cases} \mathbf{i}x - \mathbf{j}y + \mathbf{k}z & z > 0, \\ 0 & \text{when} \quad z = 0, \\ -\mathbf{i}x + \mathbf{j}y + \mathbf{k}z & z < 0. \end{cases}$$

Show that $\oint \mathbf{n} \cdot \mathbf{f} \, dS = 0$ over any closed surface.

9. Apply the divergence theorem to $\mathbf{P} \times \text{rot } \mathbf{Q}$ to prove the identities

$$\int (\text{rot } \mathbf{P}) \cdot (\text{rot } \mathbf{Q}) \, dV - \int \mathbf{P} \cdot \text{rot rot } \mathbf{Q} \, dV = \oint \mathbf{n} \cdot \mathbf{P} \times \text{rot } \mathbf{Q} \, dS,$$

$$\int (\mathbf{Q} \cdot \text{rot rot } \mathbf{P} - \mathbf{P} \cdot \text{rot rot } \mathbf{Q}) \, dV = \oint \mathbf{n} \cdot (\mathbf{P} \times \text{rot } \mathbf{Q} - \mathbf{Q} \times \text{rot } \mathbf{P}) \, dS.$$

10. Compute $\oint (ax^2 + by^2 + cz^2) \, dS$ over the sphere $x^2 + y^2 + z^2 = 1$. [Use (52.1); $\mathbf{n} = [x, y, z]$; find $\mathbf{f}$.]

11. Compute $\oint (a^2x^2 + b^2y^2 + c^2z^2)^{-1/2} \, dS$ and $\oint (a^2x^2 + b^2y^2 + c^2z^2)^{1/2} \, dS$ over the ellipsoid $ax^2 + by^2 + cz^2 = 1$. [Use (52.1); find $\mathbf{n}$, then $\mathbf{f}$.]

53. Generalized Divergence Theorem. We may use equations (3), (4), (5) of the preceding article to prove the more general

THEOREM. *If the vector* $\mathbf{f(r)}$ *has continuous first partial derivatives in a region V bounded by a closed surface S,*

$$(1) \qquad \int_V \nabla \mathbf{f}\, dV = \oint_S \mathbf{n}\,\mathbf{f}\, dS.$$

Proof. The volume integral in (1) equals

$$(i) \qquad \mathbf{i} \int \mathbf{f}_x\, dV + \mathbf{j} \int \mathbf{f}_y\, dV + \mathbf{k} \int \mathbf{f}_z\, dV;$$

and, since

$$\mathbf{n} = \mathbf{i}\,\mathbf{i}\cdot\mathbf{n} + \mathbf{j}\,\mathbf{j}\cdot\mathbf{n} + \mathbf{k}\,\mathbf{k}\cdot\mathbf{n},$$

the surface integral equals

$$(ii) \qquad \mathbf{i} \oint \mathbf{i}\cdot\mathbf{n}\,\mathbf{f}\, dS + \mathbf{j} \oint \mathbf{j}\cdot\mathbf{n}\,\mathbf{f}\, dS + \mathbf{k} \oint \mathbf{k}\cdot\mathbf{n}\,\mathbf{f}\, dS.$$

Since the corresponding integrals in (i) and (ii) are equal, (1) is established.

The dyadic equation (1) gives two others on taking scalar and vector invariants under the integral signs as in §52. Since the scalar invariant of $\nabla \mathbf{f}$ is div $\mathbf{f}$, the first of these equations is again the divergence theorem. But the vector invariant of $\nabla \mathbf{f}$ is rot $\mathbf{f}$, and we obtain the new theorem:

$$(2) \qquad \int_V \mathrm{rot}\, \mathbf{f}\, dV = \oint_S \mathbf{n} \times \mathbf{f}\, dS.$$

If in (1) we put $\mathbf{f} = f\mathbf{e}$, where the scalar $f(\mathbf{r})$ has continuous first partial derivatives and $\mathbf{e}$ is a constant vector, we obtain

$$(3) \qquad \int_V \nabla f\, dV = \oint_S \mathbf{n} f\, dS.$$

Example 1. Put $f = 1$ in (3); then

$$(4) \qquad \oint \mathbf{n}\, dS = \mathbf{0}.$$

Put $\mathbf{f} = \mathbf{r}$ in (2); since rot $\mathbf{r} = \mathbf{0}$,

$$(5) \qquad \oint \mathbf{r} \times \mathbf{n}\, dS = \mathbf{0}.$$

From (4) and (5) we conclude that a closed surface is in equilibrium under any system of normal pressures $-\mathbf{n}p$ of constant magnitude p; for their vector sum and vector moment about O are zero.

Example 2. Put $f = \frac{1}{2}r^2$ in (3); then $\nabla f = \mathbf{r}$, and the left member

$$\oint \mathbf{r}\, dV = V\mathbf{r}^*,$$

where $\mathbf{r}^*$ locates the centroid of V; hence

(6) $$V\mathbf{r}^* = \frac{1}{2} \oint r^2\mathbf{n}\, dS.$$

54. Solenoidal Vectors. A vector function $\mathbf{f(r)}$ is said to be solenoidal in a region V if div $\mathbf{f} = 0$ in V.

THEOREM 1. *The vector rot* $\mathbf{g}$ *is solenoidal in any region in which* $\mathbf{g(r)}$ *has continuous second partial derivatives.*

Proof. Let $\mathbf{g} = \mathbf{i}g_1 + \mathbf{j}g_2 + \mathbf{k}g_3$; then (§40)

(1) $$\text{rot } \mathbf{g} = \left(\frac{\partial g_3}{\partial y} - \frac{\partial g_2}{\partial z}\right)\mathbf{i} + \left(\frac{\partial g_1}{\partial z} - \frac{\partial g_3}{\partial x}\right)\mathbf{j} + \left(\frac{\partial g_2}{\partial x} - \frac{\partial g_1}{\partial y}\right)\mathbf{k},$$

and

$$\text{div rot } \mathbf{g} = \frac{\partial}{\partial x}\left(\frac{\partial g_3}{\partial y} - \frac{\partial g_2}{\partial z}\right) + \frac{\partial}{\partial y}\left(\frac{\partial g_1}{\partial z} - \frac{\partial g_3}{\partial x}\right) + \frac{\partial}{\partial z}\left(\frac{\partial g_2}{\partial x} - \frac{\partial g_1}{\partial y}\right) = 0,$$

since the mixed derivatives cancel in pairs.

COROLLARY. *The vector* $\nabla u \times \nabla v$ *is solenoidal*; for

$$\nabla u \times \nabla v = \text{rot } (u\nabla v) \qquad\qquad (41.5).$$

We shall now prove the converse of Theorem 1. To avoid complications we consider the case when the region V is a rectangular prism.

THEOREM 2. *If* div $\mathbf{f} = 0$ *in a rectangular prism* V, *a vector point function* $\mathbf{g}$ *can be defined in* V *so that*

(2) $$\underline{\mathbf{f} = \text{rot } \mathbf{g}.}$$

$div\ \bar{f} = \bar{\iota} \cdot \bar{f}_x + \bar{\jmath} \cdot \bar{f}_y + \bar{k} \cdot \bar{f}$

Proof. If $\mathbf{f} = \mathbf{i}f_1 + \mathbf{j}f_2 + \mathbf{k}f_3$,

(3) $$\text{div } \mathbf{f} = \frac{\partial f_1}{\partial x} + \frac{\partial f_2}{\partial y} + \frac{\partial f_3}{\partial z} \qquad\qquad (40.5).$$

We shall first obtain a particular solution $\mathbf{G}$ of (2) for which $G_3 = 0$:

$$\mathbf{G} = \mathbf{i}G_1 + \mathbf{j}G_2.$$

In view of (1), $\mathbf{f} = \text{rot } \mathbf{G}$ is equivalent to three scalar equations:

(4) $$f_1 = -\frac{\partial G_2}{\partial z}, \qquad f_2 = \frac{\partial G_1}{\partial z}, \qquad f_3 = \frac{\partial G_2}{\partial x} - \frac{\partial G_1}{\partial y}.$$

If (x_0, y_0, z_0) is any fixed point of V, the first two equations of (4) are satisfied by

$$(5) \quad G_2 = - \int_{z_0}^{z} f_1(x, y, z) \, dz, \qquad G_1 = \int_{z_0}^{z} f_2(x, y, z) \, dz + \alpha(x, y).$$

In these integrations x and y are regarded as constant parameters, and $\alpha(x, y)$ is a function as yet undetermined. In order that G_1, G_2 satisfy the third equation of (4) we must have

$$- \int_{z_0}^{z} \left(\frac{\partial f_1}{\partial x} + \frac{\partial f_2}{\partial y} \right) dz - \frac{\partial \alpha}{\partial y} = f_3,$$

or, in view of (3),

$$\int_{z_0}^{z} \frac{\partial f_3}{\partial z} \, dz - \frac{\partial \alpha}{\partial y} = f_3(x, y, z).$$

When we perform the integration this reduces to

$$-f_3(x, y, z_0) - \frac{\partial \alpha}{\partial y} = 0,$$

an equation that is satisfied by taking

$$\alpha(x, y) = - \int_{y_0}^{y} f_3(x, y, z_0) \, dy.$$

Hence the vector $\mathbf{G}$ whose components are

$$(6) \quad G_1 = \int_{z_0}^{z} f_2(x, y, t) \, dt - \int_{y_0}^{y} f_3(x, t, z_0) \, dt, \qquad G_2 = - \int_{z_0}^{z} f_1(x, y, t) \, dt,$$
$$G_3 = 0,$$

is a particular solution of (2)—as we readily verify by computing rot $\mathbf{G}$.

If $\mathbf{g}$ is any other solution of (2),

$$\text{rot } (\mathbf{g} - \mathbf{G}) = \mathbf{f} - \mathbf{f} = 0.$$

Thus $\mathbf{g} - \mathbf{G}$ is irrotational and may be expressed as a gradient vector ∇F (Theorem 45.2). Hence $\mathbf{g} - \mathbf{G} = \nabla F$, and the general solution of (2) is

$$(7) \qquad\qquad\qquad \mathbf{g} = \mathbf{G} + \nabla F,$$

where $F(\mathbf{r})$ is an arbitrary twice-differentiable scalar function. The rectangular components of **g** are obtained by adding $\partial F/\partial x$, $\partial F/\partial y$, $\partial F/\partial z$ to the components of **G** given in (6).

In mathematical physics the solenoidal vector **f** = rot **g** is said to be derived from the *vector potential* **g**.

If C is a closed curve in the region V, and S is any surface spanning C that satisfies the requirements of Stokes' theorem, the normal flux

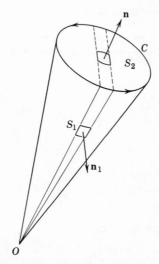

Fig. 54. Closed conical region.

through S of a solenoidal vector **f** = rot **g** depends only on C and the vector potential **g**; for from (50.1)

$$\int_S \mathbf{n} \cdot \mathbf{f} \, dS = \int_S \mathbf{n} \cdot \text{rot } \mathbf{g} \, dS = \oint_C \mathbf{g} \cdot d\mathbf{r}.$$

The vector potential of a solenoidal vector **f** may be found without resort to components.† From the divergence theorem

(8) $$\oint_S \mathbf{n} \cdot \mathbf{f} \, dS = 0 \quad \text{if} \quad \text{div } \mathbf{f} = 0,$$

for any closed surface S. Let S_1 denote the lateral surface of a cone with vertex at O and having the closed curve C as directrix and boundary (Fig. 54). We now apply (8) to the *closed* surface formed by S_1 and the

† Cf. Louis Brand, "*The Vector Potential of a Solenoidal Vector,*" *Am. Math. Monthly,* vol. 57, 1950, pp. 161–167.

"base" S_2 of the cone (a portion of a surface bounded by C). By Stokes' theorem, S_2 contributes

$$(9) \qquad \int_{S_2} \mathbf{n} \cdot \mathbf{f} \, dS = \int_{S_2} \mathbf{n} \cdot \text{rot } \mathbf{g} \, dS = \oint_C \mathbf{g} \cdot \mathbf{T} \, ds \qquad (50.1)$$

to the integral (8). If $\mathbf{r} = \mathbf{r}(s)$ is the equation of C, S_1 has the vector equation

$$\mathbf{r}_1 = t \, \mathbf{r}(s), \qquad 0 < t \leqq 1;$$

and its vector element of area in the direction of the external normal $\mathbf{n}_1$ is

$$\mathbf{n}_1 \, dS = \frac{\partial \mathbf{r}_1}{\partial s} \times \frac{\partial \mathbf{r}_1}{\partial t} \, ds \, dt = t\mathbf{T} \times \mathbf{r}(s) \, ds \, dt.$$

Hence the contribution of S_1 to (8) is

$$(10) \quad \int_{S_1} \mathbf{n}_1 \cdot \mathbf{f} \, dS = \int\int_{S_1} \mathbf{f}(t\mathbf{r}) \cdot \mathbf{T} \times \mathbf{r} \, t \, dt \, ds = \left[\oint_C \int_0^1 \mathbf{r} \times \mathbf{f}(t\mathbf{r}) t \, dt \right] \cdot \mathbf{T} \, ds.$$

Since the sum of the integrals (9) and (10) is zero, we have

$$\oint_C \left[\mathbf{g} + \int_0^1 \mathbf{r} \times \mathbf{f}(t\mathbf{r}) t \, dt \right] \cdot \mathbf{T} \, ds = 0.$$

As this holds for an arbitrary closed curve C, the vector in brackets is zero; hence,

$$(11) \qquad \mathbf{g} = -\mathbf{r} \times \int_0^1 \mathbf{f}(t\mathbf{r}) t \, dt$$

whenever the integral exists.

When $\mathbf{f}(\mathbf{r})$ is homogeneous of degree n, $\mathbf{f}(t\mathbf{r}) = t^n \, \mathbf{f}(\mathbf{r})$, and

$$(12) \qquad \mathbf{g} = - \mathbf{r} \times \mathbf{f}(\mathbf{r}) \int_0^1 t^{n+1} \, dt = \frac{\mathbf{f} \times \mathbf{r}}{n+2}, \qquad n > -2.$$

When $n < -2$, (12) is still valid; for we can integrate from $t = \infty$ to $t = 1$ over the portion of the cone beyond S_2.

Example 1. When $\mathbf{f} = [y, z, x]$, div $\mathbf{f} = 0$. Equation (6) gives the vector potential

$$\mathbf{G} = \left[\int_0^z t \, dt - \int_0^y x \, dt, \quad - \int_0^z y \, dt, \quad 0 \right] = [\tfrac{1}{2}z^2 - xy, -yz, 0].$$

Since $\mathbf{f}$ is homogeneous of degree 1, (12) gives

$$\mathbf{g} = \tfrac{1}{3}\mathbf{f} \times \mathbf{r} = \tfrac{1}{3}[z^2 - xy,\, x^2 - yz,\, y^2 - zx].$$

The difference

$$\mathbf{G} - \mathbf{g} = \tfrac{1}{3}[\tfrac{1}{2}z^2 - 2xy,\, -2yz - x^2,\, -y^2 + zx]$$

is irrotational. We can readily express $\mathbf{G} - \mathbf{g}$ as ∇F by means of (45.7):

$$F = \frac{1}{3}\int_0^x \left(\frac{1}{2}z^2 - 2xy\right)dx - \frac{1}{3}\int_0^y 2yz\,dy = \frac{1}{3}\left(\frac{1}{2}xz^2 - x^2 y - y^2 z\right).$$

Example 2. The vector $\mathbf{f} = \mathbf{a} \times \mathbf{r}$ is solenoidal; for from (41.6)

$$\operatorname{div}(\mathbf{a} \times \mathbf{r}) = \mathbf{r} \cdot \operatorname{rot}\mathbf{a} - \mathbf{a} \cdot \operatorname{rot}\mathbf{r} = 0.$$

Since $\mathbf{f}$ is homogeneous of degree 1, the vector potential given by (12) is

$$\mathbf{g} = \tfrac{1}{3}\mathbf{f} \times \mathbf{r} = \tfrac{1}{3}(\mathbf{a} \times \mathbf{r}) \times \mathbf{r}.$$

PROBLEMS

1. Show that a constant vector $\mathbf{c}$ has the scalar potential $\varphi = -\mathbf{c} \cdot \mathbf{r}$ and the vector potential $\mathbf{g} = \tfrac{1}{2}(\mathbf{c} \times \mathbf{r})$.

2. Find the vector potential of $\mathbf{f} = (\mathbf{r} - \mathbf{a}) \times (\mathbf{r} - \mathbf{b})$.

3. Find the vector potential of the given solenoidal vector $\mathbf{f}$ from (6) and also from (12), and verify that $\mathbf{g} - \mathbf{G}$ is irrotational.

(a) $\mathbf{f} = [x, x, -z]$;   (b) $\mathbf{f} = [z - y, x - z, y - x]$;

(c) $\mathbf{f} = [xy, -y^2, yz]$;   (d) $\mathbf{f} = [z, x, y]$.

4. Find the vector potential of $\mathbf{f}$ from (11) when

(a) $\mathbf{f} = r^3 \mathbf{c} \times \mathbf{r}$;   (b) $\mathbf{f} = [x, 1, -z]$.

5. If ρ, φ, z are cylindrical coordinates (Ex. 42.1), show that $\nabla \log \rho$ and $\nabla \varphi$ are solenoidal vectors in any region not containing the origin.

6. If r, θ, φ are spherical coordinates (Ex. 42.2), show that $\nabla \log \tan \tfrac{1}{2}\theta$ is solenoidal in any region that does not include the z-axis.

7. Show that a vector $\mathbf{f}$ is irrotational and solenoidal in a rectangular prism R when and only when it is the gradient of a harmonic function in R.

8. Show that $\mathbf{f} = \mathbf{r}/r^3$ irrotational and solenoidal at all points except the origin.

55. Green's Identities.

We shall now use the divergence theorem to prove three important identities due to George Green.†

Let φ and ψ be scalar point functions having continuous derivatives of the first and second orders, respectively, in a region V bounded by a closed surface S. The divergence theorem (52.1) applied to the vector $\mathbf{f} = \varphi\,\nabla\psi$ now gives

$$\int_V \operatorname{div}(\varphi\,\nabla\psi)\,dV = \oint_S \varphi\,\frac{d\psi}{dn}\,dS.$$

† George Green, *Essay on the Application of Mathematical Analysis to the Theory of Electricity and Magnetism*, Nottingham, 1828.

In case ψ is not defined outside of S, we replace $d\psi/dn$ by the negative of the derivative along the internal normal $-\mathbf{n}$. Now, from (41.4),

$$\operatorname{div}(\varphi\,\nabla\psi) = \nabla\varphi \cdot \nabla\psi + \varphi\,\nabla^2\psi,$$

since $\operatorname{div}\nabla\psi = \nabla^2\psi$ (40.9); therefore on writing $\mathbf{n} \cdot \nabla\psi = d\psi/dn$,

(1)
$$\int_V \nabla\varphi \cdot \nabla\psi\,dV + \int_V \varphi\,\nabla^2\psi\,dV = \oint \varphi\,\frac{d\psi}{dn}\,dS.$$

This formula is known as *Green's first identity*.

If both φ and ψ have continuous derivatives of the first and second orders, we may interchange φ and ψ in (1). On subtracting this result from (1), we obtain *Green's second identity*:

(2)
$$\int_V (\varphi\,\nabla^2\psi - \psi\,\nabla^2\varphi)\,dV = \oint_S \left(\varphi\,\frac{d\psi}{dn} - \psi\,\frac{d\varphi}{dn}\right)dS.$$

We now take $\psi = 1/r$, where r is the distance from a point P. If P is *interior* to S, we cannot apply (2) to the entire region enclosed for $1/r$ becomes infinite at P. We therefore exclude P by surrounding it by a small sphere σ of radius ε and apply (2) to the region V' between S and σ; then, since

$$\nabla^2\left(\frac{1}{r}\right) = 0 \quad \text{in } V' \qquad\qquad (\text{Ex. 41.1}),$$

we have

(2)′
$$-\int_{V'} \frac{1}{r}\,\nabla^2\varphi\,dV = \oint_S \left[\varphi\,\frac{d}{dn}\left(\frac{1}{r}\right) - \frac{1}{r}\,\frac{d\varphi}{dn}\right]dS$$

$$+ \oint_\sigma \left[\varphi\,\frac{d}{dn}\left(\frac{1}{r}\right) - \frac{1}{r}\,\frac{d\varphi}{dn}\right]dS.$$

On the sphere σ, $r = \varepsilon$, and the external normal is directed toward P; hence

$$\frac{d}{dn}\left(\frac{1}{r}\right) = -\frac{d}{dr}\left(\frac{1}{r}\right) = \frac{1}{r^2} = \frac{1}{\varepsilon^2}, \qquad \frac{d\varphi}{dn} = -\frac{\partial\varphi}{\partial r};$$

and $dS = \varepsilon^2\,d\Omega$, where Ω is the solid angle subtended by dS at P. The integral over σ is therefore

$$\oint_\sigma \left(\frac{\varphi}{\varepsilon^2} + \frac{1}{\varepsilon}\frac{\partial\varphi}{\partial r}\right)\varepsilon^2\,d\Omega = \int \left(\varphi + \varepsilon\frac{\partial\varphi}{\partial r}\right)d\Omega$$

and approaches $4\pi\,\varphi(P)$ as $\varepsilon \to 0$. Moreover, as $\varepsilon \to 0$, the volume integral

$$\int_{V'} \frac{1}{r}\,\nabla^2\varphi\,dV \to \int_V \frac{1}{r}\,\nabla^2\varphi\,dV;$$

for the integrand remains finite since we may take $dV = r^2\,d\Omega\,dr$ as the element of volume in the neighborhood of P.   Thus, on passing to the limit $\varepsilon \to 0$, (2)′ yields *Green's third identity*:

(3) $\quad 4\pi\, \varphi(P) = -\int_V \frac{\nabla^2\varphi}{r}\, dV + \oint_S \left[\frac{1}{r}\frac{d\varphi}{dn} - \varphi\,\frac{d}{dn}\left(\frac{1}{r}\right)\right] dS, \qquad P$ inside S.

When P is *exterior* to S, we may put $\psi = 1/r$ directly in (2); we then obtain

(4) $\qquad 0 = -\int_V \frac{\nabla^2\varphi}{r}\, dV + \oint_S \left[\frac{1}{r}\frac{d\varphi}{dn} - \varphi\,\frac{d}{dn}\left(\frac{1}{r}\right)\right] dS, \qquad P$ outside S.

In order to apply Green's identities to the infinite region V_∞ consisting of a closed surface S and all of space beyond it, we require that the functions φ and ψ vanish at infinity in accordance with the following

DEFINITION. A function φ is said to be *regular at infinity* when $r|\varphi|$ and $r^2|\nabla\varphi|$ are uniformly bounded as $r \to \infty$:

(5) $\qquad\qquad r|\varphi| \quad$ and $\quad r^2|\nabla\varphi| < M \qquad$ when $\quad r > R$,

a suitably large value; or, in the O-notation†

(5)′ $\qquad\qquad \varphi = O\left(\frac{1}{r}\right), \qquad |\nabla\varphi| = O\left(\frac{1}{r^2}\right).$

This condition implies that the vectors $\varphi\,\nabla\psi$ and $\psi\,\nabla\varphi$ have the property (7) required in Theorem 52.2. For example, $r^3\,|\varphi\,\nabla\,\psi| < M^2$ when $r > R$, and hence

$$r^2\varphi\,|\nabla\psi| < \varepsilon \qquad \text{when} \quad r > M^2/\varepsilon.$$

Thus the divergence theorem may be applied to the vectors $\varphi\,\nabla\psi$ and $\psi\,\nabla\varphi$ in the infinite region V_∞ beyond S; then $\mathbf{n}$ is a unit normal external to V_∞ and points toward the interior of S.

Noting that $1/r$ is regular at infinity, we conclude that Green's identities (1), (2), (3), (4) are all valid in V_∞. It may be shown that (3) and (4) are even valid when $\nabla^2\varphi$ is continuous in the *interior* of the region, but not necessarily on its boundary S, provided that the integral $\int r^{-1}\,\nabla^2\varphi\, dV$ converges.‡

Suppose now that φ is regular at infinity and $\nabla^2\varphi$ is continuous throughout space except at P. Then, if we apply (3) to the region V_∞ beyond S and let S shrink down to the point P, we obtain

(6) $\qquad\qquad \varphi(P) = -\frac{1}{4\pi}\int_\infty \frac{\nabla^2\varphi}{r}\, dV \qquad$ (over all space),

provided the integral converges.

† *Advanced Calculus*, p. 129.
‡ Cf. O. D. Kellogg, *Foundations of Potential Theory*, Berlin, 1929, pp. 119, 219.

PROBLEMS

1. Verify (3) by finding $\varphi(0)$ when $\varphi(r) = ar^2 + br + c$ and S is the sphere $r = 1$.

2. Verify (6) by finding $\varphi(0)$ when

$$\varphi(r) = 3 - 3\frac{r}{a} + \frac{r^2}{a^2} \quad (r < a) \qquad \varphi(r) = \frac{a}{r} \quad (r \geqq a).$$

Is $\nabla^2\varphi$ continuous at $r = 0$? at $r = a$?

3. Verify (6) by finding $\varphi(0)$ when $\varphi(r) = 1/(a + r)$.

$$[\nabla^2\varphi = -2a/r(r + a)^3, \ (42.21).]$$

4. $\varphi(r)$, $\nabla\varphi$, and $\nabla^2\varphi$ are everywhere continuous except that $\nabla^2\varphi \to \infty$ as $r \to 0$. Show that the volume integral in (6) will converge to $-4\pi\varphi(0)$, provided φ is regular at infinity.

$$\left[\nabla^2\varphi = \frac{1}{r^2}\frac{d}{dr}[r^2\varphi'(r)] \text{ from (42.21).}\right]$$

56. **Harmonic Functions.** A solution of Laplace's equation $\nabla^2\varphi = 0$ is called a *harmonic function*. The function φ is said to be *harmonic at a point P* if its second derivatives are continuous in some neighborhood of P and satisfy Laplace's equation. If φ is harmonic at all interior points of a region and continuous throughout the region, it is said to be *harmonic in the region*. In an *open* region, all points are interior, and the continuity of φ follows from the continuity of its derivatives. For a *closed* region, the values of φ in the interior must connect continuously with its boundary values.

In Green's identities we shall now suppose that φ is harmonic in the region V bounded by a closed surface S.

If we put $\psi = \varphi$ in (55.1), we have

$$(1) \qquad \int_V |\nabla\varphi|^2 \, dV = \oint_S \varphi \frac{d\varphi}{dn} \, dS.$$

Consequently, if either

$$(a) \quad \varphi = 0 \qquad \text{or} \qquad (b) \quad \frac{d\varphi}{dn} = 0 \quad \text{on } S,$$

the volume integral is zero. Since $|\nabla\varphi|$ is *continuous* and never negative, $\nabla\varphi = 0$ throughout V; for, if $|\nabla\varphi|$ were positive at a point P, we could embed P in a subregion V' of V in which $|\nabla\varphi| > 0$, and the integral of $|\nabla\varphi|^2$ over V', and hence also over V, would be positive. Thus, in both cases (a) and (b),

$$\nabla\varphi = 0 \qquad \text{and} \qquad \varphi = \text{const} \quad \text{in } V.$$

In particular, $\varphi = 0$ in case (a).

Now let φ_1 and φ_2 be two harmonic functions in V which have the same values on S; then $\varphi = \varphi_1 - \varphi_2$ is harmonic in V and zero on S; consequently $\varphi = 0$, or $\varphi_1 = \varphi_2$, throughout V. We have thus proved

THEOREM 1. *A function that is harmonic in a closed region bounded by a surface S is completely determined by its values on the boundary.*

If φ and ψ are both harmonic in the region V, the volume integral in (55.2) is zero, and we have

$$(2) \qquad \oint_S \left(\varphi \frac{d\psi}{dn} - \psi \frac{d\varphi}{dn} \right) dS = 0.$$

In particular, if $\psi = 1$, (2) becomes

$$(3) \qquad \oint_S \frac{d\varphi}{dn} dS = 0.$$

THEOREM 2. *If a function is harmonic in a closed region bounded by a surface S, the integral of its normal derivative over S is zero.*

This property is characteristic of harmonic functions; for it can be shown that, if (3) holds for all spheres in a region V, φ is harmonic in V.[†]

Finally, if we put $\nabla^2 \varphi = 0$ in (55.3–4) we obtain the important

THEOREM 3. *If φ is harmonic in a closed region V bounded by a surface S and r is the distance from a point P,*

$$(4) \qquad 4\pi \, \varphi(P) = \oint_S \left[\frac{1}{r} \frac{d\varphi}{dn} - \varphi \frac{d}{dn} \left(\frac{1}{r} \right) \right] dS, \qquad P \text{ inside } V;$$

$$(5) \qquad 0 = \oint_S \left[\frac{1}{r} \frac{d\varphi}{dn} - \varphi \frac{d}{dn} \left(\frac{1}{r} \right) \right] dS, \qquad P \text{ outside } V.$$

Observe that (4) gives the value of a harmonic function at any interior point P of a closed region in terms of the values of φ and $d\varphi/dn$ on its boundary. Thus the integrand of (4) is a function, say $F(x, y, z)$, of the coordinates of P (which enter in $1/r$ and its normal derivative). Now it may be shown that the integral can be differentiated under the integral sign, and, since $F(x, y, z)$ admits derivatives of all orders, the same is true of the integral and $\varphi(P)$. Thus $\varphi(P)$ is a function $\varphi(x, y, z)$ that admits derivatives of all orders; and, since the existence of all derivatives of order n implies the continuity of all derivatives of order $n - 1$, $\varphi(P)$ has *continuous* derivatives of all orders. This remarkable result flows from a mere condition $\nabla^2 \varphi = 0$ on the *second* derivatives of φ.

[†] Cf. O. D. Kellogg, *Foundations of Potential Theory*, Berlin, 1929, p. 227.

We have seen that (4) gives $\varphi(P)$ in terms of the boundary values of φ and $d\varphi/dn$. But, since φ is uniquely determined by its boundary values alone (Theorem 1), we might expect to find a formula giving φ within S in terms of its continuous boundary values on S. This more difficult problem was solved by Green by use of a function (known now as *Green's function*) which he defined as a potential due to certain electric charges. The purely mathematical treatment of this question is known as

DIRICHLET'S PROBLEM.   *Does a harmonic function φ exist in a closed region bounded by a surface S which assumes a given set of continuous values on the boundary?*

The answer to this famous problem is *yes* for surfaces of a very general type; but it has been shown that there are some surfaces for which there is no solution.

If we apply (4) to a sphere $\sum$ of radius r about P,

$$\frac{d}{dn}\left(\frac{1}{r}\right) = \frac{d}{dr}\left(\frac{1}{r}\right) = -\frac{1}{r^2}.$$

Since r is constant over $\sum$, the first integral in (4) vanishes by virtue of (3), and we obtain

(6)
$$\varphi(P) = \frac{1}{4\pi r^2} \oint_{\Sigma} \varphi \, dS.$$

Since the surface area of $\sum$ is $4\pi r^2$, (6) expresses the *mean-value theorem of Gauss:*

THEOREM 4.   *If a function is harmonic in a sphere, its value at the center is the arithmetic mean of its values on the surface.*

This property also proves to be characteristic of harmonic functions.[†] From this theorem it is easy to prove

THEOREM 5.   *A function that is harmonic, but not constant, in a closed region attains its extreme values only on the boundary.*

Proof.   If φ is harmonic in a closed region V, it must assume its extreme values in V by virtue of its continuity.[‡]   Consider the set of points at which $\varphi = M$, its maximum value. Since φ is not constant, this set cannot contain *all* interior points. Moreover, the set cannot contain *any* interior point; for, if it did, it would have a frontier point P in the interior of V. Then there would be a sphere about P lying entirely in V and

† Cf. Kellogg, *Foundations of Potential Theory*, p. 224–227
‡ Cf. *Advanced Calculus*, p. 152, Theorem 4.

passing through some points where $\varphi < M$. The mean of its surface values therefore could not be $\varphi(P) = M$, as required by Gauss' theorem.

Formulas (1), (2), (4), (5) also hold for functions that are harmonic in the infinite region consisting of a closed surface and all of space beyond, provided φ and ψ are regular at infinity; for Green's identities from which they are derived hold for infinite regions (§55).

Formula (3), however, is *not* in general true; for it was derived from (2) by taking $\psi = 1$, a function not regular at infinity. Indeed (3) is false when $\varphi = 1/r$, where r is the distance from a point P within S; although $1/r$ is harmonic beyond S and regular at infinity, we have from (52.9)

$$(7) \qquad \oint_S \frac{d}{dn}\left(\frac{1}{r}\right) dS = -4\pi, \qquad \mathbf{n} \text{ external to } S.$$

We can, however, prove

THEOREM 6.   *If φ is harmonic in the closed region between the closed surfaces S_1 and S_2 (surrounding S_1), then*

$$(8) \qquad \oint_{S_1} \frac{d\varphi}{dn_1} dS = \oint_{S_2} \frac{d\varphi}{dn_2} dS.$$

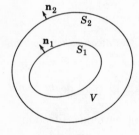

where $\mathbf{n}_1$ and $\mathbf{n}_2$ both point from the inside to the outside of the surfaces.

Proof. Apply the divergence theorem to the vector $\nabla\varphi$ in the closed region V between S_1 and S_2. Then, since $-\mathbf{n}_1$ and $\mathbf{n}_2$ are external normals to the region V (Fig. 56a),

$$0 = \int_V \operatorname{div} \nabla\varphi\, dV = -\oint_{S_1} \frac{d\varphi}{dn_1} dS + \oint_{S_2} \frac{d\varphi}{dn_2} dS.$$

Fig. 56a. Region between closed surfaces.

Thus (8) is proved.

Example 1.   If we apply (4) and (5) to the harmonic function $\varphi = 1$, we obtain

$$(9) \qquad \left.\begin{matrix} 4\pi \\[6pt] 0 \end{matrix}\right\} = -\oint_S \frac{d}{dn}\left(\frac{1}{r}\right) dS, \qquad \begin{matrix} P \text{ inside } S, \\[6pt] P \text{ outside } S. \end{matrix}$$

in agreement with (52.9).

Example 2.   *If P is any point within a sphere Σ of radius a and center O, and r is the distance from P,*

$$(10) \qquad \oint_\Sigma \frac{1}{r}\, dS = 4\pi a$$

If R is the distance from O (Fig. 56b), the functions $\varphi = 1/r$ and $\psi = 1/R$ are harmonic *outside* of Σ and regular at infinity.   Hence from (2)

$$\oint_\Sigma \left[\frac{1}{r} \frac{d}{dn} \left(\frac{1}{R} \right) - \frac{1}{R} \frac{d}{dn} \left(\frac{1}{r} \right) \right] dS = 0.$$

If **n** denotes the external normal to Σ, this gives, since $R = a$ on Σ,

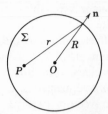

$$-\frac{1}{a^2} \oint_\Sigma \frac{1}{r} dS = \frac{1}{a} \oint_\Sigma \frac{d}{dn} \left(\frac{1}{r} \right) dS = -\frac{4\pi}{a}$$

from (7).   Thus (10) is proved; it also states that the mean of $1/r$ over Σ is $1/a$.

Fig. 56b. Region with a spherical boundary.

Example 3.   If r_1 and r_2 denote the distances from P_1 and P_2, the functions $1/r_1$ and $1/r_2$ are harmonic everywhere except at P_1 and P_2, respectively.   Consider the integral over any closed surface S:

$$I = \oint_S \left[\frac{1}{r_1} \frac{d}{dn} \left(\frac{1}{r_2} \right) - \frac{1}{r_2} \frac{d}{dn} \left(\frac{1}{r_1} \right) \right] dS.$$

If P_1 and P_2 lie outside of S, $1/r_1$ and $1/r_2$ are harmonic inside S and $I = 0$ by (2).   If P_1 and P_2 lie inside of S, $1/r_1$ and $1/r_2$ are harmonic outside of S and regular at infinity; again $I = 0$.   But, if P_1 lies inside of S, P_2 outside of S, $1/r_2$ is harmonic within S and, on putting $r = r_1$, $\varphi = 1/r_2$ in (4),

$$I = 4\pi \left(\frac{1}{r_2} \right)_{P_1} = \frac{4\pi}{P_1 P_2}.$$

PROBLEMS

1. If φ is harmonic in a closed region V bounded by a surface S, and $\varphi = C$ in S, prove that $\varphi = C$ throughout V.

2. If φ and ψ are harmonic functions in a closed region V bounded by a surface S, and $d\varphi/dn = d\psi/dn$ on S, prove that $\psi = \varphi + $ const throughout V.

3. If φ and $f(\varphi)$ are both harmonic in a region V and φ is not constant, show that

$$f(\varphi) = a + b\varphi.$$

$$[\nabla f(\varphi) = f'(\varphi) \, \nabla\varphi, \; \nabla^2 f(\varphi) = f''(\varphi) \, \nabla\varphi \cdot \nabla\varphi + f'(\varphi) \, \nabla^2\varphi.]$$

4. Prove that, if φ is harmonic throughout space and regular at infinity, then $\varphi = 0$.
[Apply (1) when V is the region within a sphere Σ centered at O and of radius r. Show the surface integral $\to 0$ as $r \to \infty$.]

57. **Retrospect.**   In computing the derivative of a scalar point function $f(\mathbf{r})$ in the direction **e**, we found that a single vector point function ∇f, the *gradient of f*, combined all the directional derivatives df/ds at a point in a single package in accordance with the formula:

$$\frac{df}{ds} = \mathbf{e} \cdot \nabla f.$$

In this expression the unit vector $\mathbf{e}$ gives the *direction*, whereas ∇f depends only on the *point* where the derivatives are computed. Thus a single vector ∇f enables us to compute an infinite number of scalars. However the gradient ∇f is a more complex quantity than a single scalar; it is, in effect, defined by the three numbers, its components. · Thus the three components of ∇f, enable us to combine an infinity of scalars df/ds in a single package. In order to simplify directional differentiation in space of *three* dimensions, we have been led from scalars (with $3^0 = 1$ component) to vectors (with $3^1 = 3$ components). Technically speaking, we have advanced from *tensors of valence zero to tensors of valence one.*

Passing next to the directional differentiation of vector point functions $\mathbf{f(r)}$, we obtain a formula

$$\frac{d\mathbf{f}}{ds} = \mathbf{e} \cdot \nabla \mathbf{f}$$

of the same form as before. Here again the vector $\mathbf{e}$ gives the direction, whereas $\nabla \mathbf{f}$, the *gradient of* $\mathbf{f}$, depends only on the point where the derivatives are computed. The package that holds an infinite number of vector derivatives $d\mathbf{f}/ds$ is now a new kind of quantity which we call a *dyadic*. In the form of a 3×3 matrix it is fully represented by nine numbers. Through our efforts to simplify and understand directional differentiation of vectors in space of three dimensions, we have been led from vectors (with $3^1 = 3$ components) to dyadics (with $3^2 = 9$ components). We have again advanced, this time *from tensors of valence one to tensors of valence two.* The higher valence is the price we pay for lucidity, concision, and the better understanding that they bring about.

In order to differentiate a dyadic directionally we must introduce a *triadic*, a tensor of valence three with $3^3 = 27$ components. But tensors of higher valence do not concern us here although they are indispensable for formulating certain portions of geometry and mathematical physics— especially the theory of relativity, which is both geometry and physics.

The basic property of tensors is the law for changing their components when the coordinate system is changed. Thus a vector $\mathbf{f} = [f_1, f_2, f_3]$ has different components in each rectangular coordinate system; and the relation that connects the components in different coordinate systems is actually the essential character of a vector. The same is true for tensors of higher valence, such as dyadics and triadics. In all these changes, however, certain functions of the components do not change; these are the *invariants* of the tensor. For a vector

$$\mathbf{f} = f_1\mathbf{i} + f_2\mathbf{j} + f_3\mathbf{k}, \qquad \mathbf{f} \cdot \mathbf{f} = f_1^2 + f_2^2 + f_3^2$$

is an invariant. For a dyadic

$$\mathbf{F} = \sum \mathbf{a}_i\mathbf{b}_i = f_{11}\mathbf{ii} + f_{12}\mathbf{ij} + \cdots + f_{33}\mathbf{kk},$$

the two most important invariants are the scalar

$$F_s = \sum \mathbf{a}_i \cdot \mathbf{b}_i = f_{11} + f_{22} + f_{33}$$

and the vector

$$\mathbf{f} = \sum \mathbf{a}_i \times \mathbf{b}_i = (f_{23} - f_{32})\mathbf{i} + (f_{31} - f_{13})\mathbf{j} + (f_{12} - f_{21})\mathbf{k}.$$

Since the invariants of tensors are independent of the system of coordinates employed, the theorems of geometry and the laws of physics are expressed in terms of invariants. This is the reason for studying them. This is the key to their importance.

The gradient of a vector $\mathbf{f}$, namely the dyadic

$$\text{grad } \mathbf{f} = \nabla \mathbf{f} = \mathbf{i}\, \mathbf{f}_x + \mathbf{j}\, \mathbf{f}_y + \mathbf{k}\, \mathbf{f}_z,$$

has the scalar and vector invariants

$$\text{div } \mathbf{f} = \nabla \cdot \mathbf{f} = \mathbf{i} \cdot \mathbf{f}_x + \mathbf{j} \cdot \mathbf{f}_y + \mathbf{k} \cdot \mathbf{f}_y,$$

$$\text{rot } \mathbf{f} = \nabla \times \mathbf{f} = \mathbf{i} \times \mathbf{f}_x + \mathbf{j} \times \mathbf{f}_y + \mathbf{k} \times \mathbf{f}_y.$$

They appear constantly in all branches of *field theory*: fields of force, velocity fields in fluid flow, and the electromagnetic field. In the following chapters we shall study such fields.

But even in geometry the divergence and rotation are of paramount importance. The basic integral transformations all involve the gradients of tensors and are valid for tensors of any valence:†

(*A*)
$$\int_{\mathbf{r}_1}^{\mathbf{r}_2} \mathbf{T} \cdot \nabla \mathbf{f}\, ds = \mathbf{f}(\mathbf{r}_2) - \mathbf{f}(\mathbf{r}_1);$$

(*B*)
$$\int \mathbf{n} \times \nabla \mathbf{f}\, dS = \oint \mathbf{T}\, \mathbf{f}\, ds;$$

(*C*)
$$\int \nabla \mathbf{f}\, dV = \oint \mathbf{n}\, \mathbf{f}\, dS.$$

Each transforms an integral over a region to an integral over its boundary. The prototype of all such transformations is the *fundamental theorem of the calculus* given in (*A*) in generalized form.

From these transformations others can be deduced by dotting and crossing within the tensor functions, for both of these operations are distributive with respect to addition and therefore may be carried out under the integral sign.

† Cf. *Vector and Tensor Analysis*, Chapter 6.

When $\mathbf{f(r)}$ is a vector, the integrals in (B) and (C) involve dyadics. From them, by dotting between the dyad vectors, we obtain *Stokes' theorem*

$(B\cdot)$
$$\left(\int \mathbf{n} \cdot \operatorname{rot} \mathbf{f} \, dS = \oint \mathbf{T} \cdot \mathbf{f} \, ds, \right)$$

and the *divergence theorem*

$(C\cdot)$
$$\left(\int \operatorname{div} \mathbf{f} \, dV = \oint \mathbf{n} \cdot \mathbf{f} \, dS. \right)$$

From $(B\cdot)$ we see that for all closed curves in a simply connected region V,

$$\oint \mathbf{T} \cdot \mathbf{f} \, ds = 0 \quad \text{if} \quad \operatorname{rot} \mathbf{f} = \mathbf{0} \quad \text{in } V;$$

for, if V is simply connected, a surface that lies entirely in V may be spanned over the curve. *The circulation of an irrotational vector over any closed curve in a simply connected region is zero.*

From $(C\cdot)$ we see that

$$\oint \mathbf{n} \cdot \mathbf{f} \, dS = 0 \quad \text{if} \quad \operatorname{div} \mathbf{f} = 0 \quad \text{within } S.$$

The normal flux of a solenoidal vector over any closed surface is zero.

By crossing between the dyad vectors we get less famous, but still important, theorems:

$(B\times)$
$$\int \{ (\nabla \mathbf{f}) \cdot \mathbf{n} - \mathbf{n} \operatorname{div} \mathbf{f} \} \, dS = \oint \mathbf{T} \times \mathbf{f} \, ds;$$

$(C\times)$
$$\int \operatorname{rot} \mathbf{f} \, dV = \oint \mathbf{n} \times \mathbf{f} \, dS.$$

We know that div $\mathbf{f}$ and rot $\mathbf{f}$ are independent of the frame of reference and express invariant properties of the field vector $\mathbf{f}$. But what *are* they? Can these abstractions be made more tangible? The answer is *yes*; the divergence theorem and Stokes' theorem give divergence and curl the following meaning.

If V is the volume of a small sphere about a point P, we have from $(C\cdot)$ and the mean value theorem for volume integrals,

$$\operatorname{div} \bar{\mathbf{f}} = \frac{\oint \mathbf{n} \cdot \mathbf{f} \, dS}{V},$$

where div $\bar{\mathbf{f}}$ is computed at some point $\bar{P}$ within the sphere. Hence

$$\text{div } \mathbf{f} = \lim_{V \to 0} \frac{\oint \mathbf{n} \cdot \mathbf{f} \, dS}{V} \, ;$$

thus, roughly speaking, div $\mathbf{f}$ is a *flux density*:

$$\text{div } \mathbf{f} = \textit{normal flux of } \mathbf{f} \textit{ per unit volume}$$

through a small sphere about P.

As to rot $\mathbf{f}$, consider its component $\mathbf{e} \cdot \text{rot } \mathbf{f}$ in the direction of the unit vector $\mathbf{e}$. Draw a small circle of area A about P in a plane normal to $\mathbf{e}$; then, from $(B \cdot)$ and the mean value theorem for surface integrals,

$$\mathbf{e} \cdot \text{rot } \bar{\mathbf{f}} = \frac{\oint \mathbf{T} \cdot \mathbf{f} \, ds}{A} \, ,$$

where rot $\bar{\mathbf{f}}$ is computed at some point $\bar{P}$ within the circle. Hence

$$\mathbf{e} \cdot \text{rot } \mathbf{f} = \lim_{A \to 0} \frac{\oint \mathbf{T} \cdot \mathbf{f} \, ds}{A} \, .$$

Again, speaking roughly, $\mathbf{e} \cdot \text{rot } \mathbf{f}$ is a *circulation density*:

$$\mathbf{e} \cdot \text{rot } \mathbf{f} = \textit{circulation of } \mathbf{f} \textit{ per unit area}$$

over a small circle about P and in a plane normal to $\mathbf{e}$. The *sense* of circulation is that of a right-handed screw advancing in the direction $\mathbf{e}$. The vector rot $\mathbf{f}$ represents a synthesis of all such circulation densities at a given point.

We have now a synopsis of motives, methods, and results in vector and tensor analysis. The student who keeps them in mind is in position to understand geometry and mathematical physics, not merely as a collection of formulas, but as a rich diversity of results all flowing from a few central principles.

Chapter 6 _____

Dynamics

58. Dynamics of a Particle. If in a certain dynamical problem the matter composing a body may be regarded as concentrated in a single point, the body is called a *particle*. Thus the motion of the earth around the sun may be determined quite accurately by treating earth and sun as particles. But a billiard ball, whose motion may involve rolling, sliding, and spinning (*english*), certainly cannot be regarded as a particle. In brief, to know when a body can be treated as a particle depends upon the nature of the problem and the degree of accuracy to be attained. It calls for an exercise of sound judgment.

If however, the bodies involved may be treated as particles, their motion in response to forces acting upon them may be determined from three fundamental principles.

I. FORCE AND ACCELERATION. *A free particle acted upon by a force* **f** *acquires an acceleration* **a** *in the direction of the force; that is,*

(1)
$$\mathbf{f} = m\mathbf{a},$$

where m is a scalar constant whose value (for a given system of units) depends entirely on the nature of the body designated as a particle.

II. VECTOR ADDITION OF FORCES. *A system of forces acting simultaneously on the same particle may be replaced by a single force acting on this particle and equal to their vector sum.*

III. ACTION AND REACTION. *The interaction between two particles, whether in direct contact or at a distance from each other, may be represented*

160

by two forces of equal magnitude and opposite direction acting along their joining line.

Equation (1) is the *fundamental equation of dynamics.* It is Newton's *second law of motion.*

When there is no force acting on the particle, or when all the forces have a zero sum, the fundamental equation becomes (§32)

$$(2) \qquad\qquad \frac{d\mathbf{v}}{dt} = \mathbf{0}.$$

If the initial conditions are

$$\mathbf{v} = \mathbf{v}_0, \qquad \mathbf{r} = \mathbf{r}_0 \qquad \text{when} \quad t = 0,$$

integration of (2) yields $\mathbf{v} = \mathbf{v}_0$, or

$$(3) \qquad\qquad \frac{d\mathbf{r}}{dt} = \mathbf{v}_0.$$

Integrating again, we have

$$(4) \qquad\qquad \mathbf{r} = \mathbf{v}_0 t + \mathbf{r}_0,$$

which is the equation of a *ray* issuing from $\mathbf{r}_0$ in the direction of $\mathbf{v}_0$. If $\mathbf{v}_0 = 0$, $\mathbf{r} = \mathbf{r}_0$, and the body will remain at rest; otherwise it will move in a straight line with constant velocity. These results constitute the

LAW OF INERTIA. *A particle will continue in its state of rest or of uniform motion in a straight line unless acted upon by an unbalanced force.*

Galileo was the first to realize the truth of this fundamental law. It was stated in the above form by Newton as his *first law of motion.*

59. Equations of Motion. The central problem in particle dynamics is the solution of the second-order vector differential equation

$$(1) \qquad\qquad m\frac{d^2\mathbf{r}}{dt^2} = \mathbf{f}$$

subject to the initial conditions

$$(2) \qquad\qquad \mathbf{r} = \mathbf{r}_0, \qquad \mathbf{v} = \mathbf{v}_0 \qquad \text{when} \quad t = 0.$$

In some problems, such as the motion of a planet around the sun, we can solve this vector equation directly (§61). More frequently, however, it is necessary to replace it by one, two, or three scalar equations according as the motion is in a straight line, a plane, or in 3-space. For this purpose we resolve both acceleration and force into components and equate like components in equation (1). Rectangular components of acceleration are given in (32.7), plane polar components in (32.9).

If a particle P is moving in a straight line, we choose it as x-axis, selecting an origin and positive direction (**i**) at pleasure. The position, velocity, and acceleration of P, and the force acting upon it, are given by

$$\mathbf{r} = x\mathbf{i}, \qquad \mathbf{v} = \frac{dx}{dt}\mathbf{i}, \qquad \mathbf{a} = \frac{d^2x}{dt^2}\mathbf{i}, \qquad \mathbf{f} = f\mathbf{i};$$

and (1) is equivalent to the scalar equation $m\ddot{x} = f$.† The *directions* of $\mathbf{r}$, $\mathbf{v}$, $\mathbf{a}$, and $\mathbf{f}$ are now given by the *signs* of x, $\dot{x}$, $\ddot{x}$, and f; and we call the *signed numbers*

(3) $$v = \frac{dx}{dt}, \qquad a = \frac{dv}{dt} = v\frac{dv}{dx},$$

the "velocity" and "acceleration." The positive number $|v|$ is called the speed.

In many problems the solution of $m\ddot{x} = f$ may be accomplished by solving two first-order equations.

When f is a function of t or v, we solve

(4) $$m\frac{dv}{dt} = f, \qquad \frac{dx}{dt} = v,$$

in turn to find v and x as functions of t. On eliminating t from these equations, we obtain a relation between v and x.

When f is a function of x or v, we solve

(5) $$mv\frac{dv}{dx} = f, \qquad \frac{dx}{dt} = v,$$

in turn to find v as a function of x, x as a function of t.

Example 1. Falling Body. For an unresisted free fall from rest under gravity we take the origin at the initial point, the x-axis downward. The force of gravity is $mg\mathbf{i}$, and our differential equation is

$$\frac{dv}{dt} = g \quad \text{or} \quad v\frac{dv}{dx} = g.$$

On solving these with initial conditions $x = 0$, $v = 0$ when $t = 0$, we find

(6) $$v = gt, \qquad x = \tfrac{1}{2}gt^2, \qquad v^2 = 2gx.$$

For fall in which the air resistance is proportional to v^2, we put $f = m(g - kv^2)$, in which $k > 0$. The equation of motion is now

$$\frac{dv}{dt} = g - kv^2 \quad \text{or} \quad v\frac{dv}{dx} = g - kv^2.$$

---

† The dots indicate time derivatives (Newton's notation). In the Newton-Leibnitz controversy, this notation gave occasion for a celebrated pun in which the "pure deism" of Leibnitz was compared with the "dotage" of Newton.

If the body falls from a point sufficiently high, v will increase until $g - kv^2 = 0$; then $dv/dt = 0$, and from then on the body will travel at a constant *terminal velocity* V. Thus $g - kV^2 = 0$ and $k = g/V^2$; and our equation of motion becomes

$$\frac{dv}{dt} = g\left(1 - \frac{v^2}{V^2}\right) \quad \text{or} \quad v\frac{dv}{dx} = g\left(1 - \frac{v^2}{V^2}\right).$$

From these we find that

(7)　　$v = V\tanh\frac{gt}{V}, \qquad x = \frac{V^2}{g}\log\cosh\frac{gt}{V}, \qquad v^2 = V^2\left(1 - \exp\frac{-2gx}{V^2}.\right)$

As $V \to \infty$, the right-hand members approach the values given in (6). Use l'Hospital's rule to show this.

Example 2. A particle slides from rest down a smooth concave curve (Fig. 59) under the influence of gravity. The equation of motion is

$$m\mathbf{a} = m\mathbf{g} + \mathbf{R},$$

where $\mathbf{R}$ is the normal reaction of the curve. On taking tangential and normal components, we have

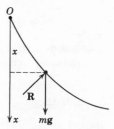

Fig. 59. Particle sliding down a curve.

(8)(9)　　$\dfrac{dv}{dt} = \mathbf{g}\cdot\mathbf{T}, \qquad m\dfrac{v^2}{\rho} = \mathbf{R}\cdot\mathbf{N} = R \quad$ (32.5).

Since

$$\frac{dv}{dt} = \frac{dv}{ds}\frac{ds}{dt} = v\frac{dv}{ds} = \frac{d}{ds}\left(\frac{1}{2}v^2\right), \qquad \mathbf{g}\cdot\mathbf{T} = \frac{d}{ds}(\mathbf{g}\cdot\mathbf{r}),$$

(8) admits the integral

$$\tfrac{1}{2}v^2 = \mathbf{g}\cdot(\mathbf{r} - \mathbf{r}_0) = gx \quad \text{or} \quad v^2 = 2gx,$$

where x is the vertical distance fallen; and $R = 2mgx/\rho$ from (9).

PROBLEMS

1. If a body falls from rest under gravity with air resistance proportional to v, show that the equation of motion is

$$\frac{dv}{dt} = g\left(1 - \frac{v}{V}\right), \qquad V = \text{terminal velocity},$$

and that

$$v = V(1 - e^{-gt/V}), \qquad x = Vt - \frac{V^2}{g}(1 - e^{-gt/V}), \qquad x = \frac{V^2}{g}\log\frac{V}{V-v} - \frac{vV}{g}.$$

2. A body is projected vertically upward with the velocity v_0. If the resistance of the air per unit mass is kv^2, show that it will rise to the height

$$h = \frac{1}{2k}\log\left(1 + \frac{kv_0^2}{g}\right)$$

and will strike the earth again with the velocity

$$V = v_0 \left(1 + \frac{kv_0^2}{g}\right)^{-1/2} .$$

Check by dimensions.

3. A projectile has the equation of motion $d\mathbf{v}/dt = \mathbf{g}$ when air resistance is neglected. If projected from the origin with $\mathbf{v}_0 = \mathbf{i}v_0 \cos \alpha + \mathbf{j}v_0 \sin \alpha$, show that it describes a parabola

$$x = v_0 t \cos \alpha, \qquad y = v_0 t \sin \alpha - \tfrac{1}{2}gt^2,$$

and that its greatest height and horizontal range are

$$h = \frac{v_0^2}{2g} \sin^2 \alpha, \qquad R = \frac{v_0^2}{g} \sin 2\alpha.$$

4. A body is attracted to the origin with a force $-k^2\mathbf{r}$ per unit of mass. Show that its equation of motion

$$\frac{d^2\mathbf{r}}{dt^2} + k^2\mathbf{r} = 0$$

has the solution

$$\mathbf{r} = \mathbf{r}_0 \cos kt + \frac{\mathbf{v}_0}{k} \sin kt.$$

If $\mathbf{r}_0 = x_0\mathbf{i}$, $\mathbf{v}_0 = v_0\mathbf{j}$, show that the particle describes an ellipse

$$\frac{x^2}{x_0^2} + \frac{y^2}{(v_0/k)^2} = 1 \quad \text{with the period } \frac{2\pi}{k}.$$

5. A body is repelled from the origin with a force $k^2\mathbf{r}$ per unit of mass. Show that its equation of motion

$$\frac{d^2\mathbf{r}}{dt^2} - k^2\mathbf{r} = 0$$

has the solution

$$\mathbf{r} = \mathbf{r}_0 \cosh kt + \frac{\mathbf{v}_0}{k} \sinh kt.$$

If $\mathbf{r}_0 = x_0\mathbf{i}$, $\mathbf{v}_0 = v_0\mathbf{j}$, show that the orbit is a hyperbola

$$\frac{x^2}{x_0^2} - \frac{y^2}{(v_0/k)^2} = 1.$$

6. If the force per unit of mass is $-k\mathbf{v}$, show that the equation of motion

$$\frac{d\mathbf{v}}{dt} + k\mathbf{v} = 0$$

admits the integrating factor e^{kt}. Hence deduce the solution

$$\mathbf{v} = \mathbf{v}_0 e^{-kt}, \qquad \mathbf{r} = \mathbf{r}_0 + \frac{\mathbf{v}_0}{k}(1 - e^{-kt}).$$

7. A falling body is subject to air resistance $-k\mathbf{v}$ per unit of mass. Show that its equation of motion

$$\frac{d\mathbf{v}}{dt} + k\mathbf{v} = \mathbf{g}$$

admits the integrating factor e^{kt}, and deduce the solution

$$\mathbf{v} = \frac{\mathbf{g}}{k} + \left(\mathbf{v}_0 - \frac{\mathbf{g}}{k}\right) e^{-kt},$$

$$\mathbf{r} = \mathbf{r}_0 + \frac{\mathbf{g}}{k} t + \left(\mathbf{v}_0 - \frac{\mathbf{g}}{k}\right) \frac{1 - e^{-kt}}{k}.$$

Find the dimensions of k and check.

8. If the force on a particle of mass m is $\mathbf{c} \times \mathbf{v}$ ($\mathbf{c}$ constant), show that
(a) the speed v is constant;
(b) $\mathbf{c} \cdot \mathbf{v} = cv \cos \alpha$ is constant;
(c) the acceleration is κv^2 N;
(d) if $\mathbf{c} \cdot \mathbf{v} \neq 0$, the orbit is a circular helix whose curvature and torsion are $\kappa = (c/mv) \sin \alpha$, $\tau = (c/mv) \cos \alpha$;
(e) if $\mathbf{c} \cdot \mathbf{v} = 0$, the orbit is a circle of radius $\rho = mv/c$.

9. The equation of motion of a particle is

$$\frac{d^2\mathbf{r}}{dt^2} + 2a \frac{d\mathbf{r}}{dt} + b^2\mathbf{r} = 0,$$

where a and b are real constants. Show that

$$\mathbf{r} \times \mathbf{v} = \mathbf{C} \, e^{-2at} \qquad (\mathbf{C} = \text{const}),$$

and deduce therefrom that the orbit is a *plane* curve. Show that, if $\gamma = \sqrt{|a^2 - b^2|}$,

$$\mathbf{r} = e^{-at} (\mathbf{A} \cosh \gamma t + \mathbf{B} \sinh \gamma t) \qquad \text{when} \quad a > b,$$

$$\mathbf{r} = e^{-at} (\mathbf{A} + \mathbf{B}t) \qquad \text{when} \quad a = b,$$

$$\mathbf{r} = e^{-at} (\mathbf{A} \cos \gamma t + \mathbf{B} \sin \gamma t) \qquad \text{when} \quad a < b,$$

where $\mathbf{A}$ and $\mathbf{B}$ are constant vectors determined by the initial conditions: $\mathbf{r} = \mathbf{r}_0$, $\mathbf{v} = \mathbf{v}_0$ when $t = 0$. What are the dimensions of a and b?

10. The equation of motion of a particle is $d\mathbf{v}/dt = \mathbf{S} \cdot \mathbf{r}$ where $\mathbf{S}$ is a constant symmetric dyadic. If $\mathbf{r} = 0$, $\mathbf{v} = \mathbf{v}_0$ when $t = 0$, show that

$$v^2 - v_0{}^2 = \mathbf{r} \cdot \mathbf{S} \cdot \mathbf{r}.$$

60. Work and Energy. If the forces acting on a particle have $\mathbf{f}$ as resultant, the equation of motion is

$$\mathbf{f} = m \frac{d\mathbf{v}}{dt}.$$

Dot-multiplying both members by $\mathbf{v}$ gives

$$(1) \qquad \mathbf{f} \cdot \mathbf{v} = m \mathbf{v} \cdot \frac{d\mathbf{v}}{dt} = \frac{1}{2} m \frac{d}{dt} (\mathbf{v} \cdot \mathbf{v}) = \frac{d}{dt} \left(\frac{1}{2} mv^2\right);$$

and, on integrating this equation between t_0 and t, we get

(2) $$\int_{t_0}^{t} \mathbf{f} \cdot \mathbf{v} \, dt = \frac{1}{2} mv^2 - \frac{1}{2} mv_0^2.$$

The scalar $\frac{1}{2}mv^2$ is called the *kinetic energy* of the particle. If we regard $\mathbf{f}$ as a function of t, the integral

(3) $$W = \int_{t_0}^{t} \mathbf{f} \cdot \mathbf{v} \, dt = \int_{t_0}^{t} \mathbf{f} \cdot \frac{d\mathbf{r}}{dt} \, dt$$

is called the *work* done by the force in the time interval. Equation (2) states the

PRINCIPLE OF WORK AND ENERGY. *The change in kinetic energy of a particle in any time interval is equal to the total work done by the forces acting on it during this interval.*

The equation

$$\text{Change in kinetic energy} = \text{work done}$$

is called the *energy equation*.

In many cases the force $\mathbf{f}$ is known when the position of the particle is given. Then $\mathbf{f}$ is a vector point function $\mathbf{f(r)}$, and we speak of a *field of force*. Then the work may be computed as a line integral over the curve C, $\mathbf{r} = \mathbf{r}(t)$, traversed by the particle. In general the work depends upon the path C between $\mathbf{r_0}$ and $\mathbf{r}$; but, if rot $\mathbf{f} = 0$ in a simply connected region $\mathscr{R}$, $\mathbf{f}$ is the gradient of a scalar point function $-\varphi(\mathbf{r})$,

(4) $$\mathbf{f} = -\nabla\varphi \qquad (45.8),$$

and the work

(5) $$W = \int_{\mathbf{r_0}}^{\mathbf{r}} \mathbf{f} \cdot d\mathbf{r} = -\int_{\mathbf{r_0}}^{\mathbf{r}} d\varphi = \varphi(\mathbf{r_0}) - \varphi(\mathbf{r})$$

is independent of the path. Hence, from (2),

$$\tfrac{1}{2}mv^2 + \varphi(\mathbf{r}) = \tfrac{1}{2}mv_0^2 + \varphi(\mathbf{r_0});$$

that is,

(6) $$\tfrac{1}{2}mv^2 + \varphi(\mathbf{r}) = \text{const}$$

at all points of the region $\mathscr{R}$.

We say now that the force $\mathbf{f}$ is derived from the *potential* φ, or that the particle has the *potential energy* φ in the field of force $\mathbf{f}$. Thus the left member in (6) is sum of two energies, kinetic and potential; the former is due to the *motion* of the particle, the latter to its *position*. The minus sign in (4) was introduced so that the energies *add* in the left member of (6). This equation is a special instance of the

LAW OF CONSERVATION OF ENERGY. *When a field of force has a potential function, the sum of the kinetic and potential energies of a particle moving in the field is constant.*

A field of force having a potential function is said to be *conservative* because the total energy, kinetic plus potential, is conserved. If the function $\varphi(\mathbf{r})$ satisfies (4), all functions $\varphi(\mathbf{r}) + \text{const}$ do likewise. The additive constant is usually determined, once for all, by prescribing the value of $\varphi(\mathbf{r})$ at some point $\mathbf{r}_0$, say where $\varphi(\mathbf{r}_0) = 0$.

Example 1. The Localized Field of the Earth. In the neighborhood of a given locality, the earth attracts a particle of mass m with the force

$$(7) \qquad \mathbf{f} = m\mathbf{g} = -mg\mathbf{k} = -mg\,\nabla z,$$

where $\mathbf{g}$ is the local acceleration of gravity and $\mathbf{k} = \nabla z$ is the unit vertical vector directed upward (37.9). For a particle at a distance z above the earth we have

$$(8) \qquad \mathbf{f} = -\nabla(mgz), \qquad \varphi = mgz.$$

Thus the field of the earth is conservative and has the potential $\varphi = mgz$. A particle moving in the earth's local field has constant total energy

$$(9) \qquad \tfrac{1}{2}mv^2 + mgz = c.$$

Thus, if a particle is projected with an initial speed v_0 at the height $z = h$, it will strike the ground with a speed V given by

$$(10) \qquad \tfrac{1}{2}mV^2 + 0 = \tfrac{1}{2}mv_0^2 + mgh, \qquad V^2 = v_0^2 + 2gh.$$

Example 2. The Field of the Sun. The sun of mass M attracts a particle of mass m with the force

$$(11) \qquad \mathbf{f} = -\gamma\,\frac{mM}{r^2}\,\frac{\mathbf{r}}{r}\,;$$

r is the radial distance of m from the sun's center, $\mathbf{r}/r$ is a unit radial vector, and γ the constant of gravitation. Since $\mathbf{r}/r = \nabla r$ (37.15),

$$\mathbf{f} = -\frac{\gamma mM}{r^2}\,\nabla r = \nabla\left(\frac{\gamma mM}{r}\right).$$

Therefore, the field of the sun is conservative and has the potential

$$(12) \qquad \varphi = -\frac{\gamma mM}{r}.$$

A particle moving in the sun's field has the constant total energy

$$(13) \qquad \frac{1}{2}mv^2 - \frac{\gamma mM}{r} = c.$$

Thus, if a meteor of mass m is at rest when $r = \infty$, $c = 0$; and it will strike the sun's surface $r = R$ with speed V given by

$$(14) \qquad \frac{1}{2}mV^2 - \frac{\gamma mM}{R} = 0, \qquad V = \sqrt{\frac{2\gamma M}{R}}.$$

If M and R denote the mass and radius of the earth, (14) gives the speed V at which a meteor enters the earth's atmosphere. Near the earth's surface $r = R$ we have from (7) and (11)

$$g = \frac{\gamma M}{R^2} \; ; \quad \text{hence} \quad V = \sqrt{2gR}.$$

Conversely, in order that a particle may leave the earth it must be projected with at least the speed V (neglecting air resistance). Thus V is often called the "speed of escape." Taking $R = 3960$ miles, $g = 32.2/5280$ miles per second per second, we find that V is about 7 miles per second.

PROBLEMS

1. Find the potential function *if one exists* for the following fields of force:
(a) $\mathbf{f} = \mathbf{c}$ (const);
(b) $\mathbf{f} = \mathbf{c} \times \mathbf{r}$;
(c) $\mathbf{f} = (\mathbf{c} \cdot \mathbf{r}) \mathbf{r}$;
(d) $\mathbf{f} = r^{n-1} \mathbf{r}$.

2. When $\mathbf{f} = \mathbf{c} \times \mathbf{r}$ show that the work done by $\mathbf{f}$ in making the circuit of a closed plane curve is $2A\mathbf{c} \cdot \mathbf{n}$ where $A\mathbf{n}$ is the vector area enclosed by the curve.

3. Show that the force

$$\mathbf{f} = [yz^2, \; xz^2 - 1, \; 2xyz - 2]$$

is conservative, and find its potential function $\varphi(x, y, z)$ for which $\varphi(0, 0, 0) = 0$.
Find the work done by $\mathbf{f}$ over a path from $(1, 2, 3)$ to $(3, 5, -1)$.

4. At a distance r_0 from the center of the sun a body is launched into its field with a speed $v_0 < \sqrt{2\gamma M/r_0}$. Show that it cannot leave the solar system.

5. If the speed of a planet at perihelion $(r = r_1)$ is v_1 find its speed v_2 at aphelion $(r = r_2)$.

6. In elliptic harmonic motion a particle of mass m is attracted to the origin with a force $\mathbf{f} = -mk\mathbf{r}$ $(k > 0)$. Find the potential, and show that $v^2 + kr^2 = \text{const}$.

7. A body of mass m is projected vertically upward from the earth (radius R) with the speed v_0. Find the height h it attains if

(a) $\mathbf{f} = -mg \, \nabla z$, where z is the distance above the ground;

(b) $\mathbf{f} = -mg \, \dfrac{R^2}{r^2} \, \nabla r$, where r is the distance from the earth's center.

61. The Solar System. Celestial mechanics is based upon Isaac Newton's

LAW OF UNIVERSAL GRAVITATION. *Any two bodies, whose dimensions are negligible in comparison with their distance apart, attract each other with forces directed along their joining line, and whose common magnitude is directly proportional to the product of the masses of the bodies and inversely proportional to the square of the distance between them.*

The consequences of this law have been verified by observation in innumerable cases. Einstein's law of gravitation, which dispenses altogether with forces acting at a distance, explains a slight discrepancy in the motion of the planet Mercury (the advance of its perihelion) and has also other theoretical advantages. But as a working tool astronomers still use Newton's law exclusively to deal with the motion of the planets and their satellites, the asteroids, the comets, and also to explain such terrestrial phenomena as the tides and the precession of the equinoxes. In brief, Newton's law is still a miracle of exactitude, and only in special problems needs to be replaced by Einstein's law.

We shall now turn to one of the most famous problems in dynamics: *How does a planet move in the sun's field of force?* The solution of this problem was first obtained empirically by Johann Kepler early in the seventeenth century. About fifty years later Newton discovered that all of Kepler's laws were consequences of his law of gravitation and his second law of motion.† We now give this deduction in vectorial form, using Newton's laws and the incomparable tool he invented, the calculus.

We regard the sun, of mass M, as fixed in space, and choose its center as the origin of position vectors. Let the planet of mass m have the position vector $\mathbf{r} = r\mathbf{R}$; since the motion turns out to be plane, we write $\mathbf{R} = \mathbf{r}/r$ for the unit radial vector. Treating sun and planet as particles, the equation of motion of the planet is

$$m\frac{d\mathbf{v}}{dt} = -\gamma\frac{Mm}{r^2}\mathbf{R}.$$

The right member represents the attraction of the sun on the planet according to Newton's law; and γ is the gravitational constant. Our equation of motion is therefore

$$(1) \qquad \frac{d\mathbf{v}}{dt} = -\frac{\gamma M}{r^2}\mathbf{R}$$

Cross-multiply (1) by $\mathbf{r}$; then, since

$$\mathbf{r}\times\frac{d\mathbf{v}}{dt} = \frac{d}{dt}(\mathbf{r}\times\mathbf{v}), \qquad \mathbf{r}\times\mathbf{R} = \mathbf{0},$$

we have

$$\frac{d}{dt}(\mathbf{r}\times\mathbf{v}) = \mathbf{0},$$

$$(2) \qquad \mathbf{r}\times\mathbf{v} = \mathbf{h}\ (\text{const}).$$

† In Newton's own words: "All this was in the two plague years of 1665 and 1666, for in those days I was in the prime of my age for invention, and minded mathematics and philosophy more than at any time since." Newton was then 22 or 23 years old.

If $\mathbf{h} = 0$, $\mathbf{v}$ is radial and the motion is rectilinear. If $\mathbf{h} \neq 0$, $\mathbf{r}$ and $\mathbf{v}$ are always perpendicular to $\mathbf{h}$ and the orbit lies in a plane through the sun. Moreover the vector area of the sector OAP (Fig. 61a) is

$$\mathbf{k}S = \frac{1}{2} \oint \mathbf{r} \times d\mathbf{r} = \frac{1}{2} \int_{t_0}^{t} \mathbf{r} \times \mathbf{v} \, dt, \tag{51.4}$$

and hence

(3) $\qquad \dfrac{dS}{dt} = \dfrac{1}{2} |\mathbf{r} \times \mathbf{v}| = \dfrac{1}{2} h, \qquad h = |\mathbf{h}| \,.$

The sectorial speed of a planet about the sun is constant.

Since

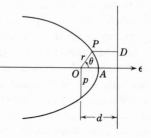

Fig. 61a. Orbit of a planet.

$$\mathbf{r} \times \mathbf{v} = r\mathbf{R} \times \left(r\frac{d\mathbf{R}}{dt} + \frac{dr}{dt}\mathbf{R} \right) = r^2 \mathbf{R} \times \frac{d\mathbf{R}}{dt},$$

(2) may be written

$$\mathbf{h} = r^2 \, \mathbf{R} \times \frac{d\mathbf{R}}{dt} \cdot$$

On cross-multiplying (1) by this equation, we find

$$\frac{d\mathbf{v}}{dt} \times \mathbf{h} = -\gamma M \mathbf{R} \times \left(\mathbf{R} \times \frac{d\mathbf{R}}{dt} \right) = \gamma M \frac{d\mathbf{R}}{dt}$$

since $\mathbf{R} \cdot (d\mathbf{R}/dt) = 0$. This may be integrated at once to give

(4) $\qquad\qquad\qquad \mathbf{v} \times \mathbf{h} = \gamma M(\mathbf{R} + \boldsymbol{\epsilon}),$

where $\boldsymbol{\epsilon}$ is vector constant of integration.

The equation of the orbit is now obtained by eliminating $\mathbf{v}$ from (2) and (4). Dot-multiply (2) by $\mathbf{h}$, (4) by $\mathbf{r}$; then

$$\mathbf{r} \times \mathbf{v} \cdot \mathbf{h} = h^2, \qquad \mathbf{r} \cdot \mathbf{v} \times \mathbf{h} = \gamma M(r + \boldsymbol{\epsilon} \cdot \mathbf{r}).$$

Since the left members are equal (13.4), the right members are also; hence on writing $\boldsymbol{\epsilon} \cdot \mathbf{r} = \varepsilon r \cos \theta$, where θ is the angle $(\boldsymbol{\epsilon}, \mathbf{r})$,

(5) $\qquad\qquad\qquad r = \dfrac{h^2/\gamma M}{1 + \varepsilon \cos \theta} \cdot$

This is the polar equation of a conic section of eccentricity ε referred to its focus as pole and axis as initial line. For from the focus-directrix definition of a conic, we have (Fig. 61a)

$$\frac{PO}{PD} = \frac{r}{d - r \cos \theta} = \varepsilon,$$

(6) $\qquad\qquad\qquad r = \dfrac{p}{1 + \varepsilon \cos \theta} \qquad (p = \varepsilon d),$

where p is the *parameter* of the conic. Since $r = p$ when $\theta = \pi/2$, p is the half-width of the conic at the focus. This is the same equation as (5) if we put $h^2/\gamma M = \varepsilon d$. The orbit is therefore an ellipse, parabola, or hyperbola, according as the eccentricity $\varepsilon < 1$, $\varepsilon = 1$, or $\varepsilon > 1$. Since the only *closed* conics are ellipses, the *planets describe ellipses with the sun at one focus*. The orbits of comets may be ellipses, parabolas, or hyperbolas.

Since the sectorial speed $\frac{1}{2}h$ is constant, the period of revolution T in an elliptic orbit is obtained by dividing the area of the ellipse by the sectorial speed. The major axis $2a$ of the orbit is $r_1 + r_2$ where r_1 and r_2 are the perihelion ($\theta = 0$) and aphelion ($\theta = \pi$) distances. Now, from (5),

$$\frac{\gamma M}{h^2}\, r_1 = \frac{1}{1 + \varepsilon}, \qquad \frac{\gamma M}{h^2}\, r_2 = \frac{1}{1 - \varepsilon},$$

and, on addition,

$$\frac{\gamma M}{h^2}\, 2a = \frac{2}{1 - \varepsilon^2}, \qquad h = \sqrt{\gamma M a(1 - \varepsilon^2)}.$$

The area of an ellipse of semiaxes a, b is πab or $\pi a^2 \sqrt{1 - \varepsilon^2}$; hence the period of revolution is

$$T = \frac{\pi a^2 \sqrt{1 - \varepsilon^2}}{\frac{1}{2}h} = \frac{2\pi}{\sqrt{\gamma M}}\, a^{3/2};$$

and

(7)
$$\frac{T^2}{a^3} = \frac{4\pi^2}{\gamma M}.$$

The ratio T^2/a^3 is the same for all the planets of the solar system. More generally this ratio is constant for all bodies revolving about the same center of attraction—the twelve moons of Jupiter for example (M in (7) is then the mass of Jupiter).

Thus the Newtonian law of gravitation has led to the proof of

KEPLER'S THREE LAWS OF PLANETARY MOTION.

I. *The planets describe ellipses with the sun at one focus.*

II. *The radius vector from the sun to a planet sweeps out equal areas in equal times.*

III. *The squares of the periods of the planets are proportional to the cubes of their mean distances† from the sun.*

† Since the major semiaxis $a = \frac{1}{2}(r_1 + r_2)$, it is called the planet's *mean distance* from the sun. For the earth, $a \simeq 92{,}900{,}000$ miles—an "astronomical unit."

These laws were stated by Kepler after a careful study of astronomical observations, the first two in 1609, the third in 1618. The discovery that these laws, so diverse in content, all flow from a single principle, the law of gravitation, is one of Newton's greatest achievements and an enduring monument to the mind of man.

The energy equation of a planet

$$(8) \qquad\qquad v^2 - \frac{2\gamma M}{r} = \text{const} \qquad\qquad (60.13)$$

gives its speed as a function of its distance from the sun. The *velocity* of the planet may be found from (4). Equation (2) shows that the direction of **h** is related to the sense in which the planet describes its orbit by the rule of the right-handed screw. If we put $\mathbf{h} = h\mathbf{k}$, where **k** is a unit vector perpendicular to the plane of the orbit, and cross-multiply (4) by **k**, we find

$$(9) \qquad\qquad \mathbf{v} = \frac{\gamma M}{h}(\mathbf{P} + \mathbf{k} \times \boldsymbol{\epsilon}).$$

Since the polar angle $\theta = (\boldsymbol{\epsilon}, \mathbf{R})$, the vector eccentricity $\boldsymbol{\epsilon} = \varepsilon\mathbf{i}$, where **i** is a unit vector in the direction $\overrightarrow{OA}$.

If we draw $\mathbf{v} = \overrightarrow{OV}$ from a fixed point, the curve traced by V is called a *hodograph*. Equation (9) now shows that

The hodograph of a planet is a circle.

Proof. Let us plot the velocity vectors $\overrightarrow{OV}$ using $\gamma M/h$ as the unit of speed; and draw $\overrightarrow{OC} = \varepsilon\mathbf{j}$. Then (9) shows that

$$\mathbf{v} = \varepsilon\mathbf{j} + \mathbf{P} \quad \text{or} \quad \overrightarrow{OV} = \overrightarrow{OC} + \overrightarrow{CV},$$

where $CV = 1$ (Fig. 61b). Thus the hodograph is a unit circle about C as center.

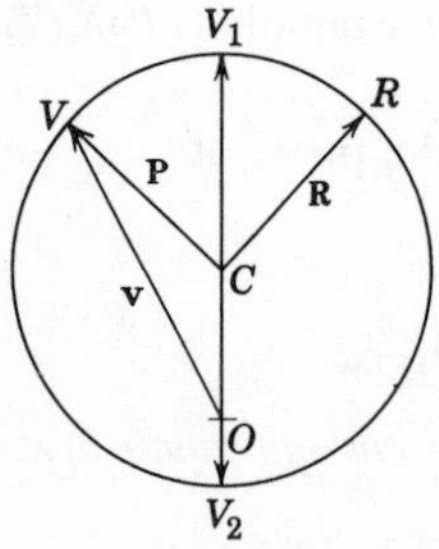

To find the velocity at any point P of the orbit, draw $\overrightarrow{CR}$ parallel to the focal radius $\overrightarrow{OP}$ of the planet, and $\overrightarrow{CV}$ 90° ahead of $\overrightarrow{CR}$; then $v = \overrightarrow{OV}$. The velocities at perihelion and aphelion are $\overrightarrow{OV}_1$ and $\overrightarrow{OV}_2$; and obviously

Fig. 61b. Hodograph of a planet.

$$\frac{v_1}{v_2} = \frac{1 + \varepsilon}{1 - \varepsilon} = \frac{a(1+\varepsilon)}{a(1-\varepsilon)} = \frac{r_2}{r_1},$$

where r_1, v_1 refer to perihelion, r_2, v_2 to aphelion. These results agree with (2); for $v_1 r_1 = v_2 r_2 = h$.

Since $\mathbf{v} = \overrightarrow{OV}$ gives the direction of the tangent to the conic at P, Fig. 61b gives a simple method of drawing tangents to a conic when only *one* focus is given. Note that, when $\varepsilon = 0$, the orbit is a circle, when $\varepsilon = 1$, a parabola.

PROBLEMS

1. The orbit of a planet or comet is the conic (6) of eccentricity ε and parameter p. Show that its sectorial speed is proportional to $\sqrt{p}$.

2. If $\mathbf{h} = 0$ in (2), show that $\mathbf{v} = v\mathbf{R}$ ($\mathbf{R}$ const) and

$$\frac{dv}{dt} = v\frac{dv}{dr} = -\frac{\gamma M}{r^2}, \qquad v^2 - \frac{2\gamma M}{r} = \text{const.}$$

3. *Halley's Comet* has a period of about 76 years. At perihelion its distance from the sun is 0.58 of an astronomical unit (the major semiaxis of the earth). Find its distance at aphelion and the eccentricity of its orbit.

4. Mercury's period is 88 days; what is its mean distance from the sun?

62. Systems of Particles. The forces acting on any system of particles may be divided into two classes: (1) the *external forces* exerted by particles not in given system, and (2) the *internal forces* consisting of the mutual actions between particles of the system. The internal forces may be grouped in pairs which represent the interaction of two particles of the system. Then, according to the principle of action and reaction, the forces of each pair are equal in magnitude, opposite in direction, and have a common line of action. Hence the vector sum of forces in each pair is zero; and the sum of their moments about any point is zero. Since the internal forces occur only in such pairs we conclude that

In any system of particles the vector sum of the internal forces, and of their moments about any point, is zero.

Consider now any particle P of mass m belonging to the system and acted on by the external forces $\mathbf{f}$ and internal forces $\mathbf{f}'$; then

$$m\mathbf{a} = \sum \mathbf{f} + \sum \mathbf{f}'.$$

Moreover, if A is any point, moving or fixed, chosen as the center of moments and $\mathbf{r} = \overrightarrow{AP}$,

$$\mathbf{r} \times m\mathbf{a} = \sum \mathbf{r} \times \mathbf{f} + \sum \mathbf{r} \times \mathbf{f}'.$$

Here $m\mathbf{a}$ is called the *mass acceleration* of the particle and $\mathbf{r} \times m\mathbf{a}$ the *moment of the mass acceleration* about A. Now form these equations for each particle of the system, and add the equations of each set.   Then, since both $\sum\sum \mathbf{f}' = \mathbf{0}$ and $\sum\sum \mathbf{r} \times \mathbf{f}' = \mathbf{0}$, we obtain

$$(1) \qquad\qquad\qquad \sum m\mathbf{a} = \sum\sum \mathbf{f},$$

$$(2) \qquad\qquad\qquad \sum \mathbf{r} \times m\mathbf{a} = \sum\sum \mathbf{r} \times \mathbf{f}.$$

These fundamental equations in the dynamics of systems may be stated as follows:

THEOREM 1.   *For any system of particles, the vector sum of the mass accelerations is equal to the sum of the external forces.*

THEOREM 2.   *For any system of particles, the vector sum of the moments of the mass accelerations about any point (fixed or moving) is equal to the sum of the moments of the external forces about the point.*

The double sums above indicate that the forces or moments are first added at each particle, and the sums then added for the entire system. In the future, however, we shall simply write $\sum \mathbf{f}$, $\sum \mathbf{r} \times \mathbf{f}$ for these total sums.

The mass accelerations $m\mathbf{a}$ are often regarded as fictitious forces acting on the particles—the so-called *inertia forces*. If we now write (1) and (2) in the form

$$(1)' \qquad\qquad\qquad \sum \mathbf{f} + \sum (-m\mathbf{a}) = \mathbf{0},$$

$$(2)' \qquad\qquad\qquad \sum \mathbf{r} \times \mathbf{f} + \sum \mathbf{r} \times (-m\mathbf{a}) = \mathbf{0},$$

we see from §23 that the external forces and the inertia forces form a system in equilibrium.   This result is known as

D'ALEMBERT'S PRINCIPLE.   *The external forces acting on a system of particles and the reversed inertia forces are equivalent to zero.*

The *momentum* of a particle P of mass m is the vector $m\mathbf{v}$; and its *moment of momentum* about O is $\mathbf{r} \times m\mathbf{v}$ ($\mathbf{r} = \overrightarrow{OP}$). For a system of particles, whether discrete or continuous, the momentum and moment of momentum are defined as the respective sums (or *integrals*) taken over all particles of the system:

$$(3) \qquad\qquad \mathbf{M} = \sum m\mathbf{v} \qquad \text{or} \qquad \int \mathbf{v}\, dm,$$

$$(4) \qquad\qquad \mathbf{H} = \sum \mathbf{r} \times m\mathbf{v} \qquad \text{or} \qquad \int \mathbf{r} \times \mathbf{v}\, dm,$$

where the integrals apply to continuous mass distributions.

We may now put the fundamental equations (1–2) in the form

$$\text{(5)} \qquad \frac{d\mathbf{M}}{dt} = \sum \mathbf{f},$$

$$\text{(6)} \qquad \frac{d\mathbf{H}}{dt} = \sum \mathbf{r} \times \mathbf{f};$$

for in computing $d\mathbf{H}/dt$ the term $\mathbf{v} \times m\mathbf{v} = \mathbf{0}$.

When $\sum \mathbf{f} = \mathbf{0}$, we obtain from (5) the important theorem on

CONSERVATION OF MOMENTUM. *If the sum of the external forces acting on a system of particles is zero, the momentum of the system remains constant.*

When the particles are associated with numbers equal to their masses, their centroid (§7) is called the *center of mass* of the system. From (7.3), the position vector $\mathbf{r}^*$ of the center of mass is given by

$$\text{(7)} \qquad (\sum m)\mathbf{r}^* = \sum m\mathbf{r} \qquad \text{(7.3)}.$$

On differentiating (3) twice with respect to the time, we obtain

$$\text{(8)} \qquad (\sum m)\mathbf{v}^* = \sum m\mathbf{v} = \mathbf{M},$$

$$\text{(9)} \qquad (\sum m)\mathbf{a}^* = \sum m\mathbf{a} = \sum \mathbf{f}.$$

These equations state that:

The momentum of the system is the same as that of a particle having the total mass of the system and moving with its center of mass.

The center of mass of a system of particles moves like a free particle having the mass of the entire system and acted upon by the sum of all the external forces.

In particular, if $\sum \mathbf{f} = \mathbf{0}$,

$$\text{(10)} \qquad \mathbf{a}^* = \frac{d\mathbf{v}^*}{dt} = \mathbf{0} \qquad \text{and} \qquad \mathbf{v}^* = \text{const.}$$

When the sum of the external forces on a material system is zero, its center of mass will remain at rest or move uniformly in a straight line.

Finally the kinetic energy E of a system of particles is defined as the sum of their kinetic energies; thus

$$\text{(11)} \qquad E = \sum \frac{1}{2} mv^2 \qquad \text{or} \qquad \frac{1}{2} \int v^2 \, dm.$$

Example. Problem of Two Bodies: To find the motions of two bodies subject only to their mutual Newtonian attractions.

In our treatment of the sun-planet problem in §61, we regarded the sun as *fixed*. If we regard all *external* forces on sun and planet as negligible, their internal forces cancel by the principle of action and reaction (§58); hence the center of mass P^* of the sun and planet moves with constant velocity $\mathbf{v}^*$. Hence, if we choose a frame of reference $\mathscr{F}^*$ moving with the velocity $\mathbf{v}^*$, we may take P^*, which is at rest in this frame, as origin. If the position vectors of sun S and planet P are now $\mathbf{s}$ and $\mathbf{r}$,

$$M\mathbf{s} + m\mathbf{r} = 0 \qquad\qquad (7.1).$$

The position vector of P relative to S is $\mathbf{p} = \mathbf{r} - \mathbf{s}$. The equations of motion of planet and sun in the frame $\mathscr{F}^*$ are now

(12)
$$m\frac{d^2\mathbf{r}}{dt^2} = -\gamma\frac{Mm}{p^2}\,\mathbf{R},$$

(13)
$$M\frac{d^2\mathbf{s}}{dt^2} = \gamma\frac{Mm}{p^2}\,\mathbf{R},$$

where $\mathbf{R}$ is a unit vector in the direction $\overrightarrow{SP}$. If we divide (12) by m, (13) by M, and subtract, we get

(14)
$$\frac{d^2\mathbf{p}}{dt^2} = -\gamma\frac{M+m}{p^2}\,\mathbf{R}.$$

This equation has the form of (61.1) with $\mathbf{p}$ in place of $\mathbf{r}$, and $M + m$ in place of M. The orbit of P relative to the sun S is therefore an ellipse in which SP sweeps out equal areas in equal times. But in place of (61.7) we now have

(15)
$$\frac{T^2}{a^3} = \frac{4\pi^2}{\gamma(M+m)}.$$

Hence T^2/a^3 is not strictly the same for all planets, as Kepler's third law asserts. But, since the mass of the sun is more than 1000 times that of Jupiter, the greatest planet, $M + m$ in (15) may be replaced by M without serious error. The third law is therefore very nearly true.

63. Body Revolving about a Fixed Axis. The particles of a rigid body revolving about the z-axis with the angular velocity $\boldsymbol{\omega} = \omega\mathbf{k}$ have the velocities $\mathbf{v} = \boldsymbol{\omega} \times \mathbf{r}$ (34.2). Its momentum is therefore

$$\mathbf{M} = \int \boldsymbol{\omega} \times \mathbf{r}\, dm = m\,\boldsymbol{\omega} \times \mathbf{r}^*,$$

where $\mathbf{r}^*$ locates its center of mass P^*. If P^* is on the axis of rotation, $\mathbf{M} = 0$, irrespective of its angular velocity $\boldsymbol{\omega}$. If forces $\mathbf{f}$ are applied to the body, the reactions $\mathbf{f}_b$ on the shaft bearings will be such that

(1)
$$\frac{d\mathbf{M}}{dt} = \sum \mathbf{f} + \sum \mathbf{f}_b.$$

In particular, if P^* is on the axis, $\mathbf{M} = 0$, $d\mathbf{M}/dt = 0$, and $\sum \mathbf{f} + \sum \mathbf{f}_b = 0$.

The moment of momentum about O is

(2)
$$\mathbf{H} = \int \mathbf{r} \times (\boldsymbol{\omega} \times \mathbf{r})\, dm;$$

therefore

(3) $$\frac{d\mathbf{H}}{dt} = \int \mathbf{r} \times (\boldsymbol{\alpha} \times \mathbf{r}) \, dm = \sum \mathbf{r} \times \mathbf{f} + \sum \mathbf{r} \times \mathbf{f}_b,$$

where

(4) $$\boldsymbol{\alpha} = \frac{d\boldsymbol{\omega}}{dt} = \frac{d\omega}{dt}\mathbf{k} = \alpha\mathbf{k}$$

is the *angular acceleration* vector. The signed number $\alpha = d\omega/dt$ is also called the angular acceleration (radians per sec.^{2}).

If bearing friction is negligible, the bearing reactions $\mathbf{f}_b$ pass through the z-axis, and we can get rid of them by taking moments about this axis. The acceleration of a particle P at a distance p from the axis (Fig. 63) has the radial and transverse components $\omega^2 p$, $p\dot\omega$ (Ex. 32.1); hence the total moment of the inertia forces about the z-axis is

$$\dot\omega \int p^2 \, dm = \dot\omega I,$$

where $I = \int p^2 \, dm$ is the *moment of inertia* of the body about the axis of rotation. Moreover the moment (or *torque*) of the external forces about this axis is

$$T = \sum \mathbf{k} \cdot \mathbf{r} \times \mathbf{f}$$

since $\mathbf{k} \cdot \mathbf{r} \times \mathbf{f}_b = 0$. The equation of motion is therefore

(5) $$I\frac{d\omega}{dt} = T.$$

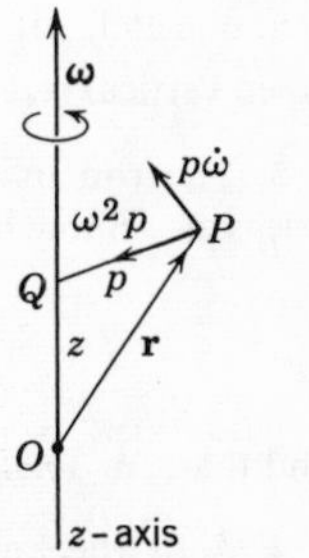

Fig. 63. Revolution about a fixed axis.

This equation may also be obtained by dot-multiplying (3) by $\mathbf{k}$; for the moment about the z-axis is the z-component of the moment about O (§19).†

Since the speed of a particle at a distance p from the axis ωp, the body has the kinetic energy

(6) $$E = \frac{1}{2}\omega^2 \int p^2 \, dm = \frac{1}{2}I\omega^2.$$

On multiplying (5) by $\omega = d\theta/dt$, we have

$$I\omega\frac{d\omega}{dt} = T\frac{d\theta}{dt};$$

† $\int \mathbf{k} \cdot \mathbf{r} \times (\boldsymbol{\alpha} \times \mathbf{r}) \, dm = \alpha \int (r^2 - z^2) \, dm = \alpha \int p^2 \, dm.$

integration between t_1 and t_2 now gives

(7)
$$\frac{1}{2} I\omega_2{}^2 - \frac{1}{2} I\omega_1{}^2 = \int_{\theta_1}^{\theta_2} T \, d\theta,$$

The left-hand member is the change in kinetic energy from time t_1 to t_2; and, if the body turns through a total of $\theta_2 - \theta_1$ radians in this time,

(8)
$$W = \int_{\theta_1}^{\theta_2} T \, d\theta$$

is the work done by the torque T during this interval (§60).

PROBLEMS

1. If a constant torque acts on a body mounted on a smooth shaft, $\alpha = d\omega/dt$ is constant. If $\theta = 0$, $\omega = \omega_0$ when $t = 0$, show that

$$\omega = \omega_0 + \alpha t, \qquad \theta = \omega_0 t + \tfrac{1}{2}\alpha t^2, \qquad \omega^2 = \omega_0{}^2 + 2\alpha\theta.$$

2. A thin uniform rod of mass m and length l is free to turn about a horizontal axis O at one end. If it is released from a horizontal position, show that its angular velocity when vertical is $\omega = \sqrt{3g/l}$ radians per second. $[I = ml^2/3.]$

3. The rod in Prob. 2 is displaced slightly from its lowest position ($\theta = 0$) and released. Show that its equation of motion is

$$\frac{d^2\theta}{dt^2} = -\frac{3g}{2l} \sin \theta,$$

and that, for *small* vibrations its period is very nearly $2\pi\sqrt{2l/3g}$ seconds.

4. A flywheel and shaft slow down from 200 to 180 rpm in 42 seconds under axle friction. Under a braking torque of 18 foot-pounds, it slows down from 200 to 180 rpm in 18 seconds. Find its moment of inertia. Take the foot, radian, pound (force), slug (mass) as units.

5. If the rod in Prob. 2 is released from a vertical position above its axis, show that $\omega = \sqrt{6g/l} \sin \tfrac{1}{2}\theta$ after it has fallen through an angle θ.

Chapter 7

Fluid Mechanics

64. Perfect Fluids. We assume as an experimental fact that the pressure exerted by a fluid *at rest* on any surface element is normal to the surface. For fluids *in motion* this is not true, since *viscous* fluids in motion exert tangential (shearing) as well as normal forces. But in many problems the tangential forces are small and may be neglected. We shall develop fluid mechanics on the hypothesis of purely normal pressure, and imply this assumption by speaking of *perfect* or *nonviscous* fluids. In brief: *a perfect fluid at rest or in motion exerts only normal pressures.*

Consider now a small fluid tetrahedron with three faces parallel to the co-ordinates planes (Fig. 64). Let the inclined face, of area A, have the unit external normal $\mathbf{n}$; then the faces normal to axes have areas

$$A_1 = A\,\mathbf{n}\cdot\mathbf{i}, \quad A_2 = A\,\mathbf{n}\cdot\mathbf{j}, \quad A_3 = A\,\mathbf{n}\cdot\mathbf{k}.$$

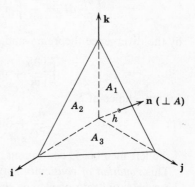

Fig. 64. Fluid tetrahedron.

The volume of the tetrahedron is $\frac{1}{3}Ah$, where h is its altitude above the face A. Let the fluid exert average pressures p_1, p_2, p_3, p on the faces A_1, A_2, A_3, A; and let ρ, $\mathbf{f}$, $\mathbf{a}$ denote averages over the tetra- hedron of the density, body force per unit mass, and acceleration.

179

Then, from d'Alembert's principle applied to the fluid in the tetra-hedron,

$$p_1 A_1 \mathbf{i} + p_2 A_2 \mathbf{j} + p_3 A_3 \mathbf{k} - pA\mathbf{n} + \tfrac{1}{3}Ah\rho(\mathbf{f} - \mathbf{a}) = 0.$$

Now replace A_1, A_2, A_3 by their values, divide out A, and let $h \to 0$; then the limiting pressures at O satisfy the relation

$$p_1(\mathbf{n} \cdot \mathbf{i})\mathbf{i} + p_2(\mathbf{n} \cdot \mathbf{j})\mathbf{j} + p_3(\mathbf{n} \cdot \mathbf{k})\mathbf{k} = p\mathbf{n}.$$

If we dot-multiply this equation by $\mathbf{i}$, $\mathbf{j}$, $\mathbf{k}$ in turn, we obtain

$$p_1 = p_2 = p_3 = p.$$

At any point within a perfect fluid the pressure is the same in all directions.

65. Equation of Continuity. Let ρ and $\mathbf{v}$ denote the density and velocity of a fluid at the point $\mathbf{r} = [x, y, z]$ at the instant t. Both ρ and v are functions of x, y, z, and t. Consider now the mass of fluid within a fixed but arbitrary closed surface S. This mass is increasing at the rate

$$\frac{\partial}{\partial t} \int \rho \, dV = \int \frac{\partial \rho}{\partial t} \, dV,$$

the time differentiation being local (fixed $\mathbf{r}$). This rate must equal the rate at which fluid is *entering* S, namely

$$- \oint \mathbf{n} \cdot \rho\mathbf{v} \, dS,$$

where $\mathbf{n}$ is the external unit normal to S. Hence

$$\int \frac{\partial \rho}{\partial t} \, dV = - \oint \mathbf{n} \cdot \rho\mathbf{v} \, dS = - \int \mathrm{div}\,(\rho\mathbf{v}) \, dV$$

by the divergence theorem; and, since

$$\int \left[\frac{\partial \rho}{\partial t} + \mathrm{div}\,(\rho\mathbf{v}) \right] dV = 0$$

for any choice of S,

(1) $$\frac{\partial \rho}{\partial t} + \mathrm{div}\,(\rho\mathbf{v}) = 0$$

if the left member is continuous.

This *equation of continuity* may be put in another form by introducing the *substantial* rate of change $d\rho/dt$ instead of the *local* time rate $\partial\rho/\partial t$. Along the actual path, or *line of motion*, of a fluid particle,

$$x = x(t), \qquad y = y(t), \qquad z = z(t),$$

the density $\rho(x, y, z, t)$ becomes a function of t alone, and

$$\frac{d\rho}{dt} = \frac{\partial \rho}{\partial t} + \frac{\partial \rho}{\partial x}\frac{dx}{dt} + \frac{\partial \rho}{\partial y}\frac{dy}{dt} + \frac{\partial \rho}{\partial z}\frac{dz}{dt} \, .$$

Now

$$\mathbf{v} = \left[\frac{dx}{dt}, \frac{dy}{dt}, \frac{dz}{dt}\right], \qquad \nabla \rho = \left[\frac{\partial \rho}{\partial x}, \frac{\partial \rho}{\partial y}, \frac{\partial \rho}{\partial z}\right],$$

and hence

(2) $$\frac{d\rho}{dt} = \frac{\partial \rho}{dt} + \mathbf{v} \cdot \nabla \rho.$$

If we now put

$$\operatorname{div}(\rho \mathbf{v}) = \mathbf{v} \cdot \nabla \rho + \rho \operatorname{div} \mathbf{v} \qquad (41.4),$$

equation (1) becomes

(3) $$\frac{d\rho}{dt} + \rho \operatorname{div} \mathbf{v} = 0.$$

Since $\operatorname{div} \mathbf{v} = -(d\rho/dt)/\rho$, we can interpret $\operatorname{div} \mathbf{v}$ as the relative rate at which the density is decreasing. Thus a positive value of $\operatorname{div} \mathbf{v}$ implies a negative $d\rho/dt$ and consequently an attenuation of the fluid at the point considered; hence the term *divergence*.

Liquids may be regarded as nearly incompressible. For an incompressible fluid the density of any fluid particle remains constant in time; hence $d\rho/dt = 0$, and, from (3),

(4) $$\operatorname{div} \mathbf{v} = 0.$$

This equation has the integral equivalent

(5) $$\oint \mathbf{n} \cdot \mathbf{v} \, dS = 0;$$

the flux of an incompressible fluid across the boundary of a fixed closed surface is zero. If an incompressible fluid is also homogeneous, ρ is constant in time and space.

We note finally that a relation of the form (2) holds for any function $F(\mathbf{r}, t)$ of time and position associated with a fluid particle moving with the velocity $\mathbf{v}$:

(6) $$\frac{dF}{dt} = \frac{\partial F}{\partial t} + \mathbf{v} \cdot \nabla F.$$

The three terms are called, respectively, *substantial*, *local*, and *stationary* rates of change. Thus the actual acceleration of a moving fluid particle is

(7) $$\frac{d\mathbf{v}}{dt} = \frac{\partial \mathbf{v}}{\partial t} + \mathbf{v} \cdot \nabla \mathbf{v};$$

here $\partial \mathbf{v}/\partial t$ is the rate of change of fluid velocity at a fixed point.

The curves which at every instant are tangent to **v** are called the *stream-lines* of the fluid.   They are not the actual paths, or *lines of motion*, of the fluid particles except when the flow is *steady*: that is, when **v** at any point does not vary with the time ($\partial v/\partial t = 0$).   Thus the stream-lines have the differential equation $\mathbf{v} \times d\mathbf{r} = 0$.

66. Euler's Equation.   The *Eulerian* or *statistical* method of treating fluid motion aims at finding the velocity **v**, density ρ, and pressure p of the fluid as functions of t and **r**, the time and position.   Thus x, y, z, t are the independent variables.

Consider the fluid within a fixed closed surface S at any instant t.   By d'Alembert's principle (§62), the body and surface forces, together with the reversed inertia forces ($-m\mathbf{a}$), may be treated as a system in statical equilibrium.   In a perfect fluid the surface force is a normal pressure $-p\mathbf{n}$.   If **f** denotes the body force per unit mass and **a** the acceleration of the fluid particles, then

(1)
$$\int (\mathbf{f} - \mathbf{a})\rho \, dV - \oint \mathbf{n} \, p \, dS = 0,$$

(2)
$$\int \mathbf{r} \times (\mathbf{f} - \mathbf{a})\rho \, dV - \oint \mathbf{r} \times \mathbf{n} \, p \, dS = 0,$$

The equations state that the sum of all forces (real and inertia) acting on the fluid inside S, and also the sum of their vector moments about O, is zero.   We now transform the surface integrals into volume integrals:

$$\oint \mathbf{n} \, p \, dS = \int \nabla p \, dV \qquad (53.3),$$

$$\oint \mathbf{n} \times \mathbf{r}p \, dS = \int \mathrm{rot} \, (p\mathbf{r}) \, dV \qquad (53.2),$$

and obtain

(1)′
$$\int [(\mathbf{f} - \mathbf{a})\rho - \nabla p] \, dV = 0,$$

(2)′
$$\int [\mathbf{r} \times (\mathbf{f} - \mathbf{a})\rho + \mathrm{rot} \, (p\mathbf{r})] \, dV = 0.$$

Since these volume integrals vanish for an arbitrary choice of S, their integrands, if continuous, must be identically zero.   We thus obtain the partial differential equations:

(3)
$$(\mathbf{f} - \mathbf{a})\rho - \nabla p = 0,$$

(4)
$$\mathbf{r} \times (\mathbf{f} - \mathbf{a})\rho + \mathrm{rot} \, (p\mathbf{r}) = 0.$$

From (41.5),

$$\text{rot}\,(p\mathbf{r}) = \nabla p \times \mathbf{r} + p\,\text{rot}\,\mathbf{r} = \nabla p \times \mathbf{r},$$

and (4) may be written

$$\mathbf{r} \times [(\mathbf{f} - \mathbf{a})\rho - \nabla p] = 0;$$

thus the moment equation (4) is a mere consequence of (3). We thus obtain from (3) Euler's equation of motion for a perfect fluid:

$$(5) \qquad \frac{d\mathbf{v}}{dt} = \mathbf{f} - \frac{1}{\rho}\,\nabla p.$$

When the density ρ is a function of p only, we introduce the function

$$(6) \qquad P = \int_{p_0}^{p} \frac{dp}{\rho}\,; \quad \text{then} \quad \nabla P = \frac{dP}{dp}\,\nabla p = \frac{1}{\rho}\,\nabla p.$$

Moreover, if the body forces are conservative,

$$(7) \qquad \mathbf{f} = -\nabla Q,$$

where $Q(\mathbf{r})$ is a single-valued scalar potential (§45). Under these conditions Euler's equation (5) becomes

$$(8) \qquad \frac{d\mathbf{v}}{dt} = -\nabla(Q + P).$$

For a liquid with body forces due to gravity, we have

$$\rho = \text{const}, \qquad P = \frac{p}{\rho};$$

$$\mathbf{f} = \mathbf{g} = -g\mathbf{k}, \qquad Q = gz,$$

when the z-axis is directed upward. Then (8) becomes

$$(9) \qquad \frac{d\mathbf{v}}{dt} = -\nabla\left(gz + \frac{p}{\rho}\right).$$

Example. If a liquid is revolving with constant angular velocity $\boldsymbol{\omega} = \omega\mathbf{k}$ about a vertical axis, its velocity distribution $\mathbf{v} = \boldsymbol{\omega} \times \mathbf{r}$ is that of a rigid body. Hence

$$\mathbf{a} = \boldsymbol{\omega} \times \mathbf{v} = \boldsymbol{\omega} \times (\boldsymbol{\omega} \times \mathbf{r}) = -\nabla\left(gz + \frac{p}{\rho}\right).$$

Now

$$\boldsymbol{\omega} \times (\boldsymbol{\omega} \times \mathbf{r}) = (\boldsymbol{\omega} \cdot \mathbf{r})\boldsymbol{\omega} - \omega^2\mathbf{r}$$
$$= \omega^2(z\mathbf{k} - x\mathbf{i} - y\mathbf{j} - z\mathbf{k})$$
$$= -\omega^2(x\,\nabla x + y\,\nabla y)$$
$$= -\tfrac{1}{2}\omega^2\,\nabla(x^2 + y^2),$$
$$\nabla\left[gz + \frac{p}{\rho} - \frac{1}{2}\,\omega^2(x^2 + y^2)\right] = 0,$$

and

$$gz + \frac{p}{\rho} - \frac{1}{2}\,\omega^2(x^2 + y^2) = \text{const}.$$

At a free surface p is constant; a free surface is therefore a paraboloid of revolution.

67. Fluid in Equilibrium.   If we put $d\mathbf{v}/dt = \mathbf{0}$ in Euler's equation (66.5), we get the equilibrium condition

$$(1) \qquad\qquad \nabla p = \rho \mathbf{f}.$$

Thus a liquid will be in equilibrium under gravity when

$$\nabla p = \rho \mathbf{g} = \rho g \mathbf{k} = \rho g\, \nabla z = \nabla(\rho g z)$$

with the z-axis directed *downward*; hence, if $p = p_0$ when $z = 0$,

$$(2) \qquad\qquad p = \rho g z + p_0.$$

If the origin is at a free surface, p_0 is the atmospheric pressure and $\rho g z$ is called the *hydrostatic pressure*.

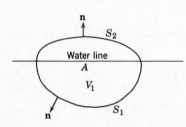

Fig. 67. Floating body.

Example. Floating Body. Let the surface S of a floating body V be divided by its plane section A at the water line into two parts: S_1 submerged, S_2 in air (Fig. 67). Then, if p_0 is the atmospheric pressure, $p_1 = \rho g z$ the hydrostatic pressure, $p_0 + p_1$ acts on S_1, p_0 on S_2; or we may say that p_0 acts over S while p_1 acts on the closed surface $S_1 + A$ ($p_1 = 0$ on A) enclosing the volume V_1 below the water line. Hence the equations of equilibrium of the body are

$$(3) \qquad \int_V \mathbf{g}\, dm - \oint_S \mathbf{n} p_0\, dS - \oint_{S_1+A} \mathbf{n} p_1\, dS = 0,$$

$$(4) \qquad \int_V \mathbf{r} \times \mathbf{g}\, dm - \int_S \mathbf{r} \times \mathbf{n} p_0\, dS - \oint_{S_1+A} \mathbf{r} \times \mathbf{n} p_1\, dS = 0.$$

We consider in turn the integrals in (3):

$$\int_V \mathbf{g}\, dm = m\mathbf{g} = W, \quad \text{the weight of the body};$$

$$\oint_S \mathbf{n} p_0\, dS = p_0 \oint_S \mathbf{n}\, dS = 0 \qquad\qquad (53.4),$$

$$\oint_{S_1+A} \mathbf{n} p_1\, dS = \int_{V_1} \nabla p_1\, dV = \int_{V_1} \rho \mathbf{g}\, dV = W \qquad (53.3),$$

the weight of the displaced liquid.   Therefore (3) states that $W = W_1$; this is the

PRINCIPLE OF ARCHIMEDES. *A floating body in equilibrium displaces its own weight of liquid.*

If we change signs throughout in (4), we have the following integrals to consider:

$$\int_V \mathbf{g} \times \mathbf{r} \, dm = \mathbf{g} \times \int_V \mathbf{r} \, dm = \mathbf{g} \times m\mathbf{r}^* = \mathbf{W} \times \mathbf{r}^*,$$

where $\mathbf{r}^*$, defined by

(5) $$m\mathbf{r}^* = \int \mathbf{r} \, dm,$$ (62.7),

locates the center of mass R^* of the body;

$$p_0 \oint_S \mathbf{n} \times \mathbf{r} \, dS = p_0 \int_V \mathrm{rot}\, \mathbf{r} \, dV = 0$$ (53.2);

$$\oint_{S_1+A} \mathbf{n} \times p_1 \mathbf{r} \, dS = \int_{V_1} \mathrm{rot}\,(p_1 \mathbf{r}) \, dV = \int_{V_1} (\nabla p_1) \times \mathbf{r} \, dV$$

$$= \mathbf{g} \times \int_{V_1} \rho \mathbf{r} \, dV = \mathbf{g} \times m_1 \mathbf{r}_1^* = \mathbf{W}_1 \times \mathbf{r}_1^*,$$

where $\mathbf{r}_1^*$ locates the center of mass R_1^* of the displaced liquid. Since $W = W_1$, (4) reduces to

$$\mathbf{W} \times (\mathbf{r}^* - \mathbf{r}_1^*) = \mathbf{W} \times \overrightarrow{R_1^* R^*} = 0,$$

so that $R_1^* R$ is parallel to $\mathbf{W}$. Therefore:

The centers of mass of a floating body and of the displaced liquid lie on the same vertical.

PROBLEMS

1. A body (surface S) totally immersed in liquid is subject to the normal pressure $p = p_0 + g\rho z$ where z is measured down from the free surface $z = 0$. Prove that

$$\oint_S p\mathbf{n} \, dS = V\rho g \, \mathbf{k},$$

the weight of the displaced liquid.

2. From the equation of fluid equilibrium $\nabla p = \rho \mathbf{f}$, show that equilibrium is only possible when $\mathbf{f} \cdot \mathrm{rot}\, \mathbf{f} = 0$.

When ρ is a function of p alone show that $\mathbf{f} = \nabla P$ and hence $\mathrm{rot}\, \mathbf{f} = 0$.

3. Assuming that the earth is a fluid sphere of radius a, of constant density ρ, and without rotation, show that the pressure at a distance r from the center is

$$p = \tfrac{1}{2} g \rho a (1 - r^2/a^2).$$

[The attraction on a unit mass at the distance r is

$$\mathbf{f} = \gamma \frac{\tfrac{4}{3}\pi r^3 \rho}{r^2} (-\mathbf{R}) = -\frac{gr}{a} \mathbf{R},$$

where $-g\mathbf{R}$ is the attraction when $r = a$. Hence

$$\mathbf{f} = -\frac{g}{a} r \nabla r \quad \text{has the potential,} \quad Q = \frac{1}{2} gr^2/a.]$$

Compute the pressure at the center if ρ is taken as the mean density of the earth ($\rho g = 5.525 \times 62.4$ lb per ft³).

4. If a fluid is bounded by a fixed surface $F(\mathbf{r}) = 0$, show that the boundary condition $\mathbf{v} \cdot \nabla F = 0$ must be satisfied.

More generally, if the bounding surface $F(\mathbf{r}, t) = 0$ varies with the time, show that the fluid satisfies the boundary condition

$$\frac{\partial F}{\partial t} + \mathbf{v} \cdot \nabla F = 0 \qquad\qquad \text{[cf. (65.6)].}$$

5. A sphere of radius a is moving in a fluid with a constant velocity $\mathbf{u}$. Show that at the surface of the sphere the velocity $\mathbf{v}$ of the fluid satisfies the condition

$$(\mathbf{v} - \mathbf{u}) \cdot (\mathbf{r} - \mathbf{u}t) = 0.$$

6. If the body forces are conservative ($\mathbf{f} = -\nabla Q$), the integrals

$$E = \int \frac{1}{2} \rho v^2 \, dV, \qquad\qquad U = \int \rho Q \, dV$$

represent the kinetic and potential energy of the fluid within the region of integration. Show that an incompressible fluid ($\rho = $ const) has the energy equation

$$\frac{d}{dt} (E + U) = -\oint p\mathbf{n} \cdot \mathbf{v} \, dS \qquad\qquad \text{[assume } \partial Q/\partial t = 0\text{].}$$

68. Vorticity.   Starting with Euler's equation in the form

(1) $$\frac{\partial \mathbf{v}}{\partial t} + \mathbf{v} \cdot \nabla \mathbf{v} = -\nabla(Q + P) \qquad\qquad (66.8),$$

we transform $\mathbf{v} \cdot \nabla \mathbf{v}$ by means of (41.9):

$$\tfrac{1}{2}\nabla(\mathbf{v} \cdot \mathbf{v}) = \mathbf{v} \cdot \nabla \mathbf{v} + \mathbf{v} \times \operatorname{rot} \mathbf{v}.$$

Thus (1) may be written

(2) $$\frac{\partial \mathbf{v}}{\partial t} - \mathbf{v} \times \operatorname{rot} \mathbf{v} = -\nabla(Q + P + \tfrac{1}{2} v^2),$$

and hence

$$\operatorname{rot} \left(\frac{\partial \mathbf{v}}{\partial t} - \mathbf{v} \times \operatorname{rot} \mathbf{v} \right) = 0 \qquad\qquad (40.10).$$

Now, since $\mathbf{r}$ and t are independent variables,

$$\frac{\partial}{\partial t} \operatorname{rot} \mathbf{v} = \operatorname{rot} \frac{\partial \mathbf{v}}{\partial t} = \operatorname{rot} (\mathbf{v} \times \operatorname{rot} \mathbf{v})$$

$$= (\operatorname{rot} \mathbf{v}) \cdot \nabla \mathbf{v} - \mathbf{v} \cdot \nabla \operatorname{rot} \mathbf{v} - (\operatorname{rot} \mathbf{v})(\operatorname{div} \mathbf{v})$$

from (4.17); and, since

$$\frac{\partial}{\partial t} \operatorname{rot} \mathbf{v} + \mathbf{v} \cdot \nabla \operatorname{rot} \mathbf{v} = \frac{d}{dt} \operatorname{rot} \mathbf{v} \qquad\qquad (65.6),$$

we have

(3) $$\frac{d}{dt} \operatorname{rot} \mathbf{v} + (\operatorname{rot} \mathbf{v})(\operatorname{div} \mathbf{v}) = (\operatorname{rot} \mathbf{v}) \cdot \nabla \mathbf{v}.$$

A rigid body having the angular velocity $\boldsymbol{\omega}$ has the velocities $\mathbf{v} = \boldsymbol{\omega} \times \mathbf{r}$ and rot $\mathbf{v} = 2\boldsymbol{\omega}$ (Ex. 40.2). For a liquid we may regard

$$(4) \qquad\qquad \boldsymbol{\omega} = \tfrac{1}{2}\,\text{rot}\,\mathbf{v}$$

as the molecular rotation or *vorticity* of the fluid particles.

In (3) we now replace rot $\mathbf{v}$ by $2\boldsymbol{\omega}$; and, from the equation of continuity (65.3),

$$\text{div } \mathbf{v} = -\frac{1}{\rho}\frac{d\rho}{dt} = \rho\,\frac{d}{dt}\left(\frac{1}{\rho}\right).$$

Then (3), after division by 2ρ, becomes

$$\frac{1}{\rho}\frac{d\boldsymbol{\omega}}{dt} + \boldsymbol{\omega}\,\frac{d}{dt}\left(\frac{1}{\rho}\right) = \frac{\boldsymbol{\omega}}{\rho}\cdot\nabla\mathbf{v},$$

that is

$$(5) \qquad\qquad \frac{d}{dt}\left(\frac{\boldsymbol{\omega}}{\rho}\right) = \frac{\boldsymbol{\omega}}{\rho}\cdot\nabla\mathbf{v}.$$

This is known as *Helmholtz's equation.*

69. Circulation Theorem. The line integral of the velocity $\int \mathbf{v}\cdot d\mathbf{r}$ over any path is called the *flow* along that path. If the path is closed, the flow is called the *circulation*.

The flow over a path Γ_0 at the instant $t = 0$ is

$$F(0) = \int_0^{s_1} \mathbf{v}\cdot\frac{\partial \mathbf{r}}{\partial s}\,ds,$$

where the arc s on the path Γ_0 is taken as parameter. At a later instant t the fluid particles forming Γ_0 move on to another curve Γ; and, since the particles that form Γ are in one-to-one correspondence with those of Γ_0, we may still use the arc s on Γ_0 as parameter in computing the flow over Γ:

$$F(t) = \int_0^{s_1} \mathbf{v}\cdot\frac{\partial \mathbf{r}}{\partial s}\,ds.$$

The velocity $\mathbf{v}$ is a function $\mathbf{v}(s, t)$ of s and t; and $\mathbf{v} = \mathbf{v}(s, 0)$ along Γ_0,

$\mathbf{v} = \mathbf{v}(s, t)$ along Γ, t having the given constant value. When Γ_0 is given, $F(t)$ is a function of t alone; hence

$$\frac{dF}{dt} = \int_0^{s_1} \left[\frac{\partial \mathbf{v}}{\partial t} \cdot \frac{\partial \mathbf{r}}{\partial s} + \mathbf{v} \cdot \frac{\partial^2 \mathbf{r}}{\partial t \partial s} \right] ds$$

$$= \int_0^{s_1} \left[\frac{\partial \mathbf{r}}{\partial s} \cdot \frac{\partial \mathbf{v}}{\partial t} + \mathbf{v} \cdot \frac{\partial^2 \mathbf{r}}{\partial s \partial t} \right] ds$$

$$= \int_0^{s_1} \left(\frac{\partial \mathbf{r}}{\partial s} \cdot \mathbf{a} + \mathbf{v} \cdot \frac{\partial \mathbf{v}}{\partial s} \right) ds$$

where $\mathbf{v} = \partial \mathbf{r}/\partial t$ and $\mathbf{a} = \partial \mathbf{v}/\partial t$ are the velocity and acceleration of the fluid particle corresponding to a certain s on Γ_0. If the body forces are conservative and ρ is a function of p (or constant), we have $\mathbf{a} = -\nabla(Q+P)$ from (66.8) and

$$\frac{\partial \mathbf{r}}{\partial s} \cdot \mathbf{a} = -\frac{\partial \mathbf{r}}{\partial s} \cdot \nabla(Q + P) = -\frac{\partial Q}{\partial s} - \frac{\partial P}{\partial s}, \quad \mathbf{v} \cdot \frac{\partial \mathbf{v}}{\partial s} = \frac{\partial}{\partial s}(\tfrac{1}{2}v^2);$$

therefore, if Γ joins the points A and B,

(1) $$\frac{dF}{dt} = \int_0^{s_1} \frac{\partial}{\partial s} \; (\tfrac{1}{2}v^2 - Q - P) \; ds = \tfrac{1}{2}v^2 - Q - P \Big|_A^B ,$$

so that dF/dt depends only on the end points of Γ. In particular, if Γ is a closed curve, $F(t)$ becomes the circulation over Γ, and

(2) $$\frac{d}{dt} \oint \mathbf{v} \cdot d\mathbf{r} = 0.$$

This is Lord Kelvin's

CIRCULATION THEOREM. *If the body forces are conservative and the density is a function of p alone or constant, the circulation over any closed curve moving with the fluid does not alter with the time.*

If, at any instant t_0, rot $\mathbf{v} = \mathbf{0}$ in a simply connected region, Stokes' theorem shows that the circulation over any closed curve Γ_0 in the region is zero:

$$\oint \mathbf{v} \cdot d\mathbf{r} = \int \mathbf{n} \cdot \text{rot } \mathbf{v} \, dS = 0 ;$$

and, as this curve moves with the fluid, the circulation around it remains zero. Thus at any later instant the circulation over any closed curve is zero, for its particles formed a closed curve Γ_0 at the prior instant t_0.

This means that the flow $\int \mathbf{v} \cdot d\mathbf{r}$ over any curve at any instant is independent of the path; hence $\mathbf{v} = -\nabla\varphi$, a gradient vector, and rot $\mathbf{v} = \mathbf{0}$.

Therefore:

If the vorticity of a fluid vanishes at any instant, it will remain zero thereafter.

70. Irrotational Motion. We have just seen that, if the body forces on a fluid are conservative and the density $\rho = \rho(p)$ or constant, the vanishing of the vorticity at any instant entails its vanishing thereafter. Then rot $\mathbf{v} = 0$ in space and time, and the motion is termed *irrotational*. In any simply connected portion of the fluid, $\mathbf{v}$ is a gradient vector (45.8):

$$(1) \qquad \mathbf{v} = -\nabla\varphi; \qquad \text{and} \qquad \varphi = -\int_{\mathbf{r}_0}^{\mathbf{r}} \mathbf{v} \cdot d\mathbf{r}$$

is called the *velocity potential*.

The equation of continuity (65.3) now becomes

$$(2) \qquad \frac{d\rho}{dt} - \rho \, \nabla^2 \varphi = 0.$$

For an incompressible fluid, $d\rho/dt = 0$, and hence $\nabla^2\varphi = 0$. Therefore:

The velocity potential of an irrotational, incompressible fluid satisfies Laplace's equation $\nabla^2\varphi = 0$.

The equation of motion (68.2) now reduces to

$$(3) \qquad \nabla\left(Q + P + \tfrac{1}{2}v^2 - \frac{\partial\varphi}{\partial t}\right) = 0$$

since

$$\frac{\partial\mathbf{v}}{\partial t} = -\nabla\frac{\partial\varphi}{\partial t};$$

for *local* time differentiation ($\mathbf{r}$ constant) and space differentiation (t constant) commute with each other. Hence

$$(4) \qquad Q + P + \tfrac{1}{2}v^2 - \frac{\partial\varphi}{\partial t} = f(t),$$

an arbitrary function of the time. If, in addition, the flow is steady, $\partial\varphi/\partial t = 0$ and

$$(5) \qquad Q + P + \tfrac{1}{2}v^2 = \text{const}$$

in time and space.

The solutions of Laplace's equation are called *harmonic functions* (§56). Every harmonic function φ represents some irrotational flow of a liquid whose velocity $\mathbf{v} = -\nabla\varphi$. The problem consists in finding a flow that conforms to the given conditions

Example. In a flow with central symmetry φ must be a function of r alone; hence, from (42.21),

$$\frac{\partial}{\partial r}\left(r^2\frac{\partial\varphi}{\partial r}\right) = 0, \qquad r^2\frac{\partial\varphi}{\partial r} = a, \qquad \varphi = b - \frac{a}{r}.$$

Now

$$\mathbf{v} = -\nabla\varphi = \frac{a}{r^2}\frac{\mathbf{r}}{r},$$

and the flux per second through any sphere of radius r about O is constant: $4\pi r^2(a/r^2) = 4\pi a$. When this flux is given, a is determined; the value of b is immaterial since it does not enter in $\mathbf{v}$.

PROBLEMS

1. For the radial flow $\mathbf{v} = (a/r^3)\mathbf{r}$ of Ex. 70, show that the normal flux through any closed surface about the origin is constant and equal to $4\pi a$.

2. A shearing flow of fluid between the parallel planes $y = 0, y = b$ is given by $\mathbf{v} = y\mathbf{i}$. Show that its vorticity $\boldsymbol{\omega} = -\frac{1}{2}\mathbf{k}$ and that $\mathbf{v}$ has a vector potential $\mathbf{A} = \frac{1}{2}y^2\mathbf{k}$ for which div $\mathbf{A} = 0$.

Prove that the circulation over any closed curve in the xy-plane is numerically equal to the area within the curve.

3. A mass of liquid is revolving about the z-axis with the angular velocity $f(r)\mathbf{k}$ where r is the perpendicular distance from the axis. If $\mathbf{R}$ is a unit vector perpendicular to the axis, prove that the velocity of the liquid is

$$\mathbf{v} = rf(r)\mathbf{k} \times \mathbf{R},$$

and

$$\text{rot } \mathbf{v} = [rf'(r) + 2f(r)]\mathbf{k}.$$

4. If the motion in Prob. 3 is irrotational, show that

$$\boldsymbol{\omega} = \frac{a}{r^2}\mathbf{k}, \qquad \mathbf{v} = \frac{a}{r}\mathbf{k} \times \mathbf{R};$$

and that the (multivalued) velocity potential

$$\varphi = b - a\theta \qquad (a, b \text{ const}),$$

where θ is the polar angle.

For a liquid of constant density ρ under the action of gravity alone, show that the pressure is given by

$$gz + \frac{p}{\rho} + \frac{1}{2}\frac{a^2}{r^2} = \text{const}.$$

5. Let r, θ, z denote cylindrical coordinates. In *Rankine's combined vortex* a body of liquid rotates as a whole when $r \leq a$ with the constant angular velocity $\omega_0\mathbf{k}$, but irrotationally with the angular velocity $(\omega_0 a^2/r^2)\mathbf{k}$ when $r \geq a$. Show that the velocity

$$\mathbf{v} = \begin{cases} \omega_0 r\, \mathbf{k} \times \mathbf{R}, & r \leq a, \\[2mm] \dfrac{\omega_0 a^2}{r}\, \mathbf{k} \times \mathbf{R}. & r \geq a, \end{cases}$$

has the potentials:

$$\text{(vector)} \quad \mathbf{A} = -\tfrac{1}{2}\omega_0 r^2\mathbf{k}, \qquad r \leq a;$$

$$\text{(scalar)} \quad \varphi = -\omega_0 a^2\theta, \qquad r \geq a.$$

6. In Rankine's combined vortex (Prob. 5), let $z = z_a$ at the free upper surface. Show that the free surface is given by

$$z = z_a - \frac{\omega_0{}^2}{2g}(a^2 - r^2), \qquad r \lessgtr a,$$

$$z = z_a + \frac{\omega_0{}^2 a^2}{2g}\left(1 - \frac{a^2}{r^2}\right), \qquad r \gtreqless a.$$

Prove that the bottom of the vortex ($r = 0$) is at a distance $\omega_0{}^2 a^2/g$ below the general level ($r = \infty$) of the liquid.

7. If the vorticity is constant throughout an incompressible fluid, prove that $\nabla^2 \mathbf{v} = \mathbf{0}$. [Cf. (40.12)].

8. If an incompressible liquid in irrotational motion occupies a simply connected region, show that

$$\int v^2 \, dV = \oint \varphi \frac{d\varphi}{dn} \, dS,$$

where φ is the velocity potential and the normal derivative $d\varphi/dn$ is taken externally to the bounding surface.

9. Under the conditions of Prob. 8, show that, if

(*a*) $\varphi = $ const over the boundary, or
(*b*) $d\varphi/dn = 0$ over the boundary,
$\varphi = $ const and $\mathbf{v} = \mathbf{0}$ throughout the region.

Hence prove that the irrotational motion of a liquid occupying a simply connected region is uniquely determined when the value of either φ or $d\varphi/dn$ is specified at each point of the boundary.

10. Prove *Kelvin's minimum-energy theorem:* The irrotational motion ($\mathbf{v}$) of an incompressible fluid occupying a simply connected region V with finite boundaries has less kinetic energy

$$E = \frac{1}{2}\rho \int v \cdot \mathbf{v} \, dV$$

than any other motion ($\mathbf{v_1}$) satisfying the same boundary conditions.
[Put $\mathbf{v_1} = \mathbf{v} + \mathbf{v}'$, then

$$\operatorname{div} \mathbf{v}' = \operatorname{div} \mathbf{v_1} - \operatorname{div} \mathbf{v} = 0 \quad \text{on boundary,}$$

$$\mathbf{n} \cdot \mathbf{v}' = \mathbf{n} \cdot \mathbf{v_1} - \mathbf{n} \cdot \mathbf{v} = 0.$$

Prove that $E_1 = E + E'$.]

71. Steady Motion. A flow is said to be *steady* when it is invariable in time. Then all local time derivatives are zero. Thus $\partial \rho/\partial t = 0$, and the equation of continuity (65.1) is simply

(1) $$\operatorname{div}(\rho \mathbf{v}) = 0.$$

Also $\partial \mathbf{v}/\partial t = \mathbf{0}$: *the stream-lines are also lines of motion.* Euler's equation (68.2) now becomes

(2) $$\mathbf{v} \times \operatorname{rot} \mathbf{v} = \nabla(Q + P + \tfrac{1}{2}v^2).$$

If **T** is a unit tangent along a stream-line ($\mathbf{T} \times \mathbf{v} = \mathbf{0}$) or a vortex-line ($\mathbf{T} \times \operatorname{rot} \mathbf{v} = \mathbf{0}$),

$$\mathbf{T} \cdot \nabla (Q + P + \tfrac{1}{2}v^2) = \frac{d}{ds}(Q + P + \tfrac{1}{2}v^2) = 0$$

along a stream-line or vortex-line. We have thus proved

BERNOULLI'S THEOREM. *In a steady flow in which the body forces have a potential Q and the density $\rho = \rho(p)$ or constant,*

$$(3) \qquad\qquad Q + \int \frac{dp}{\rho} + \tfrac{1}{2}v^2 = \text{const}$$

along any stream-line or vortex-line.

The constant will vary, in general, from one line to another. However, if the motion is irrotational as well as steady,

$$\nabla \left(Q + \int \frac{dp}{\rho} + \tfrac{1}{2}v^2 \right) = 0,$$

$$(4) \qquad\qquad Q + \int \frac{dp}{\rho} + \tfrac{1}{2}v^2 = C,$$

an absolute constant—the same throughout the fluid.

Now suppose that the fluid has a constant density ρ; this is approximately true for liquids. The equation of continuity is

$$\operatorname{div} \mathbf{v} = 0 \qquad \text{or} \qquad \oint \mathbf{n} \cdot \mathbf{v}\, dS = 0.$$

Along any tube whose surface consists of stream-lines, let the normal cross section be denoted by A. If the tube is sufficiently thin, the normal

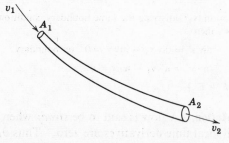

Fig. 71a. Flow through a thin tube.

flux through a portion between two sections A_1 and A_2 (Fig. 71a) is nearly $v_2 A_2 - v_1 A_1 = 0$; thus

$$(5) \qquad\qquad vA = \text{const}$$

is the equation of continuity along a tube of flow.

If the liquid is subject only to gravitational body forces, their potential is gz if the z-axis points upward from a horizontal reference plane. Thus, with

$$Q = gz, \qquad P = p/\rho,$$

we have

(6)
$$gz + \frac{p}{\rho} + \tfrac{1}{2}v^2 = \text{const}$$

along a stream-line. If z, p, v have the values z_0, p_0, v_0 at the section A_0, we have from (6)

(7)
$$\rho g(z - z_0) + (p - p_0) + \tfrac{1}{2}\rho(v^2 - v_0^2) = 0.$$

For a thin tube we may take $vA = v_0A_0$, and (7) becomes

(8)
$$p - p_0 = \rho g(z_0 - z) - \tfrac{1}{2}\rho v_0^2\left(\frac{A_0^2}{A^2} - 1\right).$$

Thus the pressure is least at the narrowest part of the tube.

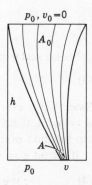

Fig. 71*b*. Flow from a tank.

Example. Torricelli's Law. When liquid escapes from an orifice near the bottom of a vessel which is kept filled to a constant level, the flow may be regarded as steady. Consider a stream tube extending from the orifice of area A to the upper surface where its area is A_0 (Fig. 71*b*). At this surface p_0 is the atmospheric pressure, and $v_0 = vA/A_0$; at the orifice $p = p_0$, and the outflow speed is v. With these values we have, from (7),

$$v^2(1 - A^2/A_0^2) = 2g(z_0 - z) = 2gh,$$

where h is the distance from the free surface to the orifice. When A_0 is large compared with A, we have approximately $v^2 = 2gh$, a result known as *Torricelli's law*.

72. Plane Motion. When the flow is the same in all planes parallel to a fixed plane (the xy-plane) and the velocity has no z-component, the motion is said to be *plane*. Velocity, density, and pressure are all functions of x and y alone; and

$$\text{rot } \mathbf{v} = \mathbf{k}\left(\frac{\partial v_2}{\partial x} - \frac{\partial v_1}{\partial y}\right)$$

is normal to the xy-plane.

The flux across any curve C in the xy-plane is defined as the volume of liquid per second crossing a right cylinder of unit height based on C.

For one who travels along the curve in the sense of increasing s, the flux crossing C from right to left is

$$(1) \qquad \int_C \mathbf{k} \times \mathbf{T} \cdot \mathbf{v} \, ds = \int_C \mathbf{v} \times \mathbf{k} \cdot d\mathbf{r};$$

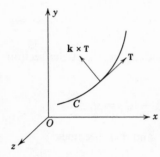

Fig. 72a. Flow across a curve.

here $\mathbf{k}$, $\mathbf{T}$, $\mathbf{k} \times \mathbf{T}$ from a dextral set of orthogonal unit vectors (Fig. 72a).

In any simply connected portion of the fluid, the line integral of $\mathbf{v} \times \mathbf{k}$ will be independent of the path when rot $(\mathbf{v} \times \mathbf{k})$ $= \mathbf{0}$.   From (41.7)

$$\operatorname{rot}(\mathbf{v} \times \mathbf{k}) = \mathbf{k} \cdot \nabla \mathbf{v} - \mathbf{k} \operatorname{div} \mathbf{v} = -\mathbf{k} \operatorname{div} \mathbf{v};$$

hence, for an incompressible fluid (div $\mathbf{v}$ $= 0$), the flux (1) will be independent of the path between end points.   Thus

$$(2) \qquad \psi(\mathbf{r}) = \int_{\mathbf{r}_0}^{\mathbf{r}} \mathbf{v} \times \mathbf{k} \cdot d\mathbf{r}$$

defines a scalar point function such that

$$(3) \qquad \mathbf{v} \times \mathbf{k} = \nabla \psi, \qquad \mathbf{v} = \mathbf{k} \times \nabla \psi \qquad \text{(Theorem 45.1)}.$$

Since $\nabla \psi$ is everywhere normal and $\mathbf{v}$ everywhere tangent to the curves $\psi = \text{const}$, these curves are the stream-lines of the motion.   Consequently the function $\psi(\mathbf{r})$ is called the *stream function*.

If we set $\mathbf{g} = -\psi \mathbf{k}$, we have

$$(4) \qquad \operatorname{rot} \mathbf{g} = \mathbf{k} \times \nabla \psi = \mathbf{v}, \qquad \operatorname{div} \mathbf{g} = -\mathbf{k} \cdot \nabla \psi = 0;$$

thus the velocity has the vector potential $-\psi \mathbf{k}$ (§54).

From (41.7) we have

$$(5) \qquad \operatorname{rot} \mathbf{v} = \operatorname{rot} (\mathbf{k} \times \nabla \psi) = \mathbf{k} \operatorname{div} \nabla \psi = \mathbf{k} \nabla^2 \psi.$$

Therefore: *The plane motion of an incompressible fluid will be irrotational when and only when the stream function is harmonic*: $\nabla^2 \psi = 0$.   When rot $\mathbf{v} = \mathbf{0}$, the velocity has a scalar potential φ, $\mathbf{v} = -\nabla \varphi$; and, since

$$\nabla^2 \varphi = -\operatorname{div} \mathbf{v} = 0,$$

the velocity potential is also harmonic.

From

$$(6) \qquad \mathbf{v} = -\nabla \varphi = \mathbf{k} \times \nabla \psi,$$

we have the relations

(7) $$\nabla\varphi = (\nabla\psi) \times \mathbf{k}, \qquad \nabla\psi = \mathbf{k} \times \nabla\varphi;$$

or, in terms of rectangular coordinates,

$$\mathbf{i}\,\frac{\partial\varphi}{\partial x} + \mathbf{j}\,\frac{\partial\varphi}{\partial y} = \mathbf{i}\,\frac{\partial\psi}{\partial y} - \mathbf{j}\,\frac{\partial\psi}{\partial x}\,.$$

Thus (7) is equivalent to the equations

(8) $$\frac{\partial\varphi}{\partial x} = \frac{\partial\psi}{\partial y}\,, \qquad \frac{\partial\varphi}{\partial y} = -\frac{\partial\psi}{\partial x}\,.$$

But these are precisely the *Cauchy–Riemann equations* which connect the real and imaginary parts of the analytic function

(9) $$w = \varphi + i\psi$$

of the complex variable $x + iy$.† We have thus proved the important

THEOREM. *In any plane, irrotational motion of an incompressible fluid, the velocity potential φ and the stream function ψ are two harmonic functions which combine into an analytic function $\varphi + i\psi$ of a complex variable $x + iy$.*

Since $-\psi + i\varphi = i(\varphi + i\psi)$, we see that, if $\varphi + i\psi$ is analytic, $-\psi + i\varphi$ is also; consequently, if φ and ψ are the velocity potential and stream function for an irrotational plane flow, $-\psi$ and φ are the corresponding functions for another flow of this type.

From (7), we have $\nabla\varphi \cdot \nabla\psi = 0$: the stream-lines ($\psi = $ const) cut the equipotential lines ($\varphi = $ const) at right angles.

Since the *complex potential* $w = \varphi + i\psi$ is an analytic function of z,

$$w' = \frac{dw}{dz} = \frac{\partial\varphi}{\partial x} + i\,\frac{\partial\psi}{\partial x} = \frac{\partial\varphi}{\partial x} - i\,\frac{\partial\varphi}{\partial y}\,;\dagger$$

or, since the velocity has the components,

$$v_x = -\mathbf{i} \cdot \nabla\varphi = -\frac{\partial\varphi}{\partial x}\,, \qquad v_y = -\mathbf{j} \cdot \nabla\varphi = -\frac{\partial\varphi}{\partial y}\,,$$

(10) $$w' = -v_x + iv_y, \qquad -\bar{w}' = v_x + iv_y,$$

where $\bar{w}'$ denotes the conjugate of w'. Thus the velocity at any point is given by the complex vector $-\bar{w}'$; its magnitude is $|w'|$:

(11) $$\mathbf{v} \sim -\operatorname{conj}\frac{dw}{dz}, \qquad |\mathbf{v}| = \left|\frac{dw}{dz}\right|.$$

† *Advanced Calculus*, §197.

Example 1. Assume the complex potential $w = az^n$ (a real); then, if we write $z = re^{i\theta}$,

$$w = ar^n e^{in\theta} = ar^n(\cos n\theta + i \sin n\theta);$$

$$\varphi = ar^n \cos n\theta, \qquad \psi = ar^n \sin n\theta.$$

The stream-lines are the curves whose polar equations are $r^n \sin n\theta = $ const.

For the cases $n = 1, 2, -1$, we put $z = x + iy$, using rectangular coordinates.

(a) $\qquad\qquad\qquad\qquad n = 1: \qquad w = az = ax + iay.$

The stream-lines are the lines $y = $ const, and the flow has the constant velocity $-\overline{w}' = -a$ in the direction of $-x$.

(b) $\qquad\qquad\qquad\qquad n = 2: \qquad w = az^2 = a(x^2 - y^2) + i\,2axy.$

The equipotential and stream-lines are the two families of equilateral hyperbolas,

$$x^2 - y^2 = \text{const}, \qquad xy = \text{const}.$$

Since the stream-line $xy = 0$ may be taken as the positive halves of the x-axis and y-axis these may be considered as fixed boundaries and the motion regarded as a steady flow of liquid in the angle between two perpendicular walls. The velocity at any point is $-\overline{w}' = -2a\overline{z}$; its magnitude varies directly as the distance from the origin.

(c) $\qquad\qquad\qquad\qquad n = -1: \qquad w = a/z = a(x - iy)/(x^2 + y^2).$

The equipotential and stream-lines are two families of circles:

$$x/(x^2 + y^2) = \text{const}, \qquad y/(x^2 + y^2) = \text{const},$$

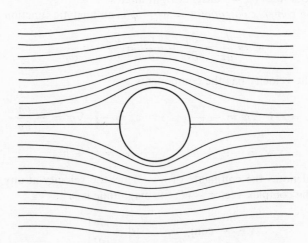

Fig. 72b. Flow about a cylinder.

tangent to y-axis and x-axis, respectively, at the origin. The velocity $-\overline{w}' = a/\overline{z}^2$ becomes infinite at the origin.

Example 2. With the complex potential,

$$w = V\left(z + \frac{a^2}{z}\right) = V(re^{i\theta} + a^2r^{-1}e^{-i\theta}), \qquad (V \text{ real}),$$

$$\varphi = V\left(r + \frac{a^2}{r}\right)\cos\theta, \qquad \psi = V\left(r - \frac{a^2}{r}\right)\sin\theta.$$

The stream-line $\psi = 0$ includes the circle $r = a$ and the x-axis $\sin\theta = 0$. Since $w' = V(1 - a^2/z^2)$, the complex velocity

$$-\overline{w}' = -V\left(1 - \frac{a^2}{\overline{z}^2}\right) \to -V \quad \text{as} \quad z \to \infty.$$

Therefore we may regard the motion as a flow to the left about an infinite cylindrical obstacle of radius a (Fig. 72b). At a great distance from the obstacle, the flow has a sensibly uniform velocity $-Vi$.

When body forces are neglected, the Bernoulli equation (71.6) gives $p/\rho + \frac{1}{2}v^2 = \text{const}$. From the symmetry of the flow about the cylinder, it is clear that the total pressure exerted by the fluid on the cylinder is zero.

PROBLEMS

1. When the motion of an incompressible fluid is steady, deduce from Helmholtz's equation (68.5) that $\boldsymbol{\omega} \cdot \nabla \mathbf{v} = \mathbf{v} \cdot \nabla \boldsymbol{\omega}$.

2. A gas flows from a reservoir, in which the pressure and density are p_0, ρ_0, into a space where the pressure is p. If the expansion takes place adiabatically, $p/\rho^\gamma = \text{const}$, where γ is the ratio of specific heats, show that

$$P = \int_{p_0}^{p} \frac{dp}{\rho} = \frac{\gamma}{\gamma - 1}\left(\frac{p}{\rho} - \frac{p_0}{\rho_0}\right).$$

Neglecting body forces and the velocity of the gas in the reservoir, show that the speed of efflux when the motion becomes steady is given by $P + \frac{1}{2}v^2 = 0$; whence

$$v^2 = \frac{2\gamma}{\gamma - 1}\frac{p_0}{\rho_0}\left[1 - \left(\frac{p}{p_0}\right)^{(\gamma-1)/\gamma}\right].$$

3. In Ex. 72.1 consider the motion when $n = \pi/\alpha$ ($0 < \alpha < \pi$). Since the lines $\theta = 0$, $\theta = \alpha$ are parts of the same stream-line $\psi = 0$, we have the steady irrotational motion of a liquid between two walls at an angle α. Find the radial and transverse components of $\mathbf{v}$ at any point (r, θ).

4. Discuss the plane irrotational motion when the complex potential $w = \varphi + i\psi$ is given by $z = \cosh w$. Show that the equipotential lines and stream-lines are the families of confocal ellipses and hyperbolas:

$$\frac{x^2}{c^2\cosh^2\varphi} + \frac{y^2}{c^2\sinh^2\varphi} = 1,$$

$$\frac{x^2}{c^2\cos^2\psi} - \frac{y^2}{c^2\sin^2\psi} = 1$$

with foci at $(\pm c, 0)$.

Show that the stream-lines $\psi = n\pi$, where n is any positive integer, correspond to the part of the x-axis from $x = \pm c$ to $x = \pm \infty$. If we regard this as a wall, we have the case of a liquid streaming through a slit of breadth $2c$ in an infinite plane.

73. Fluid Mechanics, like ordinary mechanics, has its kinematics and its dynamics. The basic kinematic principle is the *equation of continuity*, which is simply an expression of the conservation of mass. The dynamics of fluids may be studied in two ways. The one adopted here is the *Eulerian* or *statistical* method. This aims at finding the velocity, density, and pressure of the fluid as functions of place and time; the independent variables are $\mathbf{r}$ and t. In the other attack, the *Lagrangian* or *historical* method, the motion of the individual fluid particles are followed from their initial positions $\mathbf{r}_0$ to their position $\mathbf{r}$ after a time t. Thus the history of each fluid particle is traced. In any function $f(\mathbf{r})$ associated with a fluid particle, $\mathbf{r}$ is a function of the independent variables $\mathbf{r}_0$ and t. This plan leads to more subtle and difficult calculations and is not presented here; but the basic ideas and results are given in Brand's more comprehensive *Vector and Tensor Analysis*. The Lagrangian method is especially adapted to following the history of curves and surfaces composed of fluid particles. It leads moreover to a simple integral of the Helmholtz vortex equation.

Returning to the Eulerian method applied to perfect (or nonviscous) fluids, we first find by d'Alembert's principle, that at any point within the fluid, the pressure, normal to any surface element, is the same in all directions. If $F(\mathbf{r}, t)$ is any function (scalar or vector) associated with a fluid particle moving with the velocity $\mathbf{v}$, its *substantial* rate of change is

$$\frac{dF}{dt} = \frac{\partial F}{\partial t} + \mathbf{v} \cdot \nabla F,$$

where $\partial F/\partial t$ is the *local* rate of change. The Eulerian equation of continuity is

$$\frac{\partial \rho}{\partial t} + \operatorname{div}(\rho \mathbf{v}) = \frac{d\rho}{dt} + \rho \operatorname{div} \mathbf{v} = 0;$$

and, for an incompressible fluid ($d\rho/dt = 0$), becomes $\operatorname{div} \mathbf{v} = 0$. Euler's dynamical equation, also deduced from d'Alembert's principle, is

$$(E) \qquad \frac{d\mathbf{v}}{dt} = -\nabla(Q + P), \qquad P = \int \frac{dp}{\rho},$$

when the body forces have a potential Q and the density is a function of p alone. From this we can deduce Helmholtz's equation for the *vorticity* $\boldsymbol{\omega} = \frac{1}{2} \operatorname{rot} \mathbf{v}$:

$$\frac{d}{dt}\left(\frac{\boldsymbol{\omega}}{\rho}\right) = \frac{\boldsymbol{\omega}}{\rho} \cdot \nabla \mathbf{v}.$$

From this equation it can be shown that, if the vorticity of the fluid vanishes at any instant, it remains zero thereafter. We however first proved Kelvin's circulation theorem:

The circulation over a closed curve moving with the fluid is constant,

to establish this result.

For *irrotational* motion (rot $\mathbf{v} = \mathbf{0}$), the velocity is derived from a potential,

$$\mathbf{v} = -\nabla\varphi,$$

and the circulation $\oint \mathbf{v} \cdot d\mathbf{r} = 0$ over any reducible curve. Euler's equation (E) now becomes

$$Q + P + \frac{1}{2}v^2 - \frac{\partial\varphi}{\partial t} = f(t),$$

an arbitrary function of t.

For *steady motion* ($\partial\mathbf{v}/\partial t = \mathbf{0}$), equation (E) becomes

$$\mathbf{v} \times \text{rot } \mathbf{v} = \nabla(Q + P + \tfrac{1}{2}v^2);$$

whence *Bernoulli's theorem*:

$$Q + P + \tfrac{1}{2}v^2 = \text{const}$$

along a stream-line or vortex line, and this constant is absolute if the steady motion is also irrotational.

For *plane motion* of an incompressible fluid, the integral independent of the path

$$\psi(\mathbf{r}) = \int \mathbf{v} \times \mathbf{k} \cdot d\mathbf{r} \qquad (\mathbf{k} \perp \text{plane})$$

defines the *stream function*. The curves $\psi = \text{const}$ are stream-lines ($\mathbf{v} \times d\mathbf{r} = \mathbf{0}$).

For *irrotational plane motion*, both stream function and velocity potential are harmonic: $\nabla^2\psi = 0$, $\nabla^2\varphi = 0$. Then $\nabla\psi = \mathbf{k} \times \nabla\varphi$; and this is the vector form of the Cauchy–Riemann equations which guarantee that $w = \varphi + i\psi$ is an analytic function of $x + iy$. The *complex potential* w therefore has a unique derivative dw/dz; and the complex velocity vector

$$v = -\text{conjugate of } dw/dz.$$

Chapter **8**

Electrodynamics

74. Maxwell's Equations. A distribution of electric charges and currents in space gives rise to an *electromagnetic field*. The field may be characterized by means of four vectors:

$\mathbf{E}$, the *electric intensity* (electric field strength),

$\mathbf{H}$, the *magnetic intensity* (magnetic field strength),

$\mathbf{D} = \varepsilon\mathbf{E}$, the *electric flux density* (electric displacement),

$\mathbf{B} = \mu\mathbf{H}$, the *magnetic flux density* (magnetic induction);

the terms in parenthesis are also widely used. The linear relations $\mathbf{D} = \varepsilon\mathbf{E}$, $\mathbf{B} = \mu\mathbf{H}$, hold only on the case of isotropic media (whose properties are independent of direction). In nonisotropic media, such as crystals, ε and μ may be regarded as symmetric dyadics that transform $\mathbf{E}$ and $\mathbf{H}$ into $\mathbf{D}$ and $\mathbf{B}$. Moreover for ferromagnetic substances, such as iron, cobalt and nickel, the relation $\mathbf{B} = \mu\mathbf{H}$ does not apply; and, as a further complication, $\mathbf{B}$ depends upon the past history of the body.

If the medium is homogeneous as well as isotropic, ε and μ are constants; then ε is called the *permittivity* (or *dielectric constant*) and μ the *permeability* of the medium. In free space these constants are denoted by ε_0 and μ_0.

In the neighborhood of an *ordinary point* of space the physical properties of the medium are continuous. We assume also that the four field vectors are everywhere finite and, at all ordinary points, are continuous, differentiable functions of position and time. As the fundamental postulates of electrodynamics we now assume that the field vectors satisfy *Maxwell's equations*:

$$\text{(1)} \qquad \text{rot } \mathbf{E} + \frac{\partial \mathbf{B}}{\partial t} = \mathbf{0},$$

$$\text{(2)} \qquad \text{rot } \mathbf{H} - \frac{\partial \mathbf{D}}{\partial t} = \mathbf{J},$$

at all ordinary points, where the vector $\mathbf{J}$ is the *current density*.

If ρ denotes the volume density of electric charge, the total charge q (*quantity* of electricity) within a closed surface S is the volume integral

$$\text{(3)} \qquad q = \int \rho \, dV,$$

over the region V within S. To define the current density at a point P, consider a surface through P normal to the stream-lines of flow; then $\mathbf{J}$ has the direction of the current at P and a magnitude equal to the net charge that crosses a unit area of the surface about P in unit time. Both ρ and $\mathbf{J}$ are the limits of averages; and, if $\mathbf{v}$ is the average velocity of the charges near P, we may put $\mathbf{J} = \rho \mathbf{v}$.

If S is a bilateral surface and $\mathbf{n}$ its unit normal pointing from side 1 to side 2, then the current flowing through S from 1 to 2 is

$$\text{(4)} \qquad I = \int_S \mathbf{J} \cdot \mathbf{n} \, dS.$$

If S is a *closed* surface with the *external* normal $\mathbf{n}$, the total current passing *outward* through S is

$$\oint \mathbf{J} \cdot \mathbf{n} \, dS = \int \text{div } \mathbf{J} \, dV$$

by the divergence theorem. Now the charge q within S is also diminishing at the rate

$$-\frac{\partial q}{\partial t} = -\int \frac{\partial \rho}{\partial t} \, dV.$$

On equating these expressions we have

$$\int \left(\frac{\partial \rho}{\partial t} + \text{div } \mathbf{J} \right) dV = 0;$$

and, since this equation holds for any choice of S,

$$\text{(5)} \qquad \frac{\partial \rho}{\partial t} + \text{div } \mathbf{J} = 0$$

if the left member is continuous. This equation expresses the conservation of electric charge. If we put $\mathbf{J} = \rho\mathbf{v}$, (5) has exactly the same form as the equation of continuity (65.1) in hydrodynamics. We shall therefore refer to (5) as the *equation of continuity*.

On taking the divergence of equations (1) and (2), we have

$$\operatorname{div} \frac{\partial \mathbf{B}}{\partial t} = 0, \qquad \operatorname{div} \frac{\partial \mathbf{D}}{\partial t} = -\operatorname{div} \mathbf{J} = \frac{\partial \rho}{\partial t}$$

from (5). Since we may commute the spatial operator div with $\partial/\partial t$, these equations become

$$\frac{\partial}{\partial t} \operatorname{div} \mathbf{B} = 0, \qquad \frac{\partial}{\partial t} (\operatorname{div} \mathbf{D} - \rho) = 0.$$

Thus div $\mathbf{B}$ and div $\mathbf{D} - \rho$ are constant in time; and, if in the past history of the field these quantities were ever zero, they must thenceforth remain zero. We thus add to the postulated equations (1) and (2) two others,

(6) $$\operatorname{div} \mathbf{B} = 0,$$

(7) $$\operatorname{div} \mathbf{D} = \rho.$$

The entire set (1), (2), (6), (7) are usually called *Maxwell's equations*.

If S is any closed surface enclosing a region in which $\mathbf{B}$ and $\mathbf{D}$ are continuous, we have from the divergence theorem,

(8) $$\oint \mathbf{B} \cdot \mathbf{n} \, dS = 0,$$

(9) $$\oint \mathbf{D} \cdot \mathbf{n} \, dS = \int \rho \, dV = q,$$

where q is the charge enclosed by S. If $\mathbf{B}$ and $\mathbf{D}$ change very rapidly but continuously at the bounding surfaces of bodies, these equations are still valid when S encloses different media.

Mathematically, however, it is more convenient to regard $\mathbf{B}$ and $\mathbf{D}$ as *discontinuous* at such boundaries and *postulate* the truth of (8) and (9) in general. Then, if we apply these equations to a "pillbox" (Fig. 74) of height h, with one base in medium 1, the other in medium 2, and pass to the limit $h \to 0$, we get

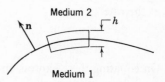

Fig. 74. Surface separating two media.

(10) $$(\mathbf{B}_2 - \mathbf{B}_1) \cdot \mathbf{n} = 0,$$

(11) $$(\mathbf{D}_2 - \mathbf{D}_1) \cdot \mathbf{n} = \omega,$$

where $\mathbf{n}$ is a unit normal to the bounding surface in the direction 1–2 and ω is the density of the surface charge (coulombs per square meter).

Thus the normal component of **B** is continuous over a bounding surface; but the normal component of **D** has a finite jump equal to the local surface density of charge.

75. Integral Form of Maxwell's Equations. Let S be a surface spanned over a closed curve C. Then, if S and C fulfill the requirements of Stokes' theorem (§50), we may express the field equations

$$\text{(1)} \qquad\qquad \operatorname{rot} \mathbf{E} = - \frac{\partial \mathbf{B}}{\partial t} \qquad\qquad \text{(74.1)},$$

$$\text{(2)} \qquad\qquad \operatorname{rot} \mathbf{H} = \mathbf{J} + \frac{\partial \mathbf{D}}{\partial t} \qquad\qquad \text{(74.2)},$$

in integral form by taking surface integrals over S and transforming the left members by Stokes' theorem:

$$\text{(3)} \qquad\qquad \oint_C \mathbf{E} \cdot d\mathbf{r} = - \int_S \frac{\partial \mathbf{B}}{\partial t} \cdot \mathbf{n} \, dS,$$

$$\text{(4)} \qquad\qquad \oint_C \mathbf{H} \cdot d\mathbf{r} = \int_S \mathbf{J} \cdot \mathbf{n} \, dS + \int_S \frac{\partial \mathbf{D}}{\partial t} \cdot \mathbf{n} \, dS.$$

The second integral in (4),

$$\int_S \mathbf{J} \cdot \mathbf{n} \, dS = I \qquad\qquad \text{(74.4)},$$

the total current passing through S in the direction of **n**. Moreover, if C and S are fixed, the operation $\partial/\partial t$ may be performed on the entire integral. We thus obtain

$$\text{(5)} \qquad\qquad \oint_C \mathbf{E} \cdot d\mathbf{r} = - \frac{\partial}{\partial t} \int_S \mathbf{B} \cdot \mathbf{n} \, dS,$$

$$\text{(6)} \qquad\qquad \oint_C \mathbf{H} \cdot d\mathbf{r} = I + \frac{\partial}{\partial t} \int_S \mathbf{D} \cdot \mathbf{n} \, dS,$$

as integral equivalents of the field equations.

The integral

$$\Phi = \int_S \mathbf{B} \cdot \mathbf{n} \, dS$$

is called the *magnetic flux* through S. Since div **B** $= 0$, the divergence theorem shows that Φ is the same for all surfaces spanned over C; and

$$\text{(5)}' \qquad\qquad \oint_C \mathbf{E} \cdot d\mathbf{r} = - \frac{\partial \Phi}{\partial t}$$

is a statement of Faraday's

LAW OF INDUCTION. *The time rate of decrease of the magnetic flux through a closed curve is equal to the circulation of the electric intensity* **E** *about the curve.*†

The partial derivative in (5) implies a flux whose density **B** varies with the time but which links a *fixed* contour. But Faraday's experiments have shown that the law of induction is even valid when Φ is changed by varying the contour; and to express this fact (5) is usually written

(5)″
$$\oint \mathbf{E} \cdot d\mathbf{r} = - \frac{d\Phi}{dt}.$$

For a stationary field $\partial \mathbf{D}/\partial t = 0$, and from (4) or (6) we obtain

(7)
$$\oint_C \mathbf{H} \cdot d\mathbf{r} = I.$$

This equation states

AMPÈRES' LAW: *The conduction current linked by a circuit is equal to the circulation of the magnetic intensity* **H** *about the curve.*

In general, when **D** is variable, (4) may be written

(4)′
$$\oint_C \mathbf{H} \cdot d\mathbf{r} = \int_S (\mathbf{J} + \mathbf{J}') \cdot \mathbf{n} \, dS \qquad \text{where} \quad \mathbf{J}' = \frac{\partial \mathbf{D}}{\partial t}.$$

Thus the vector **D** contributes to the magnetic field a portion which would be produced by a conduction current of density $\partial \mathbf{D}/\partial t$. For this reason Maxwell called $\partial \mathbf{D}/\partial t$ the density of the "displacement current" and **D** the "electric displacement."

76. Ohm's Law. The current density **J** in a liquid or solid is related to the electric field strength **E** by *Ohm's law*,

(1)
$$\mathbf{J} = \sigma \mathbf{E},$$

where the number σ is called the *conductivity* of the medium. All bodies conduct electricity to some extent, but the conductivity σ (mhos per meter) of various materials covers an enormous range of values; thus, for fused quartz $\sigma = 10^{-17}$ approximately, whereas for silver $\sigma = 6.1 \times 10^7$. Intermediate between such extreme values we have $\sigma \simeq 10^{-4}$ for distilled water, $\sigma \simeq 4$ for sea water.

For a stationary current

$$\text{div } \mathbf{J} = - \frac{\partial \rho}{\partial t} = 0 \qquad (74.5).$$

† As in Stokes' theorem, the circulation is right-handed relative to **n**.

The divergence theorem now shows that the surface integral of $\mathbf{J}$ over any thin tube formed by stream-lines of current between the normal sections A_1 and A_2 is zero:

$$\oint_1^2 \mathbf{n} \cdot \mathbf{J}\, dS = A_2 J_2 - A_1 J_1 = 0;$$

thus the current $I = AJ$ through any cross section is the same. Now, along any stream line of current of length l,

$$AJ \cdot d\mathbf{r} = I\, ds,$$

(2)
$$\int_{\mathbf{r}_1}^{\mathbf{r}_2} \mathbf{E} \cdot d\mathbf{r} = \int_{\mathbf{r}_1}^{\mathbf{r}_2} \frac{1}{\sigma} \mathbf{J} \cdot d\mathbf{r} = I \int_0^l \frac{1}{\sigma A}\, ds.$$

The factor

(3)
$$R = \int_0^l \frac{1}{\sigma A}\, ds$$

is called the *resistance* of the conductor between the points 1 and 2. Thus the resistance of a homogeneous wire of length l and uniform section A is given by

(4)
$$R = \frac{l}{\sigma A};$$

and $1/\sigma$ is called the *resistivity*. The equation (2) may now be written

$$\int_{\mathbf{r}_1}^{\mathbf{r}_2} \mathbf{E} \cdot d\mathbf{r} = RI.$$

For *steady* currents, $\partial \mathbf{B}/\partial t = 0$ and (74.1) gives rot $\mathbf{E} = 0$. Then $\mathbf{E} = -\nabla \varphi$, where φ is the scalar potential, and the last equation becomes

(5)
$$\varphi_1 - \varphi_2 = RI.$$

The potential difference $\varphi_1 - \varphi_2$ is written V and called the *electromotive force* (emf) between the points; and $V = RI$ is the familiar form of Ohm's law.

In a homogeneous conductor σ is constant; hence, from (1),

$$\operatorname{div} \mathbf{J} = \sigma \operatorname{div} \mathbf{E},$$

and the equation of continuity (74.5) becomes

$$\sigma \operatorname{div} \mathbf{E} + \frac{\partial \rho}{\partial t} = 0.$$

But, since $\varepsilon \operatorname{div} \mathbf{E} = \rho$ from (74.7), we obtain the differential equation

$$\frac{\partial \rho}{\partial t} + \frac{\sigma}{\varepsilon}\, \rho = 0.$$

If $\rho = \rho_0$ when $t = 0$, its solution

(6) $$\rho = \rho_0 \, e^{-(\sigma/\varepsilon)t}$$

shows that within a conductor charge decays exponentially with the time. The time $\tau = \varepsilon/\sigma$ required for the charge ρ_0 to decay to ρ_0/e is called the *relaxation time* of the conductor. Even for poor conductors τ is very small; thus for distilled water τ is less than a millionth of a second. However for the best insulators τ may assume large values.

If the conducting body lies in an insulating medium, the total charge on the conductor must be conserved. The decay of interior charge thus results in a rapid flow of current to the outer surface of the conductor, where it will be arrested by the negligible conductivity of the insulator. Thus charges on conductors appear almost immediately as surface charges.

77. Units and Dimensions. When the meter, the kilogram, and second are chosen as the fundamental units of length, mass, and time, the unit of force, the *newton*, will accelerate one kilogram one meter per second per second; thus

$$1 \text{ newton} = 10^3 \times 10^2 \text{ dynes} = 10^5 \text{ dynes}.$$

The unit of work, or energy, the *joule*, is the work done by 1 newton acting through one meter; hence

$$1 \text{ joule} = 1 \text{ newton-meter} = 10^7 \text{ ergs}.$$

The unit of power, the *watt*, is work done at the rate of 1 joule per second; thus

$$1 \text{ watt} = 1 \text{ joule per sec} = 10^7 \text{ ergs per sec.}$$

The dimensions of force (**F**), work (W), and power (P) are

$$[F] = MLT^{-2},$$

$$[W] = ML^2T^{-2},$$

$$[P] = ML^2T^{-3}.$$

By adding a fourth electrical unit to the meter, kilogram, and second we obtain the mks system of Giorgi, which has found wide acceptance in electrotechnics as it leads naturally to the "practical" electrical units. We give here the mks system augmented by the coulomb,† the unit of charge; its dimensional symbol is Q. The dimensions of electromagnetic quantities may then be expressed in terms of M, L, T, and Q.

---

† The international coulomb is the charge transported by a current of one ampere in one second. The international ampere deposits silver from a silver nitrate solution at the rate of 1.11800×10^{-6} kg per sec.

An electric field exerts a force $\mathbf{F}$ on a point charge q proportional to q. The field strength $\mathbf{E}$ is defined by the equation

(1) $$\mathbf{F} = q\mathbf{E};$$

that is, $\mathbf{E}$ is force in newtons per coulomb. The dimensions of $\mathbf{E}$ are therefore

$$[E] = MLT^{-2}Q^{-1}.\dagger$$

The dimensions of all other electromagnetic quantities now follow from Maxwell's equations. Noting that

$$[\rho] = L^{-3}Q,$$
$$[I] = T^{-1}Q,$$
$$[J] = [I]L^{-2} = L^{-2}T^{-1}Q,$$

we have from (74.2) and (74.7)

$$[H] = [J]L = L^{-1}T^{-1}Q,$$
$$[D] = [\rho]L = L^{-2}Q,$$
$$[\varepsilon] = [D/E] = M^{-1}L^{-3}T^2Q^2.$$

Now from (74.1)

$$[B] = [E]L^{-1}T = MT^{-1}Q^{-1},$$
$$[\mu] = [B/H] = MLQ^{-2}.$$

Since $[\varepsilon\mu] = L^{-2}T^2$, $1/\sqrt{\varepsilon\mu}$ has the dimensions of velocity:

$$[1/\sqrt{\varepsilon\mu}] = LT^{-1}.$$

Moreover $\sqrt{\varepsilon}\mathbf{E}$ and $\sqrt{\mu}\mathbf{H}$ have the same dimensions; in fact

$$[\varepsilon E^2] = [\mu H^2] = ML^{-1}T^{-2},$$

the dimensions of energy density: ML^2T^{-2}/L^3. In fact, we shall see that

(2) $$w = \tfrac{1}{2}\varepsilon E^2 + \tfrac{1}{2}\mu H^2$$

may be interpreted as the energy per unit volume (joules per cubic meter) of the electromagnetic field.

For the conductivity we have from (76.1)

$$[\sigma] = [J/E] = M^{-1}L^{-3}TQ^2.$$

Thus $\tau = \varepsilon/\sigma$ in (76.6) has the dimensions of time and is called the *relaxation time* of the medium, for from (76.6) we see that a charge ρ_0 will decay to ρ_0/e in the time τ.

† Here $E = |\mathbf{E}|$; similarly H, D, B, J, denote magnitudes of $\mathbf{H}$, $\mathbf{D}$, $\mathbf{B}$, $\mathbf{J}$.

In the mks system the units of electrical quantities are precisely the practical units used in technology. Thus the unit of current I, or coulomb per second, is the *ampere*. The unit of electromotive force V (or difference of potential $\varphi_1 - \varphi_2$) is called the *volt*; and from $\mathbf{E} = -\nabla\varphi$ we have

$$[V] = [E]L = ML^2T^{-2}Q^{-1}.$$

The unit of resistance is the *ohm*; and from (76.5)

$$[R] = [V/I] = ML^2T^{-1}Q^{-2}.$$

The unit of *magnetic flux* $\Phi = \int \mathbf{n} \cdot \mathbf{B} \, dS$ is called the *weber*; and

$$[\Phi] = [B]L^2 = ML^2T^{-1}Q^{-1}.$$

Thus $\mathbf{B}$, the magnetic flux density, is expressed in webers per square meter.

The dimensions of *capacitance* C, defined in §84, are

$$[C] = [q/V] = M^{-1}L^{-2}T^2Q^2;$$

its unit is the *farad* (coulombs per volt). The *inductance* $\mathscr{L}$† is the magnetic flux in webers per ampere through a surface spanning a closed current I; hence

$$[\mathscr{L}] = [\Phi/I] = ML^2Q^{-2},$$

and its unit is the *henry* (webers per ampere). The dimensions of ε and μ given above show that

$$[\varepsilon] = [C/L], \qquad [\mu] = [\mathscr{L}/L];$$

hence the units of ε and μ are *farads per meter* and *henrys per meter*.

A systematic table of quantities, mechanical and electrical, their dimensions and units, is given at the end of the book. This table may be used to check any rational formula in physics; for

(i)   all additive terms must have the same dimensions in M, L, T and Q; and

(ii) the arguments of all nonalgebraic functions (as the sine, exponential, logarithm) must be dimensionless.

PROBLEMS

1. Derive the dimensions of $\mathbf{D}$, $\mathbf{H}$, and $1/\sqrt{\varepsilon\mu}$ by making use of Maxwell's equations (74.1–2) only.

2. Find the dimensions of γ, the constant of gravitation (§61). Check Kepler's third law (61.7) by dimensions.

3. Check Bernoulli's equation (71.4) by dimensions.

4. Check Coulomb's law (79.4) by dimensions.

5. In Prob. 59.9 find the dimensions of a, b, γ, $\mathbf{A}$, $\mathbf{B}$, $\mathbf{C}$.

† We use $\mathscr{L}$ instead of L, the usual symbol, to avoid confusion with length.

78. Wave Equation. In a medium in which ε and μ are constant and $\rho = 0$, the electromagnetic field equations may be written

$$(1) \qquad \operatorname{rot} \mathbf{E} + \frac{\partial \mathbf{B}}{\partial t} = \mathbf{0},$$

$$(2) \qquad \operatorname{rot} \mathbf{B} - \mu\varepsilon \frac{\partial \mathbf{E}}{\partial t} = \mu\sigma\mathbf{E},$$

$$(3)(4) \qquad \operatorname{div} \mathbf{E} = 0, \qquad \operatorname{div} \mathbf{B} = 0.$$

If we take the curl of (1) and eliminate rot $\mathbf{B}$ by means of (2), we find

$$\operatorname{rot} \operatorname{rot} \mathbf{E} + \mu\varepsilon \frac{\partial^2 \mathbf{E}}{\partial t^2} + \mu\sigma \frac{\partial \mathbf{E}}{\partial t} = \mathbf{0}.$$

In similar fashion the elimination of $\mathbf{E}$ gives

$$\operatorname{rot} \operatorname{rot} \mathbf{B} + \mu\varepsilon \frac{\partial^2 \mathbf{B}}{\partial t^2} + \mu\sigma \frac{\partial \mathbf{B}}{\partial t} = \mathbf{0}.$$

Now, from (40.12), we have

$$\operatorname{rot} \operatorname{rot} \mathbf{E} = -\nabla^2 \mathbf{E}, \qquad \operatorname{rot} \operatorname{rot} \mathbf{B} = -\nabla^2 \mathbf{B},$$

in view of (3) and (4). Hence, both $\mathbf{E}$ and $\mathbf{B}$ satisfy the same propagation equation:

$$(5) \qquad \nabla^2 \mathbf{F} - \mu\varepsilon \frac{\partial^2 \mathbf{F}}{\partial t^2} - \mu\sigma \frac{\partial \mathbf{F}}{\partial t} = \mathbf{0}.$$

The last term, which represents a dissipation of energy, is absent in an insulating medium for which $\sigma = 0$; then (5) becomes the *wave equation*

$$(6) \qquad \nabla^2 \mathbf{F} - \varepsilon\mu \frac{\partial^2 \mathbf{F}}{\partial t^2} = \mathbf{0}$$

for a speed of propagation $1/\sqrt{\varepsilon\mu}$.

In §77 we saw that Maxwell's equations implied that $1/\sqrt{\varepsilon\mu}$ had the dimensions LT^{-1} of velocity. Now experiment has shown that in free space

$$\varepsilon_0 \simeq (1/36\pi)10^{-9} = 8.85525 \times 10^{-12} \text{ farad per meter,}$$

$$\mu_0 = (4\pi)10^{-7} = 1.25664 \times 10^{-6} \text{ henry per meter;}$$

and hence the speed of propagation is

$$1/\sqrt{\varepsilon_0\mu_0} = 2.99776 \times 10^8 \simeq 3 \times 10^8 \text{ meters per second.}$$

Within the limits of experimental error this is the speed of light in free space. Thus the field vectors $\mathbf{E}$ and $\mathbf{B}$ (and also $\mathbf{D}$ and $\mathbf{H}$) are propagated with the speed of light in free space.

79. Coulomb's Law.   If we integrate the equation

$$\text{div } \mathbf{D} = \rho \tag{74.7}$$

over the volume within a closed surface S and apply the divergence theorem, we have

$$(1) \qquad \oint \mathbf{D} \cdot \mathbf{n} \, dS = \int \rho \, dV = q \tag{74.9},$$

where q is the total charge enclosed by S.   This result is known as

GAUSS' THEOREM.   *The surface integral of the electric displacement* $\mathbf{D}$ *over any closed surface equals the enclosed charge.*

In a homogeneous and isotropic medium the permittivity ε is constant, $\mathbf{D} = \varepsilon \mathbf{E}$, and (1) becomes

$$(2) \qquad \oint \mathbf{E} \cdot \mathbf{n} \, dS = \frac{q}{\varepsilon}.$$

If the field $\mathbf{E}$ is due to a point charge q_1 at O, it must have radial symmetry about O; then $\mathbf{E} = E(r)\mathbf{R}$ where $\mathbf{R}$ is a unit radial vector issuing from O. If the closed surface is a sphere of radius r, $\mathbf{n} = \mathbf{R}$ and (2) becomes

$$\oint E(r) \, dS = 4\pi r^2 \, E(r) = \frac{q_1}{\varepsilon},$$

$$(3) \qquad \mathbf{E} = \frac{1}{4\pi\varepsilon} \frac{q_1}{r^2} \mathbf{R}.$$

A charge of q_2 coulombs at a distance of r meters from O will now experience a force $\mathbf{F} = q_2 \mathbf{E}$ (77.1) or

$$(4) \qquad \mathbf{F} = \frac{1}{4\pi\varepsilon} \frac{q_1 q_2}{r^2} \mathbf{R} \quad \text{newtons},$$

due to the field $\mathbf{E}$.   If $q_1 q_2 > 0$, the charge q_2 will be repelled and $\mathbf{F}$ will have the direction of $\mathbf{R}$.   Equation (4) is *Coulomb's law.*   Like the law of gravitation it is an inverse-square law; but the charges are repelled or attracted according as they have the same or opposite signs.

If we write (3) in the form

$$\mathbf{E} = \frac{1}{4\pi\varepsilon} \frac{q}{r^2} \nabla r = -\frac{q}{4\pi\varepsilon} \nabla \left(\frac{1}{r}\right),$$

we see that the field of a point charge q has the potential

$$(5) \qquad \varphi = \frac{1}{4\pi\varepsilon} \frac{q}{r}.$$

We assume that $\mathbf{E}$ due to n point charges $q_1, q_2, \cdots, q_n$ is the sum $\sum \mathbf{E}_i$ of their separate intensities: then

$$(6) \qquad \mathbf{E} = -\frac{1}{4\pi\varepsilon} \nabla \left(\frac{q_1}{r_1} + \frac{q_2}{r_2} + \cdots + \frac{q_n}{r_n}\right),$$

where r_i is the distance from the charge q_i to the point P where $\mathbf{E}$ is computed. Consequently the potential due to this system of charges is

$$(7) \qquad \varphi = \frac{1}{4\pi\varepsilon} \left(\frac{q_1}{r_1} + \frac{q_2}{r_2} + \cdots + \frac{q_n}{r_n}\right).$$

The potential at P due to a charge $-q$ at Q and $+q$ at Q' is

$$\frac{-q}{r} + \frac{q}{r'} = q\left(\frac{1}{r'} - \frac{1}{r}\right).$$

If $Q' \to Q$ and at the same time the product

$$q \overrightarrow{QQ'} = \mathbf{m}$$

remains constant, the limiting result is called a *dipole of moment* $\mathbf{m}$. The potential of this dipole at P is

$$(8) \qquad \varphi = \frac{1}{4\pi\varepsilon} \lim_{Q' \to Q} q(QQ') \frac{1/PQ' - 1/PQ}{QQ'} = \frac{1}{4\pi\varepsilon} \mathbf{m} \cdot \nabla_Q \frac{1}{r} \, ;$$

for the limit of the fraction in the second member is the directional derivative of $1/PQ$ at Q in the direction $\overrightarrow{QQ'}$.

For a continuous charge distribution of density ρ over a volume V, (7) suggests the potential

$$(9) \qquad \varphi = \frac{1}{4\pi\varepsilon} \int_V \frac{\rho}{r} \, dV$$

at points outside of V. Similarly, for a charge distribution of surface density ω over a surface S,

$$(10) \qquad \varphi = \frac{1}{4\pi\varepsilon} \int_S \frac{\omega}{r} \, dS.$$

A continuous distribution of dipoles over a surface with moments everywhere in the direction of the unit normal $\mathbf{n}$ is called a *double layer*.

If $\tau\mathbf{n}$ is the dipole moment per unit area over the surface S, the potential at P of this double layer, suggested by (8), is

$$(11) \qquad \varphi = \frac{1}{4\pi\varepsilon} \int_S \tau\mathbf{n} \cdot \nabla_Q \frac{1}{r} \, dS,$$

where $r = PQ$. From (52.8)

$$-\mathbf{n} \cdot \nabla_Q \frac{1}{r} \, dS = d\Omega,$$

the solid angle subtended by dS at P; hence (11) may be written

$$(12) \qquad \varphi = -\frac{1}{4\pi\varepsilon} \int_S \tau \, d\Omega.$$

When τ is constant over S, this becomes

$$(13) \qquad \varphi = -\frac{\tau\Omega}{4\pi\varepsilon},$$

where Ω is the total solid angle subtended by S at P.

80. Poynting's Vector. If we dot-multiply Maxwell's equations,

$$(1) \qquad \text{rot } \mathbf{E} + \mu\frac{\partial\mathbf{H}}{\partial t} = \mathbf{0},$$

$$(2) \qquad \text{rot } \mathbf{H} - \varepsilon\frac{\partial\mathbf{E}}{\partial t} = \mathbf{J},$$

by $\mathbf{H}$ and $\mathbf{E}$, respectively, and subtract, we obtain

$$(3) \qquad \mathbf{H}\cdot\text{rot } \mathbf{E} - \mathbf{E}\cdot\text{rot } \mathbf{H} + \frac{\partial}{\partial t}\left(\mu\mathbf{H}\cdot\frac{\partial\mathbf{H}}{\partial t} + \varepsilon\mathbf{E}\cdot\frac{\partial\mathbf{E}}{\partial t}\right) + \mathbf{E}\cdot\mathbf{J} = 0.$$

Now

$$\mathbf{H}\cdot\text{rot } \mathbf{E} - \mathbf{E}\cdot\text{rot } \mathbf{H} = \text{div }(\mathbf{E}\times\mathbf{H}) \qquad (41.6),$$

$$\mu\mathbf{H}\cdot\frac{\partial\mathbf{H}}{\partial t} + \varepsilon E\cdot\frac{\partial\mathbf{E}}{\partial t} = \frac{\partial}{\partial t}\left(\frac{1}{2}\varepsilon E^2 + \frac{1}{2}\mu H^2\right);$$

hence on writing

$$(4) \qquad w = \tfrac{1}{2}\varepsilon E^2 + \tfrac{1}{2}\mu H^2,$$

$$(5) \qquad \mathbf{E}\cdot\mathbf{J} = J^2/\sigma \qquad (76.1),$$

(3) becomes

$$(6) \qquad \text{div }(\mathbf{E}\times\mathbf{H}) + \frac{\partial w}{\partial t} + \frac{J^2}{\sigma} = 0.$$

If we integrate this expression over the volume included by a closed surface S, we obtain, on using the divergence theorem,

$$(7) \qquad \oint \mathbf{n} \cdot \mathbf{E} \times \mathbf{H} \, dS + \frac{\partial}{\partial t} \int w \, dV + \int \frac{J^2}{\sigma} \, dV = 0.$$

Each term of this equation has the dimensions ML^2T^{-3}, a rate of doing work (joules per second). We therefore proceed to interpret (7) as an *energy equation.*

If we regard w as the energy of the field per unit volume,

$$\int w \, dV = \text{electromagnetic energy within } S,$$

and this energy increases at the rate

$$(7)' \qquad \frac{\partial}{\partial t} \int w \, dV = -\oint \mathbf{n} \cdot \mathbf{E} \times \mathbf{H} \, dS - \int \frac{J^2}{\sigma} \, dV.$$

Since $-\mathbf{n}$ is the *internal* unit normal to the surface S, we may regard the surface integral $-\oint \mathbf{n} \cdot \mathbf{E} \times \mathbf{H} \, dS$ as the energy in joules per second that flows into the region bounded by S. Therefore the vector $\mathbf{E} \times \mathbf{H}$ represents the intensity of energy flow in watts per square meter. Since this interpretation was first given by Poynting in 1884, the vector

$$(8) \qquad\qquad\qquad \mathbf{S} = \mathbf{E} \times \mathbf{H}$$

is known as *Poynting's vector.*

On the other hand, the integral $\oint J^2/\sigma \, dV$ represents the rate at which the energy of the electric field $\mathbf{E}$ is changing into heat. The energy of the magnetic field does not undergo a corresponding "relaxation."

We therefore interpret (7)' as follows:

The rate of increase of electromagnetic energy within a closed surface equals the rate at which energy is flowing in through the boundary minus the rate at which the energy of the electric field within is dissipated into heat.

In a stationary field $\partial w/\partial t = 0$, and (6) reduces to

$$(9) \qquad\qquad\qquad \text{div } \mathbf{S} + \frac{J^2}{\sigma} = 0.$$

81. Potentials. Since div $\mathbf{B} = 0$, the solenoidal vector $\mathbf{B}$ admits a vector potential $\mathbf{A}$:

$$(1) \qquad\qquad\qquad \mathbf{B} = \text{rot } \mathbf{A},$$

where $\mathbf{A}(\mathbf{r}, t)$, a function of position and time, is arbitrary to an additive gradient $\nabla \psi$ of a scalar function (§54). The first Maxwell equation now gives

$$\text{rot } \mathbf{E} + \frac{\partial \mathbf{B}}{\partial t} = \text{rot} \left(\mathbf{E} + \frac{\partial \mathbf{A}}{\partial t} \right) = 0;$$

hence the irrotational vector $\mathbf{E} + \partial \mathbf{A}/\partial t$ admits a scalar potential φ:

$$\mathbf{E} + \frac{\partial \mathbf{A}}{\partial t} = -\nabla \varphi,$$

where $\varphi(\mathbf{r}, t)$ is arbitrary to an additive function of the time; and

$$(2) \qquad\qquad \mathbf{E} = -\frac{\partial \mathbf{A}}{\partial t} - \nabla \varphi.$$

If $\mathbf{A}_0$, φ_0 are particular values of the potentials, and $\psi(\mathbf{r}, t)$ is an arbitrary function, the potentials

$$(3) \qquad\qquad \mathbf{A} = \mathbf{A}_0 + \nabla \psi, \qquad \varphi = \varphi_0 - \frac{\partial \psi}{\partial t}$$

will give the same field ($\mathbf{B}$ and $\mathbf{E}$).

For a homogeneous isotropic medium ε and μ are constants, and

$$(4)(5) \qquad \mathbf{H} = \frac{1}{\mu} \text{ rot } \mathbf{A}, \qquad \mathbf{D} = -\varepsilon \left(\nabla \varphi + \frac{\partial \mathbf{A}}{\partial t} \right).$$

If we substitute these values in

$$\text{rot } \mathbf{H} - \frac{\partial \mathbf{D}}{\partial t} = \mathbf{J} \qquad\qquad (74.2),$$

we find that

$$\text{rot rot } \mathbf{A} + \varepsilon \mu \left(\nabla \frac{\partial \varphi}{\partial t} + \frac{\partial^2 \mathbf{A}}{\partial t^2} \right) = \mu \mathbf{J};$$

or, replacing rot rot $\mathbf{A}$ by ∇ div $\mathbf{A} - \nabla^2 \mathbf{A}$ (40.12),

$$\nabla^2 \mathbf{A} - \varepsilon \mu \frac{\partial^2 \mathbf{A}}{\partial t^2} - \nabla \left(\text{div } \mathbf{A} + \varepsilon \mu \frac{\partial \varphi}{\partial t} \right) = -\mu \mathbf{J}.$$

Moreover, since div $\mathbf{D} = \rho$, we have from (5)

$$\nabla^2 \varphi + \frac{\partial}{\partial t} \text{ div } \mathbf{A} = -\frac{\rho}{\varepsilon}.$$

The degree to which $\mathbf{A}$ and φ are arbitrary allows us to impose the further condition

$$(6) \qquad\qquad \operatorname{div} \mathbf{A} + \varepsilon\mu \frac{\partial \varphi}{\partial t} = 0$$

on the potentials; for, from (3), we need only choose ψ to satisfy the equation

$$(7) \qquad\qquad \operatorname{div} \mathbf{A_0} + \nabla^2 \psi + \varepsilon\mu \left(\frac{\partial \varphi_0}{\partial t} - \frac{\partial^2 \psi}{\partial t^2} \right) = 0.$$

When this is done, both $\mathbf{A}$ and φ satisfy differential equations of the same form:

$$(8) \qquad\qquad \nabla^2 \mathbf{A} - \varepsilon\mu \frac{\partial^2 \mathbf{A}}{\partial t^2} = -\mu \mathbf{J},$$

$$(9) \qquad\qquad \nabla^2 \varphi - \varepsilon\mu \frac{\partial^2 \varphi}{\partial t^2} = -\frac{\rho}{\varepsilon}.$$

For *stationary fields* the time derivatives are zero. Then $\mathbf{A}$ and φ are functions of position alone and the field vectors are given by

$$\mathbf{B} = \operatorname{rot} \mathbf{A}, \qquad \mathbf{E} = -\nabla\varphi.$$

The condition (6) becomes $\operatorname{div} \mathbf{A} = 0$. The potentials now satisfy the *Poisson equations*:

$$(8)' \qquad\qquad \nabla^2 \mathbf{A} = -\mu \mathbf{J},$$

$$(9)' \qquad\qquad \nabla^2 \varphi = -\rho/\varepsilon.$$

Since $\operatorname{div} \mathbf{J} = 0$ for stationary currents (74.5), the condition $\operatorname{div} \mathbf{A} = 0$ is consistent with (8)'.

82. Electrostatics. In a stationary field the vectors $\mathbf{E}$ and $\mathbf{D}$ satisfy the Maxwell equations

$$(1) \qquad\qquad \operatorname{rot} \mathbf{E} = \mathbf{0} \qquad\qquad (74.1),$$

$$(2) \qquad\qquad \operatorname{div} \mathbf{D} = \rho \qquad\qquad (74.7).$$

Equation (1) shows that $\mathbf{E}$ has a scalar potential:

$$(3) \qquad\qquad \mathbf{E} = -\nabla\varphi.$$

In a homogeneous isotropic medium, ε is constant,

$$\operatorname{div} \mathbf{D} = \varepsilon \operatorname{div} \mathbf{E} = -\varepsilon \, \nabla^2\varphi,$$

and (2) shows that φ satisfies Poisson's equation

$$(4) \qquad\qquad \nabla^2\varphi = -\rho/\varepsilon.$$

If we put $\nabla^2 \varphi = -\rho/\varepsilon$ in Green's identities (55.3–4), we have, for any closed surface S enclosing a volume V,

$$(5) \quad 4\pi \, \varphi(P) = \frac{1}{\varepsilon} \int_V \frac{\rho}{r} \, dV + \oint_S \left[\frac{1}{r} \frac{d\varphi}{dn} - \varphi \frac{d}{dn}\!\left(\frac{1}{r}\right) \right] dS, \qquad P \text{ inside } S,$$

$$(6) \qquad 0 = \frac{1}{\varepsilon} \int_V \frac{\rho}{r} \, dV + \oint_S \left[\frac{1}{r} \frac{d\varphi}{dn} - \varphi \frac{d}{dn}\!\left(\frac{1}{r}\right) \right] dS, \qquad P \text{ outside } S.$$

In these formulas r is the distance from P, the point of observation, to a point Q in the volume or surface element; hence the volume and surface integrals in (5) are not the same as those in (6).

If φ is regular at infinity (55.5), (5) and (6) may be applied to the region V_∞ outside of S; the normal to S exterior to V_∞ is now $-\mathbf{n}$, and we have

$$(7) \quad 4\pi \, \varphi(P) = \frac{1}{\varepsilon} \int_{V_\infty} \frac{\rho}{r} \, dV - \oint_S \left[\frac{1}{r} \frac{d\varphi}{dn} - \varphi \frac{d}{dn}\!\left(\frac{1}{r}\right) \right] dS, \qquad P \text{ outside } S.$$

$$(8) \qquad 0 = \frac{1}{\varepsilon} \int_{V_\infty} \frac{\rho}{r} \, dV - \oint_S \left[\frac{1}{r} \frac{d\varphi}{dn} - \varphi \frac{d}{dn}\!\left(\frac{1}{r}\right) \right] dS, \qquad P \text{ inside } S,$$

for when P is outside S it is inside V_∞. If we now add (5) and (8), or (6) and (7), the surface integrals cancel, and we have for all positions of P

$$(9) \qquad\qquad \varphi(P) = \frac{1}{4\pi\varepsilon} \int_\infty \frac{\rho}{r} \, dV$$

on integrating over the whole of space.

In any actual case the charges occupy only a finite region V_1 beyond which $\rho = 0$, say the region V_1 bounded by a surface S_1; then

$$(10) \qquad\qquad \varphi(P) = \frac{1}{4\pi\varepsilon} \int_{V_1} \frac{\rho}{r} \, dV.$$

We may now compute $\mathbf{E} = -\nabla\varphi$ at P by taking the gradient of (10) under the integral sign; and, since $\nabla_P \, r^{-1} = -r^{-2}\mathbf{R}$ where $\mathbf{R}$ is a unit vector in the direction $\overrightarrow{QP}$,

$$(11) \qquad\qquad \mathbf{E} = \frac{1}{4\pi\varepsilon} \int_{V_1} \frac{\rho}{r^2} \mathbf{R} \, dV.$$

In differentiating functions of $r = PQ$ we may vary either P or Q, holding the other point fixed. Thus

$$(12) \qquad\qquad \nabla_P \, r = \mathbf{R}, \qquad \nabla_Q \, r = -\mathbf{R},$$

when P and Q, respectively, are varied; and in general

$$(13) \qquad \nabla_P f(r) = f'(r) \, \nabla_P \, r = -f'(r) \, \nabla_Q \, r = -\nabla_Q f(r).$$

If O is a fixed origin within V_1, and Q a variable point of V_1, the ratio $QP/OP \to 1$ as $P \to \infty$; hence, at distances from V_1 that are very great relative to the dimensions of V_1, the potential

$$(14) \qquad \varphi(P) \simeq \frac{1}{4\pi\varepsilon} \frac{q}{|OP|},$$

where $q = \int \rho \, dV$ is the total charge. Similarly the electric intensity

$$(15) \qquad \mathbf{E}(P) \simeq \frac{1}{4\pi\varepsilon} \frac{q}{|OP|^2} \mathbf{R},$$

where $\mathbf{R}$ is a unit vector in the direction OP. If the charge is concentrated in a small volume, these expressions have a wide range of validity; and for a "point charge" at O they may be regarded as exact. Thus we again obtain (79.3) and are led to *Coulomb's law*. We note also that (14) and (15) show that $|OP||\varphi|$ and $|OP|^2 |\mathbf{E}|$ are uniformly bounded. Thus the potential due to a finite distribution of charge is *regular at infinity* (55.5).

When there are charges inside and outside of S, the potential at points inside of S is given by (5). If we write

$$(16) \qquad \varphi_1(P) = \frac{1}{4\pi\varepsilon} \int_V \frac{\rho}{r} \, dV,$$

$$(17) \qquad \varphi_2(P) = \frac{1}{4\pi\varepsilon} \oint_S \left[\frac{1}{r} \varepsilon \frac{d\varphi}{dn} - \varepsilon\varphi \frac{d}{dn}\left(\frac{1}{r}\right) \right] dS,$$

we have $\varphi = \varphi_1 + \varphi_2$, where φ_1 is a particular solution of $\nabla^2\varphi = -\rho/\varepsilon$ valid within S, and φ_2 is a solution of $\nabla^2\varphi = 0$ corresponding to the boundary values of φ and $d\varphi/dn$ (Theorem 56.3). Thus φ_1 and φ_2 are the respective potentials due to the charges inside and outside of S. If we put

$$\omega = \varepsilon \frac{d\varphi}{dn}, \qquad \tau = -\varepsilon\varphi,$$

in (17), we have

$$(18) \qquad \varphi_2(P) = \frac{1}{4\pi\varepsilon} \oint_S \frac{\omega}{r} \, dS + \frac{1}{4\pi\varepsilon} \int_S \tau \frac{d}{dn}\left(\frac{1}{r}\right) dS.$$

Hence, in view of (79.10–11), we may state

THEOREM 1. *The charges outside of a closed surface S produce the same potential at an interior point as a single layer of density $\varepsilon \, d\varphi/dn$ and a double layer of moment density $-\varepsilon\varphi$ over S.*

In a similar fashion we may deduce from (7) the

THEOREM 2. *The charges inside of a closed surface S produce the same potential at an exterior point as a single layer of density* $-\varepsilon \, d\varphi/dn$ *and a double layer of moment density* $\varepsilon\varphi$ *over S.*

The surface S divides space into two regions V and V_∞ (Fig. 82a). Theorem 2 follows from Theorem 1 if V is regarded as "outside" of V_∞; then ω and τ change sign because $-\mathbf{n}$ is now the external normal. In case S is an equipotential surface, τ is constant, and the integral for the

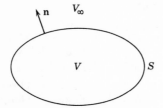   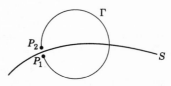

Fig. 82a. Two regions formed   Fig. 82b. To illustrate continuity
by a closed surface.   of ρ.

double layer vanishes by (56.3); for $1/r = 1/PQ$ is harmonic within S when P is outside of S.

At the surface of separation S of two media, $\mathbf{D} = \varepsilon\mathbf{E}$, and $\mathbf{E}$ satisfy the *boundary conditions*:

(19) $\mathbf{n} \cdot (\mathbf{D}_2 - \mathbf{D}_1) = \omega$ (74.11),

(20) $\mathbf{n} \times (\mathbf{E}_2 - \mathbf{E}_1) = 0.$

The argument for (19) was given in §74; and similar considerations lead to (20). For $\operatorname{rot}\mathbf{E} = 0$ implies that $\oint \mathbf{E} \cdot d\mathbf{r} = 0$ over any reducible curve, provided we regard $\mathbf{E}$ and its space derivatives as changing rapidly but continuously in a transition layer about S. It is more convenient, however, to regard $\mathbf{E}$ as discontinuous at S but in such a manner that $\oint \mathbf{E} \cdot d\mathbf{r} = 0$ for all closed curves, even those cutting S. We then find as in §46 that the tangential component of $\mathbf{E}$ is continuous over S, as stated in (20). Thus, if we write $\mathbf{E} = E_t\mathbf{T} + E_n\mathbf{n}$ on S,

(21) $E_{2t} - E_{1t} = 0, \qquad \varepsilon_2 E_{2n} - \varepsilon_1 E_{1n} = \omega.$

Nevertheless *the potential is continuous.* For, if P_1, P_2 are points near S but on opposite sides, the line integral over a curve Γ (Fig. 82b) is

$$\int_{\mathbf{r}_1}^{\mathbf{r}_2} \mathbf{E} \cdot d\mathbf{r} = -\int_{\mathbf{r}_1}^{\mathbf{r}_2} \nabla\varphi \cdot d\mathbf{r} = \varphi(P_1) - \varphi(P_2).$$

As P_1 and P_2 approach a point on S,

$$\int_{\mathbf{r}_1}^{\mathbf{r}_2} \mathbf{E} \cdot d\mathbf{r} \to \oint \mathbf{E} \cdot d\mathbf{r} = 0 \quad \text{and} \quad \varphi(P_1) - \varphi(P_2) \to 0.$$

Example. Let us compute the field $\mathbf{E}$ due to a sphere of radius a having a uniform charge density $\rho = q/\frac{4}{3}\pi a^3$. Since the field has radial symmetry, $E = E(r)\mathbf{R}$ is a vector function of r directed outward from the center. Instead of computing the integrals (10) and (11), it is simpler to use Gauss' theorem (79.1) to find $\mathbf{E}$.

The normal flux over a sphere of radius r is

$$4\pi r^2 E = \begin{cases} \dfrac{q}{\varepsilon} & \text{when } r > a, \\[2ex] \dfrac{q}{\varepsilon}\dfrac{r^3}{a^3} & \text{when } r < a. \end{cases}$$

where q is the total charge on the sphere; hence

$$E = \begin{cases} \dfrac{q}{4\pi\varepsilon}\dfrac{1}{r^2}, & r > a, \\[2ex] \dfrac{q}{4\pi\varepsilon}\dfrac{r}{a^3}, & r < a. \end{cases}$$

To find the potential φ, we integrate

$$\frac{d\varphi}{dr} = \mathbf{R} \cdot \nabla\varphi = -\mathbf{R} \cdot \mathbf{E} = -E,$$

and determine the constants so that $\varphi(\infty) = 0$, and $\varphi(r)$ is continuous when $r = a$. We thus obtain

$$\varphi = \frac{q}{4\pi\varepsilon}\frac{1}{r}, \qquad r > a,$$

$$\varphi = -\frac{q}{8\pi\varepsilon}\frac{r^2}{a^3} + C, \quad r < a.$$

Equating these values when $r = a$, we find $C = 3q/8\pi\varepsilon a$; hence

$$\varphi = \begin{cases} \dfrac{q}{4\pi\varepsilon}\dfrac{1}{r}, & r > a, \\[2ex] \dfrac{q}{8\pi\varepsilon}\dfrac{3a^2 - r^2}{a^3}, & r < a. \end{cases}$$

83. Conductors. In a *conductor* interior charges move rapidly to its surface (§76). Consequently a conductor in electrostatic equilibrium has only surface charges. Thus, if a charge q is placed inside an isolated conductor K, the charge will distribute itself over the surface with a density ω so that $\displaystyle\int_K \omega \, dS = q$.

In the interior of a conductor $\mathbf{J} = 0$ and

(1) $$\mathbf{E} = \mathbf{J}/\sigma = 0 \qquad (76.1),$$

and, since $\mathbf{E} = -\nabla\varphi$,

(2) $$\nabla\varphi = 0, \qquad \varphi = \text{const}.$$

Moreover φ has this same constant value at the surface of the conductor by reason of its continuity (§82); hence

The boundary of a conductor is an equipotential surface.

If a conductor K_1 is surrounded by a dielectric medium 2 of permittivity ε, the boundary conditions (82.19–20) take the form

(3) $$\mathbf{E}_1 = \mathbf{D}_1 = 0, \qquad \mathbf{n} \times \mathbf{E}_2 = 0, \qquad \mathbf{n} \cdot \mathbf{D}_2 = \omega,$$

where $\mathbf{n}$ is a unit normal external to K. In terms of potential, these become

(4) $$\varphi = \text{const}, \qquad \frac{d\varphi}{dn} = -\frac{\omega}{\varepsilon} \quad \text{on } K;$$

hence at the surface of a conductor the potential satisfies the boundary conditions

(5)(6) $$\varphi = \text{const}, \qquad \oint_K \frac{d\varphi}{dn}\, dS = -\frac{q}{\varepsilon}.$$

A fundamental problem in electrostatics may be formulated as follows. A number of finite conductors bounded by surfaces K_i are placed in a dielectric of constant permittivity ε which is free from charges. If each K_i is given a charge q_i, together they produce an electrostatic field whose potential φ satisfies Laplace's equation

(7) $$\nabla^2\varphi = 0 \qquad (82.4)$$

in the uncharged ($\rho = 0$) dielectric. On the surface of each conductor K_i, φ satisfies the boundary conditions

(8)(9) $$\varphi = \varphi_i \,(\text{const}), \qquad \int_{K_i} \frac{d\varphi}{dn}\, dS = -\frac{q_i}{\varepsilon},$$

where the constants φ_i are in general unknown. We then seek a solution of Laplace's equation which satisfies the boundary conditions and is regular at infinity. *If this problem has a solution it is unique.*

Proof. If φ_1 and φ_2 are solutions, $\psi = \varphi_1 - \varphi_2$ satisfies $\nabla^2\psi = 0$ with the boundary conditions on each K_i:

$$\psi = \psi_i \,(\text{const}), \qquad \oint_{K_i} \frac{d\psi}{dn}\, dS = 0.$$

For any function ψ regular at infinity we may apply the divergence theorem to $\psi \nabla \psi$ in the infinite region V_∞ outside of the conductors; since

$$\text{div} (\psi \nabla \psi) = |\nabla \psi|^2,$$

we then obtain

$$\int_{V_\infty} |\nabla \psi|^2 \, dV = - \sum_{i=1}^{n} \psi_i \int_{K_i} \frac{d\psi}{dn} \, dS = 0$$

from the boundary conditions (8–9); as to the minus sign, note that the normals external to V_∞ are internal to the conductors. Since $\mathbf{E} = -\nabla \varphi$ is everywhere continuous in the dielectric, $|\nabla \psi|$ is continuous and the volume integral cannot vanish unless $\nabla \psi = 0$. Hence $\psi = \text{const}$, and the constant is zero owing to the regularity of ψ at infinity; thus $\varphi_1 = \varphi_2$.

When the conductors are given charges q_i', let the corresponding potential be φ'. It is then obvious that the charges $q_i + q_i'$ give rise to the potential $\varphi + \varphi'$, and the corresponding field $-\nabla(\varphi + \varphi') = \mathbf{E} + \mathbf{E}'$. This is the *law of superposition of electrical effects*.

If we apply (56.2) to the harmonic functions φ and φ' in the infinite region outside of the conductors, we have

$$\sum_{i=1}^{n} \oint_{K_i} \left(\varphi \frac{d\varphi'}{dn} - \varphi' \frac{d\varphi}{dn} \right) dS = 0,$$

or, in view of the conditions (8) and (9),

$$(10) \qquad \sum_{i=1}^{n} \varphi_i q_i' = \sum_{i=1}^{n} \varphi_i' q_i.$$

This result is known as *Green's reciprocation theorem*.

Example 1. If a charge q is placed inside an isolated metal sphere of radius a, it will spread to its surface with the density

$$\omega = \frac{q}{4\pi a^2} .$$

If the sphere is surrounded by an unbounded medium of permittivity ε, and we apply Gauss' theorem to a sphere of radius $r > a$, we have

$$\varepsilon \, 4\pi r^2 E = q = 4\pi a^2 \omega;$$

hence

$$E = \begin{cases} \dfrac{\omega}{\varepsilon} \dfrac{a^2}{r^2}, & r > a, \\ 0, & r < a. \end{cases}$$

Thus E jumps from 0 to ω/ε at the surface of the sphere. Since

$$\frac{d\varphi}{dr} = -E, \qquad \varphi(\infty) = 0,$$

we find

$$\varphi = \begin{cases} \dfrac{\omega}{\varepsilon}\dfrac{a^2}{r}, & r > a, \\[2ex] \dfrac{\omega}{\varepsilon}\,a, & r \leqq a, \end{cases}$$

since φ is continuous at the surface.

Example 2. Circular Disk. A thin circular disk of radius a (Fig. 83a) is given a uniform charge of surface density $\tfrac{1}{2}\omega$ on each side; the total charge is then $\pi a^2\omega$. If

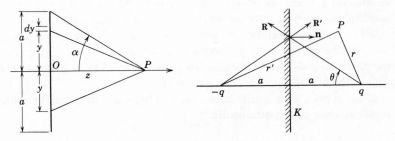

Fig. 83a. Charged disk.   Fig. 83b. Conducting plane.

dV is the volume of a ring of area $dA = 2\pi y\,dy$, $\rho\,dV = \omega dA$, and at a point P on the axis of the disk,

$$\varphi(P) = \frac{1}{4\pi\varepsilon}\int \frac{\omega}{r}\,dA = \frac{\omega}{4\pi\varepsilon}\int_0^a \frac{2\pi y\,dy}{\sqrt{y^2 + z^2}}$$

$$= \frac{\omega}{2\varepsilon}\left(\sqrt{a^2 + z^2} - z\right)$$

On the axis $\mathbf{E} = \pm E\mathbf{k}$ according as P lies to the right or left of the disk; and

$$E = -\frac{\partial\varphi}{\partial z} = \frac{\omega}{2\varepsilon}\left(1 - \frac{z}{\sqrt{a^2 + z^2}}\right) = \frac{\omega}{2\varepsilon}(1 - \cos\alpha).$$

Near the disk $\alpha \simeq \tfrac{1}{2}\pi$ and $E \simeq \omega/2\varepsilon$; and, as we cross the disk from left to right, φ is continuous, but $\mathbf{E}$ changes from

$$-\frac{\omega}{2\varepsilon}\mathbf{k} \quad\text{to}\quad \mathbf{0} \quad\text{to}\quad \frac{\omega}{2\varepsilon}\mathbf{k}$$

in conformity with (82.21).

As $a \to \infty$, the disk becomes an infinite plane and $E = \omega/2\varepsilon$ at *all* points.

Example 3. Induced Charge on a Conducting Plane. Consider two point charges q and $-q$ in a dielectric of permittivity ε (Fig. 83b). If r and r' denote the distance of a point P from these charges, the potential of the field they produce at P is

$$\varphi = \frac{q}{4\pi\varepsilon}\left(\frac{1}{r} - \frac{1}{r'}\right).$$

The median plane K $(r = r')$ is the equipotential surface $\varphi = 0$. Since φ is regular at infinity, we may apply Green's theorem to the "closed" surface K. Then, by Theorem 82.2, the charge $-q$ to the left of K produces the same potential to the right of K as the surface density

$$\omega = -\varepsilon \frac{d\varphi}{dn} = \varepsilon\, \mathbf{n} \cdot \mathbf{E}$$

spread over K. Now

$$\mathbf{E} = -\nabla\varphi = \frac{q}{4\pi\varepsilon}\left(\frac{\mathbf{R}}{r^2} - \frac{\mathbf{R}'}{r'^2}\right),$$

and, as we approach the plane $r = r'$,

$$E \to \frac{q}{4\pi\varepsilon r^2}(\mathbf{R} - \mathbf{R}') = -\frac{q\cos\theta}{2\pi\varepsilon r^2}\,\mathbf{n} = -\frac{q\cos^3\theta}{2\pi\varepsilon a^2}\,\mathbf{n}.$$

Therefore "Green's equivalent layer" is

$$\omega = -\frac{q\cos^3\theta}{2\pi a^2}.$$

Suppose now that the charge q is placed to the right of a *conducting plane* K. Since K extends to infinity, its potential will be zero. The field of q must therefore be modified so that $\varphi = 0$ on K. Transient currents will flow in K and produce a charge density ω to attain this result. This surface charge induced by q is most simply determined by replacing it by the equivalent point charge $-q$, the *image* of q in K. In passing through K from left to right, $\mathbf{n} \cdot \mathbf{D}$ will jump from 0 to ω by (3), provided ω has the value given above.

To find the total charge $\int \omega\, dA$ on K we use annular elements of area

$$dA = 2\pi y\, dy = 2\pi\, a \tan\theta\, (a \sec^2\theta\, d\theta);$$

then

$$\int_K \omega\, dA = -q \int_0^{\frac{1}{2}\pi} \sin\theta\, d\theta = -q$$

Since $\omega = \mathbf{n} \cdot \mathbf{D}$, this is a consequence of Gauss' theorem (79.1):

$$\int_K \mathbf{n} \cdot \mathbf{D}\, dA = -q.$$

84. Capacitance. *Case* 1. Consider an isolated conductor K with a charge q in a dielectric of permittivity ε. The potential φ due to this charge satisfies $\nabla^2\varphi = 0$ outside of K, the boundary conditions

$$\varphi = \text{const}, \qquad \oint_K \frac{d\varphi}{dn}\, dS = -\frac{q}{\varepsilon} \quad \text{on } K \qquad (83.5\text{–}6),$$

and is regular at infinity. If the charge were q', the potential φ' would satisfy $\nabla^2\varphi' = 0$ outside of K and the boundary conditions

$$\varphi' = \text{const}, \qquad \oint_K \frac{d\varphi'}{dn}\, dS = -\frac{q'}{\varepsilon} \quad \text{on } K.$$

If the φ is a solution of the first problem,

(1) $$\varphi' = \frac{q'}{q}\, \varphi$$

is a solution of the second; and, as the solution is unique, it is the only solution. Hence the ratio of the charge on K to its potential is a constant

(2) $$C = \frac{q}{\varphi} = \frac{q'}{\varphi'}.$$

The constant C is called the *capacitance* of K, or, more precisely, of the *capacitor* (K, K_∞) where K_∞ is a conductor at potential zero (the earth).

Case 2. Consider next two isolated conductors K_1 and K_2. If K_1 is given a charge q, induced charges will appear on K_2 of total amount zero, and the potential due to this system of charges satisfies $\nabla^2\varphi = 0$ and the boundary conditions

$$\varphi = \varphi_1 \,(\text{const}), \qquad \oint_{K_1} \frac{d\varphi}{dn}\, dS = -\frac{q}{\varepsilon} \quad \text{on } K_1,$$

$$\varphi = \varphi_2 \,(\text{const}), \qquad \oint_{K_2} \frac{d\varphi}{dn}\, dS = 0 \quad \text{on } K_2.$$

If K_1 is given the charge q', the potential φ' is again given by (1); and, since q', φ'_1, φ'_2 are q'/q times q_1, φ_1, φ_2, the ratio

(3) $$C = \frac{q}{\varphi_1 - \varphi_2} = \frac{q'}{\varphi'_1 - \varphi'_2}$$

is the same in both cases. The constant C is now called the capacitance of K_1 and K_2, or, more precisely, of the capacitor (K_1, K_2, K_∞).

Case 3. With the same conductors K_1, K_2, let K_2 be kept at a constant potential while K_1 is being given the charge q. Thus K_2 may be *grounded* (connected to K_∞) so that its potential is always zero. Then the charge q on K_1 will induce a negative charge q_2 on K_2. Then the potential φ due to these charges satisfies $\nabla^2\varphi = 0$ and the boundary conditions

$$\varphi = \varphi_1 \,(\text{const}), \qquad \oint_{K_1} \frac{d\varphi}{dn}\, dS = -\frac{q}{\varepsilon} \quad \text{on } K_1,$$

with $\varphi = 0$ on K_2. When φ is known, the induced charge on K_2 is given by

(4) $$q_2 = -\varepsilon \oint_{K_2} \frac{d\varphi}{dn}\, dS.$$

Evidently, if q is replaced by q', the potential φ' is again given by (1); and the ratio

$$(5) \qquad C = \frac{q}{\varphi_1 - \varphi_2} = \frac{q}{\varphi_1}$$

is the same in both cases.   Now C is called the *capacitance* of the capacitor $(K_1, K_2 + K_\infty)$.

If φ is the potential in case 2, $\psi = \varphi - \varphi_2$ is evidently the potential in case 3. The capacitance in both cases are exactly the same; for $\psi_1 = \varphi_1 - \varphi_2$.

Example 1. Concentric Spheres. A metal sphere K_1 of radius a has a charge q and is surrounded by a concentric spherical shell K_2 of radii b, c (Fig. 84a). The field has radial symmetry, and $\varphi(r)$ is a function of r alone; and the most general function of r that satisfies $\nabla^2\varphi = 0$ is

$$\varphi = \frac{A}{r} + B \qquad (42.22).$$

The constant A is found from the boundary condition

$$\int_{K_1} \frac{d\varphi}{dr}\, dS = -\frac{A}{a^2}\, 4\pi a^2 = -\frac{q}{\varepsilon}\,.$$

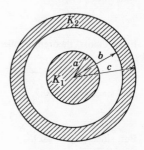

Hence $A = q/4\pi\varepsilon$ and

$$\varphi(a) - \varphi(b) = \frac{q}{4\pi\varepsilon}\left(\frac{1}{a} - \frac{1}{b}\right);$$

the capacitance of (K_1, K_2, K_∞) is therefore

$$(6) \qquad C = \frac{q}{\varphi(a) - \varphi(b)} = 4\pi\varepsilon\,\frac{ab}{b - a}\,.$$

When $r \geqq c$, $\varphi(r) = A'/r$ since $\varphi(\infty) = 0$; and the condition that the charge on K_2 is zero, namely

Fig. 84a. Spherical shell surrounding a sphere.

$$\int_{K_2} \frac{d\varphi}{dn}\, dS = -\int_{r=b} \frac{d\varphi}{dr}\, dr + \int_{r=c} \frac{d\varphi}{dr}\, dr = \frac{A}{b^2}\, 4\pi b^2 - \frac{A'}{c^2}\, 4\pi c^2 = 4\pi(A - A') = 0,$$

gives $A' = A = q/4\pi\varepsilon$. Finally $\varphi(b) = \varphi(c)$ gives

$$\frac{A}{b} + B = \frac{A'}{c}\,, \qquad B = \frac{q}{4\pi\varepsilon}\left(\frac{1}{c} - \frac{1}{b}\right).$$

The potential function is therefore

$$(7) \qquad \varphi(r) = \begin{cases} \dfrac{q}{4\pi\varepsilon}\left(\dfrac{1}{r} + \dfrac{1}{c} - \dfrac{1}{b}\right), & a \leqq r \leqq b, \\[2mm] \dfrac{q}{4\pi\varepsilon}\,\dfrac{1}{c}\,, & b \leqq r \leqq c, \\[2mm] \dfrac{q}{4\pi\varepsilon}\,\dfrac{1}{r}\,, & r \geqq c. \end{cases}$$

These results are more quickly computed by use of Gauss' theorem, but the derivation above illustrates the general procedure.

When K_2 is grounded and K_1 has the charge q, we apply Gauss' theorem to a sphere of radius r between K_1 and K_2; then

$$4\pi r^2 E = \frac{q}{\varepsilon}, \qquad \frac{d\varphi}{dr} = -E = -\frac{q}{4\pi\varepsilon}\frac{1}{r^2},$$

and, since $\varphi(b) = 0$,

$$\varphi = \frac{q}{4\pi\varepsilon}\left(\frac{1}{r} - \frac{1}{b}\right), \qquad a \leqq r \leqq b.$$

The capacitance of $(K_1, K_2 + K_\infty)$ is still given by (6); and, if we let $b \to \infty$, we obtain the capacitance $4\pi\varepsilon a$ of the isolated sphere, or the capacitor (K_1, K_∞).

When K_1 is grounded and K_2 has the charge q, we put $q = q_b + q_c$, where q_b is on the inner face $r = b$, q_c on the outer face $r = c$. If we apply Gauss' theorem to a sphere within K_2, we find that K_1 has the induced charge $-q_b$. Now from Gauss' theorem applied to a sphere of radius $r > c$, we find

$$4\pi r^2 E = -\frac{q_c}{\varepsilon}, \qquad \frac{d\varphi}{dr} = -E = -\frac{q_c}{4\pi\varepsilon}\frac{1}{r^2},$$

and, since $\varphi(\infty) = 0$,

$$\varphi(r) = \frac{q_c}{4\pi\varepsilon r}, \qquad r \geqq c.$$

From Gauss' theorem applied to a sphere of radius $r(a < r < b)$, we find

$$4\pi r^2 E = \frac{-q_b}{\varepsilon}, \qquad \frac{d\varphi}{dr} = \frac{q_b}{4\pi\varepsilon}\frac{1}{r^2}, \qquad \varphi(r) = \frac{-q_b}{4\pi\varepsilon r} + \text{const};$$

and, since $\varphi(a) = 0$,

$$\varphi(r) = \frac{q_b}{4\pi\varepsilon}\left(\frac{1}{a} - \frac{1}{r}\right), \qquad a \leqq r \leqq b.$$

But, since $\varphi(b) = \varphi(c)$,

$$q_b\left(\frac{1}{a} - \frac{1}{b}\right) = q_c\frac{1}{c} \qquad \text{and} \qquad q_b : q_c : q = \frac{1}{c} : \left(\frac{1}{a} - \frac{1}{b}\right) : \left(\frac{1}{a} - \frac{1}{b} + \frac{1}{c}\right).$$

The capacity of $(K_1 + K_\infty, K_2)$ is therefore

$$C = \frac{q}{\varphi(c)} = 4\pi\varepsilon c\,\frac{q}{q_c} = 4\pi\varepsilon\left(\frac{ab}{b-a} + c\right).$$

Example 2. Parallel Plates. Two parallel plates K_1, K_2 of equal area A are separated by a distance h very small relative to their dimensions. Neglecting fringe effects at the edges, we regard K_1 as having a uniform surface charge ω. Except near the edges, the field between K_1 and K_2 is nearly perpendicular to the plates. If K_1 is the plane $z = 0$ and the z-axis is drawn toward K_2, we have from (83.4)

$$\frac{d\varphi}{dz} = -\frac{\omega}{\varepsilon}, \qquad \varphi(z) = -\frac{\omega}{\varepsilon}z + \text{const.}$$

If K_2 is grounded, $\varphi(h) = 0$ and the constant is determined; thus

$$\varphi(z) = \frac{\omega}{\varepsilon}(h - z), \qquad \varphi(0) = \frac{\omega h}{\varepsilon},$$

and the capacitance of the plates is very nearly

$$(8) \qquad C = \frac{q}{\varphi(0)} = \frac{A\omega}{\omega h/\varepsilon} = \frac{\varepsilon A}{h}.$$

PROBLEMS

1. An uncharged conductor K_2 is raised to the potential φ by giving K_1 a charge q. If K_1 is uncharged, find its potential when K_2 is given a charge q.   [Use (83.10).]

2. A point charge q at P induces a charge q_1 on the grounded conductor K_1 ($\varphi_1 = 0$). When K_1 is isolated and raised to the potential φ_1', the potential of its field at P is $\varphi'P$. Show that

$$q_1 = -\frac{\varphi_P'}{\varphi_1'} q. \qquad\qquad \text{[Use (83.10]}$$

3. In Prob. 2, K_1 is a grounded sphere of radius a and P is at a distance r from its center. Show that a charge q at P will induce a charge $q_1 = -aq/r$ on K_1.   [Ex. 83.1]

4. If $b = a + h$ in (6), where a is large and h relatively small, show that $C \simeq \varepsilon A/h$, the capacitance of a parallel plate capacitor.

5. Three concentric spherical shells A, B, C, of radii $a < b < c$ are separated by a dielectric of permittivity ε. If A and C are grounded and B is given a charge q, show that the inner and outer faces of B will have the

charges

$$q_1 = \frac{a(c-b)}{b(c-a)} q, \qquad q_2 = \frac{c(b-a)}{b(c-a)} q;$$

and that the potential of B

$$\varphi(b) = \frac{q}{4\pi\varepsilon} \frac{(c-b)(b-a)}{b^2(c-a)}.$$

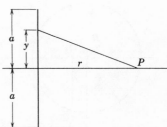

Moreover $q/\varphi(b)$ is the sum of the capacitances of AB and BC.

6. A straight thin wire of length $2a$ is uniformly charged with $2a\lambda$ coulombs. (Fig. 84b). In a plane that bisects the wire show that the potential and field at a point P at a distance r from the wire are given by

Fig. 84b. Uniform wire.

$$\varphi = \frac{\lambda}{2\pi\varepsilon} \log \frac{a + \sqrt{a^2 + r^2}}{r}, \qquad \mathbf{E} = \frac{\lambda}{2\pi\varepsilon} \frac{a}{r\sqrt{a^2 + r^2}} \mathbf{R}.$$

7. If the wire in Prob. 6 is infinite and charged with a linear density λ, show that the potential and field at all points is

$$\varphi = C - \frac{\lambda}{2\pi\varepsilon} \log r, \qquad \mathbf{E} = \frac{\lambda}{2\pi\varepsilon} \frac{\mathbf{R}}{r}.$$

Find the constant C if $\varphi = \varphi_0$ when $r = r_0$.

8. Let O_1 and O_2 represent two thin parallel wires (lines perpendicular to the paper) of infinite length and a distance $2b$ apart (Fig. 84c). If their charge densities are λ and $-\lambda$ per unit length, show that the potential in any plane normal to the wires is

$$\varphi = C + \frac{\lambda}{2\pi\varepsilon} \log \frac{r_2}{r_1}.$$

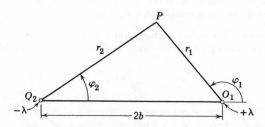

Fig. 84c. Two infinite parallel wires.

Show that the equipotential lines are a family of circles having O_1 and O_2 as inverse points, and that the field lines are the family of circles passing through O_1 and O_2.

[If O_1, O_2 are the origins of bipolar coordinates r_1, θ_1, and r_2, θ_2, the equipotential lines are the circles $r_1/r_2 = $ const; these are cut at right angles by the circles $\varphi_2 - \varphi_1 = $ const, the field lines. Cf. Prob. 37.9.]

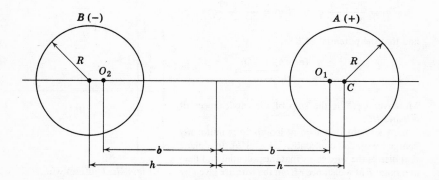

Fig. 84d. Two parallel cylindrical conductors.

9. Two parallel cylindrical conductors A, B, of infinite length and radius R, have their centers a distance $2h$ apart (Fig. 84d). If their charge densities are λ and $-\lambda$ per unit of length, show that their field may be computed by replacing them by similarly charged lines at a distance $2b$ apart (Prob. 8) where $b = \sqrt{h^2 - R^2}$. Hence deduce from Prob. 3 that

$$\varphi_A - \varphi_B = \frac{\lambda}{\pi\varepsilon} \log \frac{b + (h - R)}{b - (h - R)} = \frac{\lambda}{\pi\varepsilon} \log \frac{h + b}{R}.$$

[O_1 and O_2 are inverse points to a circle of center C and radius R, provided $CO_1 \cdot CO_2 = (h - b)(h + b) = R^2$.]

10. In Fig. 84*e*, *O* represents a charged infinite wire parallel to the infinite conducting plane *p*. If *O* has the linear charge density λ, show that the potential in a plane normal to *O* (the paper) and to the right of *p* is

$$\varphi = \frac{\lambda}{2\pi\varepsilon} \log \frac{r'}{r},$$

where r, r' are radial distances from *O* and its image *O'*, and that

$$\omega = -\frac{\lambda \cos \theta}{\pi r}$$

is the charge density induced on *p* by the wire *O*.

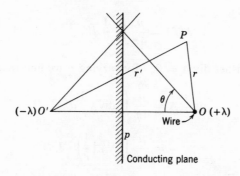

Fig. 84*e*. Infinite wire parallel to conducting plane.

85. Magnetostatics. In a stationary field the magnetic vectors **H** and **B** satisfy the equations

(1)   rot **H** = **J**   (74.2),

(2)   div **B** = 0   (74.6).

In addition the equation of continuity now becomes

(3)   div **J** = 0   (74.5).

B may now be derived from a vector potential

(4)   **B** = rot **A**

such that

(5)   div **A** = 0   (81.6).

If the medium is homogeneous, isotropic, and not ferromagnetic (§74), we have **B** = μ**H**. Equation (1) now gives

$$\text{rot } \mathbf{B} = \text{rot rot } \mathbf{A} = \mu\mathbf{J},$$

or, since rot rot **A** = $-\nabla^2$**A** in view of (5),

(6) $\nabla^2 \mathbf{A} = -\mu\mathbf{J}.$

This vector equation is equivalent to three scalar Poisson equations,

(6)′ $$\nabla^2 A_i = -\mu J_i, \qquad (i = 1, 2, 3),$$

where A_i, J_i denote the rectangular components of **A** and **J**.

If the steady currents occupy a finite volume V_1 within a closed surface S_1, we may deduce just as in §82 that

$$4\pi\, A_i(P) = \mu \int_{V_1} \frac{J_i}{r}\, dV, \qquad (i = 1, 2, 3),$$

and, consequently,

(7) $$\mathbf{A}(P) = \frac{\mu}{4\pi} \int_{V_1} \frac{\mathbf{J}}{r}\, dV.$$

This vector satisfies div **A** = 0. By varying P we find that

$$\operatorname{div}_P \mathbf{A} = \frac{\mu}{4\pi} \int_{V_1} \operatorname{div}_P \frac{\mathbf{J}}{r}\, dV$$

$$= \frac{\mu}{4\pi} \int_{V_1} \nabla_P\!\left(\frac{1}{r}\right) \cdot \mathbf{J}\, dV \qquad (41.4)$$

$$= -\frac{\mu}{4\pi} \int_{V_1} \nabla_Q\!\left(\frac{1}{r}\right) \cdot \mathbf{J}\, dV \qquad \cdot \quad (82.13).$$

Since $\operatorname{div}_Q \mathbf{J} = 0$, the integral equals

$$\int_{V_1} \operatorname{div}_Q \frac{\mathbf{J}}{r}\, dV = \oint_{S_1} \frac{\mathbf{J} \cdot \mathbf{n}}{r}\, dS$$

on applying the divergence theorem. But, if the flow of electricity is confined within the surface S_1, $\mathbf{J} \cdot \mathbf{n} = 0$ on S_1 and hence

(8) $$\operatorname{div}_P \mathbf{A} = 0.$$

Thus the vector potential given by (7) is a solenoidal vector that satisfies (6). Now **B** = rot **A** and

$$\mathbf{B} = \frac{\mu}{4\pi} \operatorname{rot}_P \int_{V_1} \frac{\mathbf{J}}{r}\, dV = \frac{\mu}{4\pi} \int_{V_1} \nabla_P\!\left(\frac{1}{r}\right) \times \mathbf{J}\, dV,$$

since **J** in the integral does not depend on P. Putting $\mathbf{B} = \mu\mathbf{H}$ and

$$\nabla_P\!\left(\frac{1}{r}\right) = -\frac{1}{r^2}\nabla_P r = -\frac{\mathbf{R}}{r^2} \qquad (82.12),$$

where $\mathbf{R}$ is a unit vector directed from the current elements toward P, we have

$$(9) \qquad \mathbf{H} = \frac{1}{4\pi} \int_{V_1} \frac{\mathbf{J} \times \mathbf{R}}{r^2} \, dV.$$

This formula is the analogue of (82.11).

We now apply (7) and (9) to a thin closed-current tube carrying a steady current I. Putting

$$\mathbf{J} \, dV = \mathbf{J} \, dA \, ds = I\mathbf{T} \, ds,$$

where $\mathbf{T}$ is a unit tangent in the direction of the current,

$$(10) \qquad \mathbf{A} = \frac{\mu I}{4\pi} \oint \frac{\mathbf{T}}{r} \, ds,$$

$$(11) \qquad \mathbf{H} = \frac{I}{4\pi} \oint \frac{\mathbf{T} \times \mathbf{R}}{r^2} \, ds.$$

Thus each current element $I \, ds$ contributes

$$(12) \qquad d\mathbf{H} = \frac{1}{4\pi} \frac{\mathbf{T} \times \mathbf{R}}{r^2} I \, ds$$

to the total magnetic field.† In 1820 Biot and Savart deduced the essential facts of this formula from their experiments; it is therefore known as the *Biot–Savart law*.‡

The current flowing through a surface S spanned over a closed curve C is, from (1),

$$I = \int \mathbf{J} \cdot \mathbf{n} \, dS = \int \mathbf{n} \cdot \operatorname{rot} \mathbf{H} \, dS;$$

hence, from Stokes' theorem,

$$(13) \qquad \oint_C \mathbf{H} \cdot \mathbf{T} \, ds = I.$$

This important result, already proved in §75, is

AMPÈRE'S LAW. *The circulation of the magnetic intensity over any simple closed curve is equal to the total current linked by the circuit.*

† If $\mathbf{f}$ is an arbitrary vector function, we can add $\mathbf{T} \cdot \nabla \mathbf{f} \, ds$ to this expression for $d\mathbf{H}$ without altering the value of the circuit integral. Although $d\mathbf{H}$ given in (12) is by no means unique, it has at least the simplest form.

‡ Also called Ampère's law by some authors.

Example 1.   Infinite Straight Current.   We shall compute $\mathbf{H}$ at the point P due to an infinite straight current I in the direction of the unit vector $\mathbf{e}$ (Fig. 85a).   If we write $\overrightarrow{OP} = a\mathbf{N}$, where $\mathbf{N}$ is a unit normal to the wire, we have at Q

$$\mathbf{R} = \mathbf{N}\cos\theta - \mathbf{e}\sin\theta, \qquad\qquad \mathbf{T}\times\mathbf{R} = \mathbf{e}\times\mathbf{N}\cos\theta,$$
$$r = a\sec\theta, \qquad\qquad s = a\tan\theta;$$

and from (12)

$$dH = \frac{I}{4\pi}\frac{\mathbf{e}\times\mathbf{N}\cos\theta}{a^2\sec^2\theta}\, a\sec^2\theta\, d\theta,$$

(14) $$\mathbf{H} = \frac{I}{4\pi a}\mathbf{e}\times\mathbf{N}\int_{-\pi/2}^{\pi/2}\cos\theta\, d\theta = \frac{I}{2\pi a}\mathbf{e}\times\mathbf{N}.$$

In the figure $\mathbf{e}\times\mathbf{N}$ points up from the page.

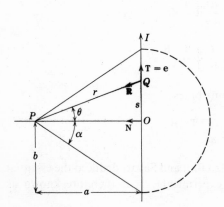

Fig. 85a. Infinite straight current.

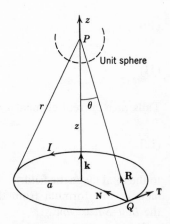

Fig. 85b. Circular current.

Since $d\mathbf{H}$ in (12) is regarded as an element due to a *closed* current, one may doubt the validity of (14).   But, if the current is closed through the dotted semicircle of radius $\sqrt{a^2 + b^2}$ in the figure, we readily find that the field at P is

(15) $$\mathbf{H} = \frac{I}{2\pi}\left(\frac{\sin\alpha}{a} - \frac{a}{\sqrt{a^2 + b^2}}\right)\mathbf{e}\times\mathbf{N}.$$

As $b \to \infty$, $\alpha \to \pi/2$, and we again obtain (14).

$\mathbf{H}$ has the same numerical value at all points of a cylinder coaxial with the current. Hence we may compute H from Ampère's law; for, as P describes a circle of radius a about the current,

$$\oint \mathbf{H}\cdot d\mathbf{r} = 2\pi aH = I.$$

Example 2.   Axial Field of a Circular Current.   We shall find $\mathbf{H}$ at a point P in the axis of a circular current I (Fig. 85b).   If $\mathbf{T}$, $\mathbf{N}$ are unit tangent and principal normal,

$$\mathbf{R} = \mathbf{k}\cos\theta + \mathbf{N}\sin\theta, \qquad\qquad \mathbf{T}\times\mathbf{R} = -\mathbf{N}\cos\theta + \mathbf{k}\sin\theta,$$

and $r = a/\sin\theta$ is constant; hence

$$H(P) = \frac{I}{4\pi} \oint \frac{T \times R}{r^2}\, ds$$

$$= \frac{I}{4\pi r^2}\left(-\cos\theta \oint N\, ds + k \sin\theta \oint ds\right).$$

Since

$$\oint N\, ds = 0, \qquad \oint ds = 2\pi a,$$

(16)

$$H(P) = \frac{I \sin^3\theta}{2a}\, k.$$

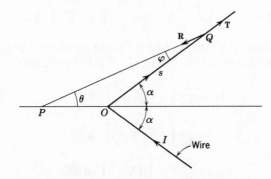

Fig. 85c. Infinite wire forming angle 2α.

Example 3. Infinite Wire Making an Angle 2α. In Fig. 85c each leg of the angle contributes $\frac{1}{2}H$ at P. If k is a unit vector pointing up from the paper,

$$T \times R = k \sin\varphi, \qquad r = a\frac{\sin\alpha}{\sin\varphi}, \qquad s = a\frac{\sin\theta}{\sin\varphi},$$

and, since $\theta + \varphi = \alpha$, $d\theta = -d\varphi$, we have

$$ds = a\frac{-\sin\varphi\cos\theta - \sin\theta\cos\varphi}{\sin^2\varphi}\, d\varphi = -a\frac{\sin\alpha}{\sin^2\varphi}\, d\varphi.$$

Hence

$$\frac{T \times R}{r^2}ds = -\frac{k}{a\sin\alpha}\sin\varphi\, d\varphi,$$

$$\int \frac{T \times R}{r^2}\, ds = -\frac{2k}{a\sin\alpha}\int_0^\alpha \sin\varphi\, d\varphi = \frac{2k}{a}\frac{1 - \cos\alpha}{\sin\alpha},$$

$$H = \frac{I}{4\pi}\frac{2k}{a}\tan\frac{1}{2}\alpha = \frac{I\tan\frac{1}{2}\alpha}{2\pi a}\, k.$$

When $\alpha = \frac{1}{2}\pi$, $H = k\, I/2\pi a$, in agreement with (14).

86. Magnetostatic Potential. A closed stationary current I generates a magnetic field $\mathbf{H}$, and in any region free from currents

(1)(2) $$\operatorname{rot} \mathbf{H} = \mathbf{0}, \quad \text{and} \quad \oint \mathbf{H} \cdot d\mathbf{r} = 0$$

over any reducible curve: that is, a curve that does not link the current. The entire region outside of the currents will be multiply connected due to their presence, but any simply connected portion will admit a single-valued scalar potential ψ for $\mathbf{H}$ so that

(3) $$\mathbf{H} = -\nabla\psi.$$

To find this *magnetostatic potential* at P we rewrite the Biot–Savart law (85.11) in the form†

$$\mathbf{H} = -\frac{I}{4\pi} \oint \frac{\mathbf{T} \times \nabla_Q r}{r^2}\, ds = \frac{I}{4\pi} \oint \mathbf{T} \times \nabla_Q \left(\frac{1}{r}\right) ds,$$

and then transform the integral by (51.3) into an integral over a surface S spanning the current circuit. Since $\operatorname{div}_Q \nabla_Q(1/r) = 0$, we thus obtain

$$
\begin{aligned}
\mathbf{H} &= \frac{I}{4\pi} \int \left(\nabla_Q \nabla_Q \frac{1}{r}\right) \cdot \mathbf{n}\, dS \\
&= \frac{I}{4\pi} \int \left(\nabla_P \nabla_P \frac{1}{r}\right) \cdot \mathbf{n}\, dS \qquad\qquad (82.13) \\
&= \frac{I}{4\pi} \nabla_P \int \left(\nabla_P \frac{1}{r}\right) \cdot \mathbf{n}\, dS \\
&= -\frac{I}{4\pi} \nabla_P \int \left(\nabla_Q \frac{1}{r}\right) \cdot \mathbf{n}\, dS.
\end{aligned}
$$

Now from (52.8)

$$\int \left(\nabla_Q \frac{1}{r}\right) \cdot \mathbf{n}\, dS = \Omega,$$

the solid angle subtended by the current loop at P; for from Fig. 86a we see that $\mathbf{n}$, the normal to S, is directed toward the observer P, whereas in (52.8) $\mathbf{n}$ is directed away from the observer. Therefore

(4) $$\mathbf{H} = -\nabla_P \left(\frac{I\Omega}{4\pi}\right),$$

and

(5) $$\psi = \frac{I\Omega}{4\pi}$$

is the desired scalar potential.

† In (85.11) ʀ has the direction $\overrightarrow{PQ}$; since Q is in the current element, $\nabla_Q r = -\mathbf{R}$.

Note that, in Fig. 86a, P is on the positive of S as determined by the sense of the circuit; in this case Ω is taken positive. If P is on the negative side of S, Ω must be taken negative.

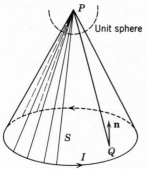

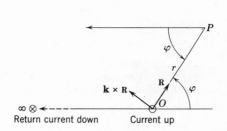

Fig. 86a. Current loop.   Fig. 86b. Infinite straight current.

Example 1. Infinite Straight Current. In Fig. 86b the infinite straight current at O is flowing up from the paper along the z-axis. If $\mathbf{k}$ is a unit vector along this axis and $\mathbf{R}$ a unit radial vector toward the point P in the xy-plane, the field at P, given by (85.14), is

$$(6) \qquad \mathbf{H} = \frac{I}{2\pi} \frac{\mathbf{k} \times \mathbf{R}}{r} = \frac{I}{2\pi} \nabla \varphi \qquad (37.16).$$

Thus $\mathbf{H}$ is derived from the scalar potential

$$\psi = -\frac{I\varphi}{2\pi}.$$

This result agrees with (5). For, if we regard the return current as situated to the *left* of O at an infinite distance, P lies on the negative side of the circuit; hence the solid angle Ω subtended by the circuit at P is the negative area of a lune of angle φ: thus

$$\Omega = -\frac{\varphi}{2\pi} 4\pi = -2\varphi,$$

where 4π is the area of the unit sphere.

If the return current were taken to the *right* of O, P would have been on the positive side of the circuit. Now the solid angle is

$$\Omega = 2(\pi - \varphi), \qquad \psi = \frac{I(\pi - \varphi)}{2\pi},$$

but $\mathbf{H} = -\nabla \psi$ is still given by (6).

Example 2. Two Infinite Parallel Currents. In Fig. 86c the paper represents the xy-plane and the currents are parallel to the z-axis (up at O_1, down at O_2). The point

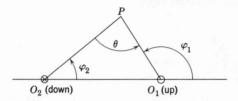

Fig. 86c. Two infinite parallel currents.

P lies on the negative side of the circuit, and the solid angle subtended by the currents at P is the negative area of a lune of angle θ; hence

$$\Omega = -\frac{\theta}{2\pi}\, 4\pi = -2\theta = -2(\varphi_1 - \varphi_2).$$

Now from (5)

$$\psi = \frac{I\Omega}{4\pi} = \frac{I}{2\pi}(\varphi_2 - \varphi_1);$$

and **H** is given by $-\nabla\psi$ or

(7) $$\mathbf{H} = -\frac{I}{2\pi}\left(\frac{\mathbf{k}\times\mathbf{R}_2}{r_2} - \frac{\mathbf{k}\times\mathbf{R}_1}{r_1}\right) = \frac{I}{2\pi}\left(\nabla\log\frac{r_2}{r_1}\right)\times\mathbf{k}.$$

Since we can write

$$\mathbf{H} = \frac{I}{2\pi}\,\mathrm{rot}\left(\mathbf{k}\log\frac{r_2}{r_1}\right) \qquad\qquad (40.10),$$

$\mathbf{B} = \mu\mathbf{H}$ is derived from the vector potential

(8) $$\mathbf{A} = \mathbf{k}\frac{\mu I}{2\pi}\log\frac{r_2}{r_1};$$

thus $\mathbf{B} = \mathrm{rot}\,\mathbf{A}$, and $\mathrm{div}\,\mathbf{A} = 0$.

In the xy-plane the equipotential lines $\psi = \mathrm{const}$ are the family of circles $\varphi_1 - \varphi_2 = \mathrm{const}$ through O_1 and O_2. The field lines of $\mathbf{H} = -\nabla\psi$ cut these circles at right angles, and, from (7), are the family of coaxial circles $r_2/r_1 = \mathrm{const}$ having O_1 and O_2 as inverse points (cf. Prob. 37.9).

Example 3. The problem of Ex. 85.2 may also be solved by means of (4). Referring to Fig. 85b, the solid angle Ω subtended at P by the current is equal to the area of a unit sphere about P intercepted by a cone with the apical angle 2θ; hence

$$\Omega = 2\pi\int_0^\theta \sin\theta\, d\theta = 2\pi(1 - \cos\theta), \qquad \psi = \frac{I}{2}(1 - \cos\theta).$$

Symmetry shows that, at points on the z-axis, $\mathbf{H}$ has only a z-component. This is given by

$$H = -\mathbf{k} \cdot \nabla \psi = -\frac{d\psi}{dz} = -\frac{d\psi}{d\theta} \bigg/ \frac{dz}{d\theta};$$

and, since $z = a \cot \theta$,

$$H = \frac{-\tfrac{1}{2}I \sin \theta}{-a/\sin^2 \theta} = \frac{I}{2a} \sin^3 \theta.$$

PROBLEMS

1. Prove equation (85.15).

2. In Ex. 1 show that $\mathbf{B} = \mu \mathbf{H}$ is derived from the vector potential

$$\mathbf{A} = -\mathbf{k} \frac{\mu I}{2\pi} \log r.$$

Hence deduce the vector potential (8) for two infinite parallel currents.

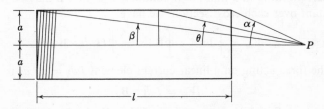

Fig. 86d. Solenoid.

3. A *solenoid* is a circle of wire wound into a circular helix. If the solenoid has n closely spaced turns in a coil of length l and radius a, prove that the magnetic intensity at a point P (Fig. 86d) due to the current I is of magnitude

$$H = \frac{nI}{2l} (\cos \beta - \cos \alpha).$$

Show that, at the center of a *very long* solenoid ($l \gg a$), $H \simeq nI/l$; and, at its ends, $H \simeq nI/2l$.

[Regard the current as a sheet of linear density $\lambda = nI/l$ amperes per meter, and use (85.16):

$$H(P) = \frac{\lambda}{2a} \int_\alpha^\beta \sin^3\theta \, d(a \cot \theta) \,]$$

87. Forces on Charges and Currents. In §77 we defined the electric field strength $\mathbf{E}$ so that a "point charge" q would be subject to the force $\mathbf{F} = q\mathbf{E}$. In terms of charges distributed with the volume density ρ, we now define $\mathbf{E}$ so that the force exerted on the charges per unit volume is $\rho \mathbf{E}$. Then the total force on the charges within a volume V is

(1) $$\mathbf{F}_e = \int_V \rho \mathbf{E} \, dV.$$

If V is so small that $\mathbf{E}$ may be regarded as constant within V,

$$\text{(2)} \qquad \mathbf{F}_e = \mathbf{E} \int \rho \, dV = q\mathbf{E}$$

in agreement with (77.1).

To relate the force exerted on a current to the magnetic field we observe from §77 that $\mathbf{J} \times \mathbf{B}$ (like $\rho \mathbf{E}$) has the dimensions of force per unit volume:

$$[J][B] = L^{-2}T^{-1}Q \cdot MT^{-1}Q^{-1} = ML^{-2}T^{-2} = [F]L^{-3}.$$

Thus we define the vector $\mathbf{B}$ so that the force exerted on currents per unit volume is $\mathbf{J} \times \mathbf{B}$. Then the total force on the currents within a volume V is

$$\text{(3)} \qquad \mathbf{F}_m = \int_V \mathbf{J} \times \mathbf{B} \, dV.$$

If the current flows in a thin linear conductor, so that $\mathbf{B}$ may be regarded as constant over each cross section, we have

$$\mathbf{F}_m = \int \mathbf{J} \, dA \times \oint \mathbf{B} \, ds = \oint I\mathbf{T} \, ds \times \mathbf{B};$$

hence the force acting on a linear current element $I \, d\mathbf{r} = I\mathbf{T} \, ds$ is

$$\text{(4)} \qquad d\mathbf{F}_m = I \, d\mathbf{r} \times \mathbf{B}.$$

In contrast to $\mathbf{F}_e$, which is exerted parallel to $\mathbf{E}$, the force $d\mathbf{F}_m$ is perpendicular to the plane of $d\mathbf{r}$ and $\mathbf{B}$.

$\mathbf{E}$ and $\mathbf{B}$ having been defined, the vectors $\mathbf{D}$ and $\mathbf{H}$ are given by $\varepsilon\mathbf{E}$ and $\mathbf{B}/\mu$, respectively. The properties of the electromagnetic field defined in this manner are compatible with Maxwell's equations and are in complete accord with experiment.

Finally, if an element of charge q is moving with the velocity $\mathbf{v}$ in an electromagnetic field, it constitutes a current element $q\mathbf{v}$; the field therefore exerts the forces

$$\mathbf{F}_e = q\mathbf{E} \qquad \text{and} \qquad \mathbf{F}_m = q\mathbf{v} \times \mathbf{B}$$

upon it. The total force on the moving charge is therefore

$$\text{(5)} \qquad \mathbf{F} = q(\mathbf{E} + \mathbf{v} \times \mathbf{B}).$$

Example 1. Charged Particle in a Stationary Electric Field. A particle of mass m and charge q has, from (5), the equation of motion

$$m \frac{d\mathbf{v}}{dt} = q\mathbf{E} = -q \, \nabla\varphi.$$

Dot-multiplying by $\mathbf{v} = d\mathbf{r}/dt$ gives

$$m\mathbf{v} \cdot \frac{d\mathbf{v}}{dt} = -q \frac{d\mathbf{r}}{dt} \cdot \nabla\varphi$$

or

$$d(\tfrac{1}{2}mv^2) = -q \, d\varphi.$$

Hence, on integrating over any path from $\mathbf{r}_0$ to $\mathbf{r}$, we have

$$\text{(6)} \qquad \tfrac{1}{2}mv^2 - \tfrac{1}{2}mv_0^2 = q(\varphi_0 - \varphi)$$

for the energy acquired (joules) by a particle of m kilograms and charged with q coulombs in "falling" through a potential difference of $V = \varphi_0 - \varphi$ volts. If the initial velocity $\mathbf{v}_0 = 0$, the velocity acquired is

$$\text{(7)} \qquad v = \sqrt{2qV/m} \quad \text{meters per second.}$$

For an electron

$$m = 9.107 \times 10^{-31} \text{ kg}, \qquad q = 1.602 \times 10^{-19} \text{ coulomb},$$

and (7) gives

$$v = 5.93 \times 10^5 \sqrt{V} \text{ meters per second.}$$

The energy acquired by an electron in falling through one volt is called one *electron-volt;* from (6)

$$1 \text{ electron volt} = 1.6 \times 10^{-19} \text{ joule.}$$

When $\mathbf{E}$ is constant, the equation of motion is readily integrated, giving

$$\mathbf{v} = \frac{q}{m}\mathbf{E}t + \mathbf{v}_0, \qquad \mathbf{r} = \frac{q}{2m}\mathbf{E}t^2 + \mathbf{v}_0 t + \mathbf{r}_0.$$

The orbit (as for any particle in a constant field of force) is a parabola if $\mathbf{v}_0$ is not parallel to $\mathbf{E}$.

In the discussion above, the mass m is regarded as constant instead of having the relativistic value $m_0(1 - v^2/c^2)^{-1/2}$, where m_0 is the rest mass and c the velocity of light. Hence, as $v \to c, m \to \infty$. But, if $v \ll c, m \simeq m_0$; thus, if $v = c/10, m = m_0/\sqrt{0.99} = 1.005\, m_0$.

Example 2.   Charged Particle in a Constant Magnetic Field.   Write the constant field vector $\mathbf{H} = H\mathbf{e}$, where $|\mathbf{e}| = 1$. Then, from (5), the charged particle has the equation of motion

$$m\frac{d\mathbf{v}}{dt} = q\mathbf{v} \times \mu\mathbf{H} = \mu q H\, \mathbf{v} \times \mathbf{e}$$

Dot-multiplying by $\mathbf{v}$ and $\mathbf{e}$ now gives

$$\mathbf{v} \cdot \frac{d\mathbf{v}}{dt} = \frac{d}{dt}\frac{v^2}{2} = 0, \qquad \mathbf{e} \cdot \frac{d\mathbf{v}}{dt} = \frac{d}{dt}(\mathbf{e} \cdot \mathbf{v}) = 0;$$

hence v and $\mathbf{e} \cdot \mathbf{v}$ are constant.   Since $\mathbf{v} = v\mathbf{T}$ (32.3), we have

$$\mathbf{e} \cdot \mathbf{T} = \cos \alpha,$$

where α is the constant angle between $\mathbf{e}$ and $\mathbf{v}$. Since the speed v is constant, the acceleration is purely normal and equals $\kappa v^2 \mathbf{N}$ (32.5); hence the equation of motion is

$$m\kappa v^2 \mathbf{N} = \mu q H v\, \mathbf{T} \times \mathbf{e}.$$

On equating magnitudes and unit vectors, this gives two equations:

$$\text{(8)(9)} \qquad m\kappa v^2 = \mu q H v \sin \alpha, \qquad \mathbf{N} = \frac{\mathbf{T} \times \mathbf{e}}{\sin \alpha}.$$

From (8) we see that κ is constant and that the curvature of the path

$$(10) \qquad \qquad \kappa = \frac{\mu q H \sin \alpha}{mv} .$$

On differentiating (9) with respect to the arc s and using Frenet's formulas (29.4), we have

$$-\kappa T + \tau B = \frac{\kappa \ N \times e}{\sin \alpha} ;$$

and, on dot-multiplying by B,

$$\tau = \frac{\kappa}{\sin \alpha} B \cdot N \times e = \frac{-\kappa}{\sin \alpha} T \cdot e = -\kappa \cot \alpha.$$

Since both κ and τ are constant, the path is a circular helix (Ex. 30.2). In particular, if v is perpendicular to H, $\alpha = \pi/2$, and, from (10), the path is a circle of radius $\rho = mv/\mu q H$. As a check, we note the ρ has the dimensions of length (§77).

Chapter 9

Vector Spaces

88. Postulates. In geometry and mathematical physics it is well to have a more general conception of a vector which is applicable to space whose dimensions are greater than three. We therefore formulate an abstract definition of a vector free from geometric concepts and applicable in many diverse cases.

A vector space $V(\mathscr{F})$ over a field† $\mathscr{F}$ of scalars is formed by a set of elements called *vectors* which have the following properties.

A_1. Two vectors $\mathbf{u}$, $\mathbf{v}$ determine a unique sum $\mathbf{u} + \mathbf{v}$.

A_2. Vector addition is associative:

$$(\mathbf{u} + \mathbf{v}) + \mathbf{w} = \mathbf{u} + (\mathbf{v} + \mathbf{w}).$$

A_3. Vector addition is commutative:

$$\mathbf{u} + \mathbf{v} = \mathbf{v} + \mathbf{u}.$$

A_4. There is a null vector $\mathbf{0}$ such that

$$\mathbf{0} + \mathbf{u} = \mathbf{u}.$$

A_5. Every vector $\mathbf{u}$ admits a negative $-\mathbf{u}$ such that

$$-\mathbf{u} + \mathbf{u} = \mathbf{0}.$$

M_1. A vector $\mathbf{u}$ from V and a scalar a from $\mathscr{F}$ determine a unique *scalar product* $a\mathbf{u}$ in V.‡

† See *Advanced Calculus*, §2, for the definition of a *field* and the deduction of the cancelation laws. The rational, the real, and the complex numbers constitute three important fields. In this chapter *scalar* means a number of $\mathscr{F}$.

‡ Henceforth $\mathbf{u} \cdot \mathbf{v}$ will be called the *inner product*.

241

M_2.   Scalar multiplication is associative:

$$(ab)\mathbf{u} = a(b\mathbf{u}).$$

M_3.   Scalar multiplication is distributive both ways:

$$a(\mathbf{u} + \mathbf{v}) = a\mathbf{u} + a\mathbf{v}, \qquad (a + b)\mathbf{u} = a\mathbf{u} + b\mathbf{u}.$$

M_4.   The unit element e of the field (denoted hereafter by 1) has the property

$$e\mathbf{u} = \mathbf{u}.$$

From these postulates we can deduce the cancelation laws

(1) $\mathbf{u} + \mathbf{w} = \mathbf{v} + \mathbf{w}$ implies $\mathbf{u} = \mathbf{v}$,

(2) $a\mathbf{u} = a\mathbf{v}$ implies $\mathbf{u} = \mathbf{v}$ if $a \neq 0$.

The null vector $\mathbf{0}$ and the zero scalar 0 are connected by the important identity

(3) $0\mathbf{u} = \mathbf{0}$ for all $\mathbf{u}$.

This follows from

$$a\mathbf{u} + 0\mathbf{u} = (a + 0)\mathbf{u} = a\mathbf{u} = a\mathbf{u} + \mathbf{0}$$

on canceling $a\mathbf{u}$.   Moreover, from

$$a\mathbf{u} + a\mathbf{0} = a(\mathbf{u} + \mathbf{0}) = a\mathbf{u} = a\mathbf{u} + \mathbf{0},$$

we have also

(4) $a\mathbf{0} = \mathbf{0}$.

Note finally that the negative of $\mathbf{u}$ (postulated in A_5) is given by

(5) $-\mathbf{u} = (-1)\mathbf{u};$

for

$$(-1)\mathbf{u} + (1\mathbf{u}) = (-1 + 1)\mathbf{u} = 0\mathbf{u} = \mathbf{0}.$$

It should be observed that addition of vectors and their multiplication by scalars produce vectors, and that V is *closed* with respect to both operations.

Example 1.   The directed line segments of Chapter 1 are vectors since they satisfy all the postulates. If these vectors $\mathbf{u}$ are represented by their components $[u_1, u_2, u_3]$ written in order, such ordered triples obey the rules

$$[u_1, u_2, u_3] + [v_1, v_2, v_3] = [u_1 + v_1, u_2 + v_2, u_3 + v_3],$$

$$\lambda[u_1, u_2, u_3] = [\lambda u_1, \lambda u_2, \lambda u_3],$$

and $[0, 0, 0] = \mathbf{0}$ is the null vector. The commutative, associative, and distributive laws A_2, A_3, M_2, M_3 are consequences of the corresponding laws in the field $\mathscr{R}$ of real numbers.

Example 2. In coplanar statics (§22), forces and couples may be fully represented by the symbol $(\mathbf{f}, \mathbf{f}_O)$. If $\mathbf{f} \neq \mathbf{0}$ is a force, $\mathbf{f}_O$ is the moment of $\mathbf{f}$ about O; if $\mathbf{f} = \mathbf{0}$ and $\mathbf{f}_O \neq \mathbf{0}$, $\mathbf{f}_O$ is the moment of a couple. The laws of statics are comprised in the operational rules

$$\lambda(\mathbf{f}, \mathbf{f}_O) = (\lambda\mathbf{f}, \lambda\mathbf{f}_O), \qquad (\mathbf{f}^1, \mathbf{f}_O^1) + (\mathbf{f}^2, \mathbf{f}_O^2) = (\mathbf{f}^1 + \mathbf{f}^2, \mathbf{f}_O^1 + \mathbf{f}_O^2),$$

and the fact that static equilibrium corresponds to

$$\Sigma\,(\mathbf{f}^i, \mathbf{f}_O^{\,i}) = (\mathbf{0}, \mathbf{0}).$$

The elements $(\mathbf{f}, \mathbf{f}_O)$ thus constitute a vector space with $(\mathbf{0}, \mathbf{0})$ as null vector. This vector space is isomorphic with the vector space of bound vectors in space issuing from the origin (§22).

Example 3. All real-valued functions of x in the interval $0 \leq x \leq 1$ constitute a vector space. For two such functions $f(x)$, $g(x)$ may be added to give a third function $f(x) + g(x)$ of the set; and, if λ is a number of the real field, $\lambda f(x)$ is also such a function. Although these functions cannot be represented by arrows, they nevertheless constitute a vector space; the value of $f(x)$ at each point of the interval may be regarded as its "component" at that point.

89. Linear Dependence. The n vectors $\mathbf{u}_1, \mathbf{u}_2, \cdots, \mathbf{u}_n$ of a vector space $V(\mathscr{F})$ are said to be *linearly dependent* if there are n scalars $\lambda_1, \lambda_2, \cdots, \lambda_n$ in $\mathscr{F}$, not all zero, such that

$$(1) \qquad \lambda_1\mathbf{u}_1 + \lambda_2\mathbf{u}_2 + \cdots + \lambda_n\mathbf{u}_n = \mathbf{0}.$$

If the vectors are not linearly dependent, they are said to be *linearly independent*. Consequently, if the relation (6) exists between n linearly independent vectors, all $\lambda_i = 0$.

If m vectors are linearly dependent, any greater number n of vectors including these are also linearly dependent. For, if

$$\lambda_1\mathbf{u}_1 + \lambda_2\mathbf{u}_2 + \cdots + \lambda_m\mathbf{u}_m = \mathbf{0},$$

we can give $\lambda_1, \lambda_2, \cdots, \lambda_m$ these values (at least one of which is not zero) and take $\lambda_{m+1} = \cdots = \lambda_n = 0$. Then (1) is satisfied, and the n vectors $\mathbf{u}_i$ are linearly dependent.

If $\lambda\mathbf{u} = \mathbf{0}$ and $\lambda \neq 0$, then $\mathbf{u} = \mathbf{0}$ (cancel λ in $\lambda\mathbf{u} = \lambda\mathbf{0}$); hence *one vector is linearly dependent only when it is the null vector.* Thus the vectors of any set that includes the zero vector are linearly dependent.

THEOREM. *The nonzero vectors $\mathbf{u}_1, \mathbf{u}_2, \mathbf{u}_3, \cdots, \mathbf{u}_n$ are linearly dependent when and only when one vector is a linear combination of its predecessors in this sequence.*

Proof. If $\mathbf{u}_{k+1} = \lambda_1 u_1 + \cdots + \lambda_k u_k$, the vectors $\mathbf{u}_1, \cdots, \mathbf{u}_{k+1}$ are linearly dependent, and the same is true of any larger set containing them.

Conversely, if $\mathbf{u}_1, \cdots, \mathbf{u}_n$ are linearly dependent, let $k + 1$ be the *highest* index in (1) for which $\lambda_{k+1} \neq 0$; we can then solve (1) for $\mathbf{u}_{k+1}$ in terms of $\mathbf{u}_1, \cdots, \mathbf{u}_k$. Note that $k + 1 > 1$; for, if $\lambda_1 \neq 0$, $\lambda_2 = \cdots = \lambda_n = 0$, we would have $\lambda_1 \mathbf{u}_1 = \mathbf{0}$ and $\mathbf{u}_1 = \mathbf{0}$, contrary to hypothesis.

Example.   For the free arrow vectors of Chapter 1 we can readily show that:

1. *Two proper vectors are linearly dependent when they are parallel.*

2. *Three proper vectors are linearly dependent when they are parallel to a plane.*

Proof of 2. If $\lambda_1 \mathbf{u}_1 + \lambda_2 \mathbf{u}_2 + \lambda_3 \mathbf{u}_3 = 0$ and $\lambda_3 \neq 0$, division by λ_3 gives $\mathbf{u}_3 = \alpha \mathbf{u}_1 + \beta \mathbf{u}_2$, and the parallelogram construction shows that $\mathbf{u}_3$ lies in the plane of $\mathbf{u}_1$ and $\mathbf{u}_2$. Conversely, if $\mathbf{u}_1, \mathbf{u}_2, \mathbf{u}_3$ are parallel to a plane, they are linearly dependent. For, if $\mathbf{u}_1$ and $\mathbf{u}_2$ are parallel, $\mathbf{u}_2 = \alpha \mathbf{u}_1 \,(\alpha \neq 0)$; and, if no two are parallel, we have $\mathbf{u}_3 = \alpha \mathbf{u}_1 + \beta \mathbf{u}_2 \,(\alpha, \beta \neq 0)$ by the parallelogram construction.

90. Subspaces.   A subset of vectors in $V(\mathscr{F})$ which itself forms a vector space is called a *vector subspace* of $V(\mathscr{F})$.

If $\mathbf{a}_1, \mathbf{a}_2, \cdots, \mathbf{a}_k$ are given vectors in $V(\mathscr{F})$, the set of all linear combinations

$$(1) \qquad \mathbf{u} = \lambda_1 \mathbf{a}_1 + \lambda_2 \mathbf{a}_2 + \cdots + \lambda_k \mathbf{a}_k \qquad (\lambda_i \text{ in } \mathscr{F})$$

is called a *linear system* L_k.

The linear system L_k is a vector subspace of $V(\mathscr{F})$, which may possibly be $V(\mathscr{F})$ itself.   For, if

$$\mathbf{u}' = \lambda_1' \mathbf{a}_1 + \lambda_2' \mathbf{a}_2 + \cdots + \lambda_k' \mathbf{a}_k \qquad (\lambda_i' \text{ in } \mathscr{F}),$$

the vectors

$$\mathbf{u} + \mathbf{u}' = \sum_{i=1}^{k} (\lambda_i + \lambda_i') \mathbf{a}_i, \qquad \lambda \mathbf{u} = \sum_{i=1}^{k} \lambda \lambda_i \mathbf{a}_i \qquad (\lambda \text{ in } \mathscr{F})$$

are members of L_k.   The subspace L_k is said to be *spanned* by the vectors $\mathbf{a}_1, \cdots, \mathbf{a}_k$.

Thus, for the arrow vectors of Chapter 1, the subspace L_1 spanned by the vector $\mathbf{a}_1 \neq \mathbf{0}$ consists of all vectors $\lambda \mathbf{a}_1$ collinear with $\mathbf{a}_1$.   The subspace L_2 spanned by two noncollinear vectors $\mathbf{a}_1$ and $\mathbf{a}_2$ consists of all vectors $\lambda_1 \mathbf{a}_1 + \lambda_2 \mathbf{a}_2$ coplanar with $\mathbf{a}_1$ and $\mathbf{a}_2$.   Finally, if $\mathbf{a}_1, \mathbf{a}_2, \mathbf{a}_3$ are not coplanar, the subspace L_3 they span consists of all vectors $\lambda_1 \mathbf{a}_1 + \lambda_2 \mathbf{a}_2 + \lambda_3 \mathbf{a}_3$; and, since any arrow vector can be put in this form, $\mathbf{a}_1, \mathbf{a}_2, \mathbf{a}_3$ span the entire vector space of three dimensions.

DEFINITION.   *A set of linearly independent vectors which spans a vector space is called a* basis *for that space.*

Thus, any three noncoplanar vectors $\mathbf{a}_1, \mathbf{a}_2, \mathbf{a}_3$ form a *basis* for the ordinary vector space of three dimensions.

We now have the fundamental

THEOREM. *If n vectors span a vector space containing k linearly independent vectors, $n \geq k$.*

Proof.† Let $\mathbf{a}_1, \mathbf{a}_2, \cdots, \mathbf{a}_n$ span the vector space V which contains the k linearly independent vectors $\mathbf{b}_1, \mathbf{b}_2, \cdots, \mathbf{b}_k$. Then $\mathbf{b}_1 \neq \mathbf{0}$ and is given by a linear combination of $\mathbf{a}_1, \mathbf{a}_2, \cdots, \mathbf{a}_n$; hence the vectors of the sequence $\{\mathbf{b}_1, \mathbf{a}_1, \mathbf{a}_2, \cdots, \mathbf{a}_n\}$ are linearly dependent. By Theorem 89 some $\mathbf{a}_i$ is a linear combination of its predecessors in this sequence; and, if it is discarded, $\mathbf{b}_1$ and the $n-1$ remaining $\mathbf{a}$'s still span V.

If we call the discarded vector $\mathbf{a}_1$, the n vectors $\mathbf{b}_1, \mathbf{a}_2, \mathbf{a}_3, \cdots, \mathbf{a}_n$ span the vector space V which contains $k-1$ linearly independent vectors $\mathbf{b}_2, \mathbf{b}_3, \cdots, \mathbf{b}_k$. We now repeat the argument above. Now $\mathbf{b}_2 \neq \mathbf{0}$ and is given by a linear combination of $\mathbf{b}_1, \mathbf{a}_2, \cdots, \mathbf{a}_n$; hence the vectors of the sequence $\{\mathbf{b}_2, \mathbf{b}_1, \mathbf{a}_2, \cdots, \mathbf{a}_n\}$ are linearly dependent. Since $\mathbf{b}_1 \neq \lambda \mathbf{b}_2$ by hypothesis, Theorem 1 shows that some $\mathbf{a}_i$ of this sequence is a linear combination of its predecessors; and, if it is discarded, $\mathbf{b}_2$, $\mathbf{b}_1$ and the $n-2$ remaining $\mathbf{a}$'s still span V.

If we call the discarded vector $\mathbf{a}_2$, the n vectors $\mathbf{b}_2, \mathbf{b}_1, \mathbf{a}_3, \mathbf{a}_4, \cdots, \mathbf{a}_n$ span the vector space V which contains $k-2$ linearly independent vectors $\mathbf{b}_3, \mathbf{b}_4, \cdots, \mathbf{b}_k$. We now repeat the above argument and find that we can discard another $\mathbf{a}_i$ from the sequence $\{\mathbf{b}_3, \mathbf{b}_2, \mathbf{b}_1, \mathbf{a}_3, \cdots, \mathbf{a}_n\}$; for the $\mathbf{b}$'s cannot be discarded as they are linearly independent.

This procedure is now repeated until

(a) all $\mathbf{a}$'s are discarded, *or*

(b) all $\mathbf{b}$'s are exhausted, but some $\mathbf{a}$'s are left.

In case (a), the $\mathbf{b}$'s will be exhausted when all $\mathbf{a}$'s are discarded; otherwise any remaining $\mathbf{b}$ would be a linear combination of the $\mathbf{b}$'s already used, contradicting the hypothesis. Hence, in case (a), $n = k$. In case (b), $n > k$. Thus $n \geq k$, and the theorem is proved.

91. Bases and Dimension. The following theorem enables us to define the dimension of a vector space which has a basis formed by a finite number of vectors.

THEOREM 1. *All bases of a vector space contain the same number of vectors provided this number is finite.*

Proof. Let $\mathbf{a}_1, \mathbf{a}_2, \cdots, \mathbf{a}_n$ and $\mathbf{b}_1, \mathbf{b}_2, \cdots, \mathbf{b}_k$ be two bases of a vector space V. Since the $\mathbf{a}$'s span V and the $\mathbf{b}$'s are linearly independent,

† We follow the argument in Birkhoff and MacLane, *A Survey of Modern Algebra*, Macmillan, 1953. Since it makes no use of the commutative law $ab = ba$, the theorem is valid when the scalars form a *division ring*.

$n \geq k$ by Theorem 90. But, since the $\mathbf{b}$'s span V and the $\mathbf{a}$'s are linearly independent, $k \geq n$. Hence, $n = k$, as stated in the theorem.

The *dimension* of a vector space is now defined as the number of vectors (if finite) in any one of its bases. Any n-dimensional vector space is a linear system L_n.

THEOREM 2. *In an n-dimensional vector space any $n+1$ vectors are linearly dependent.*

Proof. By Theorem 1, any basis of the vector space consists of exactly n vectors. If any $n+1$ vectors in L_n were linearly independent, Theorem 90 would require an impossibility: namely $n \geq n+1$. Hence any $n+1$ vectors of the space must be linearly dependent.

THEOREM 3. *Any set of n linearly independent vectors $\mathbf{e}_1, \mathbf{e}_2, \cdots, \mathbf{e}_n$ of a vector space over a field $\mathscr{F}$ form a basis; and any vector $\mathbf{u}$ of the space has a unique representation*

$$(1) \qquad \mathbf{u} = u^1\mathbf{e}_1 + u^2\mathbf{e}_2 + \cdots + u^n\mathbf{e}_n,$$

where the scalars u^i are in the field $\mathscr{F}$.†

Proof. The $n + 1$ vectors $\mathbf{u}, \mathbf{e}_1, \mathbf{e}_2, \cdots, \mathbf{e}_n$ are linearly dependent by Theorem 2; hence

$$(2) \qquad \lambda\mathbf{u} + \lambda_1\mathbf{e}_1 + \lambda_2\mathbf{e}_2 + \cdots + \lambda_n\mathbf{e}_n = \mathbf{0},$$

where the lambdas are in $\mathscr{F}$ and at least one is not zero. If $\lambda = 0$, the linear independence of $\mathbf{e}_1, \mathbf{e}_2, \cdots, \mathbf{e}_n$ would require $\lambda_1 = \lambda_2 = \cdots = \lambda_n = 0$, and *all* lambdas in (9) would vanish. Hence, $\lambda \neq 0$; and, on solving (2) for u and writing $u^i = -\lambda_i/\lambda$, we obtain (1). Since every vector of the space can be represented in this way, the vectors $\mathbf{e}_1, \mathbf{e}_2, \cdots, \mathbf{e}_n$ form a basis.

If there were a second expression for $\mathbf{u}$ of the form (1) with coefficients u_i, we would have on subtraction

$$\mathbf{0} = \sum_{i=1}^{n} (u^i - u_i)\mathbf{e}_i \qquad \text{and all} \qquad u^i - u_i = 0,$$

since $\mathbf{e}_1, \mathbf{e}_2, \cdots, \mathbf{e}_n$ are linearly independent. The expression (1) for $\mathbf{u}$ in terms of the basis is therefore unique.

The scalars $u^1, u^2, \cdots, u^n$ in (1) are called the *components* of the vector $\mathbf{u}$ relative to the basis $\mathbf{e}_1, \mathbf{e}_2, \cdots, \mathbf{e}_n$. The null vector $\mathbf{0}$ has all of its components 0. The totality of vectors $\mathbf{u}$ form a linear system (§90); we therefore denote this vector space by $L_n(\mathscr{F})$.

---

† Just as in §15, the upper indices are *not exponents* but mere identification tags.

92. Ordered Sets. Consider now the ordered set of n scalars u^i belonging to the field $\mathscr{F}$:

$$\mathbf{U} = [u^1, u^2, \cdots, u^n].$$

We define addition of such sets, and their multiplication by scalars, by the equations

(1) $$\mathbf{U} + \mathbf{V} = [u^1 + v^1, u^2 + v^2, \cdots, u^n + v^n],$$

(2) $$a\mathbf{U} = [au^1, au^2, \cdots, au^n],$$

and denote the null set by

(3) $$\mathbf{0} = [0, 0, \cdots, 0].$$

It is now easy to verify that all postulates for a vector space are satisfied by such n-tuples. These n-tuples are therefore vectors, and $\mathbf{0}$ is the null vector. In aggregate they constitute an n-dimensional vector space which we denote by $V_n(\mathscr{F})$; for the vectors

(4) $$\mathbf{E}_1 = (1, 0, 0, \cdots, 0), \quad \mathbf{E}_2 = (0, 1, 0, \cdots, 0), \quad \cdots, \quad \mathbf{E}_n = (0, 0, 0, \cdots, 1)$$

are obviously linearly independent and form a basis; we have, in fact, from (1) and (2):

(5) $$\mathbf{U} = u^1\mathbf{E}_1 + u^2\mathbf{E}_2 + \cdots + u^n\mathbf{E}_n.$$

When a basis $\mathbf{e}_1, \mathbf{e}_2, \cdots, \mathbf{e}_n$ of a linear system $L_n(\mathscr{F})$ is given, any vector $\mathbf{u}$ of the system has the unique representation

(6) $$\mathbf{u} = u^1\mathbf{e}_1 + u^2\mathbf{e}_2 + \cdots + u^n\mathbf{e}_n.$$

We may now set up a one-to-one correspondence between the vectors $\mathbf{u}$ of $L_n(\mathscr{F})$ and the vectors $\mathbf{U}$ of $V_n(\mathscr{F})$:

(7) $$u^1\mathbf{e}_1 + u^2\mathbf{e}_2 + \cdots + u^n\mathbf{e}_n \leftrightarrow [u^1, u^2, \cdots, u^n].$$

This correspondence is an *isomorphism* between the vector spaces L_n and V_n; for

$$\mathbf{u} + \mathbf{v} \leftrightarrow \mathbf{U} + \mathbf{V}, \qquad a\mathbf{u} \leftrightarrow a\mathbf{U}.$$

Therefore: *Any n-dimensional vector space is isomorphic with the vector space V_n of ordered n-tuples over the same field.*

93. Inner Product. Since length and angle have not been defined in an abstract vector space, these concepts are not available in defining the analogue of the dot product $\mathbf{u} \cdot \mathbf{v}$ of two vectors. Since $\lambda\mathbf{u}$ has been called the *scalar product*, we henceforth term $\mathbf{u} \cdot \mathbf{v}$ the *inner product*.

We now define the inner product $\mathbf{u} \cdot \mathbf{v}$ of two vectors of a vector space $L_n(\mathscr{R})$ over the field $\mathscr{R}$ of reals, as a scalar having the following properties:

(1) $\mathbf{u} \cdot \mathbf{v} = \mathbf{v} \cdot \mathbf{u}$

(2) $(\lambda\mathbf{u}) \cdot \mathbf{v} = \mathbf{u} \cdot (\lambda\mathbf{v}) = \lambda\,(\mathbf{u} \cdot \mathbf{v}),$

(3) $\mathbf{w} \cdot (\mathbf{u} + \mathbf{v}) = \mathbf{w} \cdot \mathbf{u} + \mathbf{w} \cdot \mathbf{v},$

(4) $\mathbf{u} \cdot \mathbf{u} > 0$ when $\mathbf{u} \neq \mathbf{0}.$

From (1) and (3) we have also

(3)′ $(\mathbf{u} + \mathbf{v}) \cdot \mathbf{w} = \mathbf{u} \cdot \mathbf{w} + \mathbf{v} \cdot \mathbf{w};$

and, since $\mathbf{u} \cdot \mathbf{v} = \mathbf{u} \cdot (\mathbf{v} + \mathbf{0}) = \mathbf{u} \cdot \mathbf{v} + \mathbf{u} \cdot \mathbf{0},$

(5) $\mathbf{u} \cdot \mathbf{0} = 0.$

For the sake of compactness and brevity we shall in the following frequently use the

SUMMATION CONVENTION. *Any term, in which the same index (subscript or superscript) appears twice, shall stand for the sum of all such terms obtained by giving this index its complete range of values.*

Consider now two vectors $\mathbf{u}$, $\mathbf{v}$ of an n-dimensional vector space $L_n(\mathscr{R})$:

$$\mathbf{u} = u^i\mathbf{e}_i, \qquad \mathbf{v} = v^j\mathbf{e}_j \qquad (i, j = 1, 2, \cdots, n).$$

Then, making use of properties (1), (2), (3) and (3)′, we have

$$\mathbf{u} \cdot \mathbf{v} = (u^i\mathbf{e}_i) \cdot (v^j\mathbf{e}_j) = u^i v^j \mathbf{e}_i \cdot \mathbf{e}_j.$$

The inner products $\mathbf{e}_i \cdot \mathbf{e}_j$ are now defined as

(6) $\mathbf{e}_i \cdot \mathbf{e}_j = g_{ij},$

where the n^2 real scalars g_{ij} are the coefficients of a *positive definite quadratic form*:

$$g(x, x) = g_{ij}\,x^i x^j \qquad (g_{ij} = g_{ji}).$$

For such a form $g(x, x) \geq 0$ for all sets $(x^1, x^2, \cdots, x^n)$; and $g(x, x) = 0$ only when all $x^i = 0.$† We now have

(7) $\mathbf{u} \cdot \mathbf{v} = g_{ij}u^i u^j;$

(8) $\mathbf{u} \cdot \mathbf{u} = g_{ij}u^i u^j > 0$ if $\mathbf{u} \neq \mathbf{0},$

and property (4) is sustained.

---

† Cf *Vector and Tensor Analysis*, §150.   Note that $g_{ii} > 0$ $(i = 1, 2, \cdots, n)$; for, if $x^r = \delta^r_i, g(x, x) = g_{ii} > 0.$

Two nonzero vectors $\mathbf{u}$, $\mathbf{v}$ are said to be *orthogonal* when and only when $\mathbf{u} \cdot \mathbf{v} = 0$. Thus orthogonal abstract vectors constitute a natural generalization of perpendicular arrow vectors.

A basis $\mathbf{a}_1, \mathbf{a}_2, \cdots, \mathbf{a}_n$ is said to be *orthogonal* when each $\mathbf{a}_i$ is orthogonal to all the others; then

$$(9) \qquad\qquad \mathbf{a}_i \cdot \mathbf{a}_j = 0, \qquad i \neq j.$$

The vectors of any nonzero orthogonal set $\mathbf{a}_1, \mathbf{a}_2, \cdots, \mathbf{a}_k$ *are linearly independent.* For, if the vectors are connected by a linear relation

$$\lambda_1 \mathbf{a}_1 + \lambda_2 \mathbf{a}_2 + \cdots + \lambda_k \mathbf{a}_k = \mathbf{0},$$

dot-multiplying by $\mathbf{a}_i$ gives $\lambda_i \mathbf{a}_i \cdot \mathbf{a}_i = 0$; and, since $\mathbf{a}_i \cdot \mathbf{a}_i > 0$, $\lambda_i = 0$.

Any vector $\mathbf{v}$ *orthogonal to the set* $\mathbf{a}_1, \mathbf{a}_2, \cdots, \mathbf{a}_k$ *is orthogonal to every vector of the subspace* L_k *spanned by them:* for

$$\mathbf{v} \cdot (\lambda_1 \mathbf{a}_1 + \lambda_2 \mathbf{a}_2 + \cdots + \lambda_k \mathbf{a}_k) = 0.$$

94. Euclidean Vector Space. In order to make *measurements* in an abstract vector space, we next define the *length* of a vector $\mathbf{u}$ to be

$$(1) \qquad\qquad |\mathbf{u}| = \sqrt{\mathbf{u} \cdot \mathbf{u}} = \sqrt{g_{ij} u^i u^j}.$$

Moreover, in analogy with (10.14), we define the *angle* $(\mathbf{u}, \mathbf{v})$ between $\mathbf{u}$ and $\mathbf{v}$ by

$$(2) \qquad\qquad \cos(\mathbf{u}, \mathbf{v}) = \frac{\mathbf{u} \cdot \mathbf{v}}{|\mathbf{u}| \, |\mathbf{v}|}, \qquad 0 \leq (\mathbf{u}, \mathbf{v}) \leq \pi.$$

We now show that, when $g_{ij} x^i x^j$ is a positive definite quadratic form, length defined by (1) has the familiar Euclidean properties:

$$(3) \qquad\qquad |\mathbf{u}| > 0 \quad \text{if} \quad \mathbf{u} \neq \mathbf{0}; \qquad |\mathbf{0}| = 0;$$

$$(4) \qquad\qquad |\lambda \mathbf{u}| = |\lambda| \, |\mathbf{u}|;$$

$$(5) \qquad\qquad |\mathbf{u} + \mathbf{v}| \leq |\mathbf{u}| + |\mathbf{v}| \qquad \text{(triangle inequality)}.$$

The *positiveness* of length, expressed by (3), follows at once from (93.4). The multiplicative property (4) is an immediate consequence of (1):

$$|\lambda \mathbf{u}| = \sqrt{g_{ij} (\lambda u^i)(\lambda u^j)} = |\lambda| \, |\mathbf{u}|.$$

To prove (5), consider

$$(\mathbf{u} + \lambda \mathbf{v}) \cdot (\mathbf{u} + \lambda \mathbf{v}) = |\mathbf{u}^2| + 2\lambda \mathbf{u} \cdot \mathbf{v} + \lambda^2 |\mathbf{v}|^2 \geq 0.$$

Since this may be written

$$\left(\lambda|\mathbf{v}| + \frac{\mathbf{u} \cdot \mathbf{v}}{|\mathbf{v}|}\right)^2 + \frac{|\mathbf{u}|^2 |\mathbf{v}|^2 - (\mathbf{u} \cdot \mathbf{v})^2}{|\mathbf{v}|^2} \geq 0,$$

we see that the left member will be ≥ 0 for *all* λ when and only when the last fraction ≥ 0; that is,

(6) $$|\mathbf{u} \cdot \mathbf{v}| \leq |\mathbf{u}| \, |\mathbf{v}| \qquad \text{(Schwarz inequality)}.$$

Using this inequality, we now have

$$|\mathbf{u} + \mathbf{v}|^2 = (\mathbf{u} + \mathbf{v}) \cdot (\mathbf{u} + \mathbf{v}) = |\mathbf{u}|^2 + 2\,\mathbf{u} \cdot \mathbf{v} + |\mathbf{v}|^2$$
$$\leq |\mathbf{u}^2| + 2\,|\mathbf{u}|\,|\mathbf{v}| + |\mathbf{v}^2| = \{|\mathbf{u}| + |\mathbf{v}|\}^2;$$

and, on taking the positive square root of both sides, we obtain (5).

As a consequence of the Schwarz inequality (6), we find from (2) that

(7) $$|\cos(\mathbf{u}, \mathbf{v})| \leq 1;$$

hence the unique angle defined by (2) is always real.

We thus see that the positive definite form $g_{ij}x^i x^j$ enables us to make measurements of length and angle in our vector space. Therefore $g_{ij}x^i x^j$ is called the *metric quadratic form* of the vector space; and the n^2 numbers g_{ij}† are said to define the *metric* of the space.

If all vectors of an orthogonal basis $\mathbf{a}_i$ are of length 1, the basis $\mathbf{a}_i$ is called *orthonormal*. Thus the basis $\mathbf{a}_1, \mathbf{a}_2, \cdots, \mathbf{a}_n$ is orthonormal when and only when

(8) $$\mathbf{a}_i \cdot \mathbf{a}_j = \delta_{ij},$$

where δ_{ij} is the Kronecker delta δ_i^j of §15. When vector components are referred to an orthonormal basis, the inner product assumes the simple form

(9) $$\mathbf{u} \cdot \mathbf{v} = \delta_{ij}u^i v^j = u^i v^i.$$

When the basis is orthonormal, the inner product of two vectors is the sum of the products of their corresponding components:

(9)′ $$\mathbf{u} \cdot \mathbf{v} = u^1 v^1 + u^2 v^2 + \cdots + u^n v^n.$$

This is the generalized form of (10.13).

In the vector space $V_n(\mathscr{R})$ of real n-tuples (§92) the inner product is *defined* as

$$\mathbf{U} \cdot \mathbf{V} = u^1 v^1 + u^2 v^2 + \cdots + u^n v^n.$$

---

† Owing to the symmetry $g_{ij} = g_{ji}$, at most $\frac{1}{2}n(n + 1)$ of the coefficients g_{ij} have distinct values; for there are n of the form g_{ii}, and $\frac{1}{2}n(n - 1)$ of the form g_{ij} ($i \neq j$); and $n + \frac{1}{2}n(n - 1) = \frac{1}{2}n(n + 1)$.

With this definition the base vectors $\mathbf{E}_i$ form an orthonormal set; for from (92.4) we obviously have $\mathbf{E}_i \cdot \mathbf{E}_j = \delta_{ij}$.

In the vector space $V_n(\mathscr{C})$ of complex n-tuples, the inner product $\mathbf{U} \cdot \mathbf{V}$ is defined as

(10) $$\mathbf{U} \cdot \mathbf{V} = u^1 \bar{v}^1 + u^2 \bar{v}^2 + \cdots + u^n \bar{v}^n$$

where $\bar{v}^i$ is the complex conjugate of v^i. With this definition $\mathbf{U} \cdot \mathbf{U} > 0$ if $\mathbf{U} \neq \mathbf{0}$; and $|\mathbf{U}|$, the length of $\mathbf{U}$, is given by the positive square root of $\mathbf{U} \cdot \mathbf{U}$:

(11) $$|\mathbf{U}|^2 = u^1 \bar{u}^1 + u^2 \bar{u}^2 + \cdots + u^n \bar{u}^n.$$

Unless $\mathbf{U}$ and $\mathbf{V}$ have real components, $\mathbf{U} \cdot \mathbf{V} \neq \mathbf{V} \cdot \mathbf{U}$; instead we now have *Hermitian symmetry*:

(12) $$\mathbf{V} \cdot \mathbf{U} = \overline{\mathbf{U} \cdot \mathbf{V}};$$

and for any scalar

(13) $$(\lambda \mathbf{U}) \cdot \mathbf{V} = \lambda \, \mathbf{U} \cdot \mathbf{V}, \qquad \mathbf{U} \cdot (\lambda \mathbf{V}) = \bar{\lambda} \, \mathbf{U} \cdot \mathbf{V}.$$

The distributive laws,

$$\mathbf{U} \cdot (\mathbf{V} + \mathbf{W}) = \mathbf{U} \cdot \mathbf{V} + \mathbf{U} \cdot \mathbf{W}, \qquad (\mathbf{V} + \mathbf{W}) \cdot \mathbf{U} = \mathbf{V} \cdot \mathbf{U} + \mathbf{W} \cdot \mathbf{U},$$

are still valid. Moreover both the Schwarz and triangle inequalities hold good. To prove the former, consider

$$(\mathbf{U} + \lambda \, \mathbf{V}) \cdot (\mathbf{U} + \lambda \, \mathbf{V}) = |\mathbf{U}|^2 + \lambda \, \mathbf{V} \cdot \mathbf{U} + \bar{\lambda} \, \mathbf{U} \cdot \mathbf{V} + \lambda \bar{\lambda} |\mathbf{V}|^2 \geqq 0.$$

Since this may be written

$$\left(\lambda |\mathbf{V}| + \frac{\mathbf{U} \cdot \mathbf{V}}{|\mathbf{V}|} \right) \left(\bar{\lambda} |\mathbf{V}| + \frac{\mathbf{V} \cdot \mathbf{U}}{|\mathbf{V}|} \right) + \frac{|\mathbf{U}|^2 |\mathbf{V}|^2 - |\mathbf{U} \cdot \mathbf{V}|^2}{|\mathbf{V}|^2} \geqq 0,$$

we see that the left member will be $\geqq 0$ for *all* λ when and only when the last fraction $\geqq 0$; we thus obtain the Schwarz inequality:

(14) $$|\mathbf{U} \cdot \mathbf{V}| \leqq |\mathbf{U}| \, |\mathbf{V}|.$$

The triangle inequality

(15) $$|\mathbf{U} + \mathbf{V}| \leqq |\mathbf{U}| + |\mathbf{V}|$$

now follows from (14):

$$|\mathbf{U} + \mathbf{V}|^2 = (\mathbf{U} + \mathbf{V}) \cdot (\mathbf{U} + \mathbf{V}) = |\mathbf{U}|^2 + \mathbf{U} \cdot \mathbf{V} + \mathbf{V} \cdot \mathbf{U} + |\mathbf{V}|^2$$
$$= |\mathbf{U}|^2 + \mathbf{U} \cdot \mathbf{V} + \overline{\mathbf{U} \cdot \mathbf{V}} + |\mathbf{V}|^2$$
$$\leqq |\mathbf{U}|^2 + 2|\mathbf{U} \cdot \mathbf{V}| + |\mathbf{V}|^2$$
$$\leqq |\mathbf{U}|^2 + 2|\mathbf{U}| \, |\mathbf{V}| + |\mathbf{V}|^2 = \{|\mathbf{U}| + |\mathbf{V}|\}^2.$$

If $\mathbf{U}_1, \mathbf{U}_2, \cdots, \mathbf{U}_k$ are k vectors of $V_n(\mathscr{C})$, their *Gramian* is the determinant

$$(16) \qquad G_k = \begin{vmatrix} \mathbf{U}_1 \cdot \mathbf{U}_1 & \mathbf{U}_2 \cdot \mathbf{U}_1 & \cdots & \mathbf{U}_k \cdot \mathbf{U}_1 \\ \mathbf{U}_1 \cdot \mathbf{U}_2 & \mathbf{U}_2 \cdot \mathbf{U}_2 & \cdots & \mathbf{U}_k \cdot \mathbf{U}_2 \\ \cdot & \cdot & \cdots & \cdot \\ \cdot & \cdot & \cdots & \cdot \\ \mathbf{U}_1 \cdot \mathbf{U}_k & \mathbf{U}_2 \cdot \mathbf{U}_k & \cdots & \mathbf{U}_k \cdot \mathbf{U}_k \end{vmatrix}$$

From (12) we see that $\bar{G}_k$ is obtained from G_k by an interchange of rows and columns. Thus $\bar{G}_k = G_k$; therefore *a Gramian is a real scalar.*[†]

THEOREM. *A necessary and sufficient condition that* $\mathbf{U}_1, \mathbf{U}_2, \ldots, \mathbf{U}_k$ *be linearly dependent is that their Gramian vanish.*

Proof. The condition is necessary; for, if there are k constants c_i, not all zero, such that

$$(17) \qquad c_1\mathbf{U}_1 + c_2\mathbf{U}_2 + \cdots + c_k\mathbf{U}_k = \mathbf{0},$$

we have the k homogeneous equations

$$(18) \qquad c_1\mathbf{U}_1 \cdot \mathbf{U}_i + \cdots + c_k\mathbf{U}_k \cdot \mathbf{U}_i = 0, \qquad i = 1, 2, \cdots, k.$$

Since the c's are not all zero, the determinant G_k of the system (18) must vanish.

The condition $G_k = 0$ is also sufficient. For the system (18),

$$(c_1\mathbf{U}_1 + \cdots + c_k\mathbf{U}_k) \cdot \mathbf{U}_i = 0, \qquad i = 1, 2, \cdots, k,$$

has the zero determinant G_k and therefore must admit a solution $c_1, c_2, \cdots, c_k$ not consisting of zeros. If we multiply these equations by $\bar{c}_1, \bar{c}_2, \cdots, \bar{c}_k$, respectively, and add after using (13), the resulting equation,

$$(c_1\mathbf{U}_1 + \cdots + c_k\mathbf{U}_k) \cdot (c_1\mathbf{U}_1 + \cdots + c_k\mathbf{U}_k) = 0,$$

implies (17).

95. Gram–Schmidt Process. If the vectors $\mathbf{e}_1, \mathbf{e}_2 \cdots, \mathbf{e}_n$ form a basis for an Euclidean vector space, we can derive from them by rational processes an orthogonal basis $\mathbf{a}_1, \mathbf{a}_2, \cdots, \mathbf{a}_n$ that spans the same space.

---

† $G_1 = \mathbf{U}_1 \cdot \mathbf{U}_1 \geqq 0$; and $G_2 \geqq 0$ from (14). We shall see later (§98) that, in general, $G_k \geqq 0$.

The construction, known as the *Gram–Schmidt process*, consists in forming the vector sequence

$$\mathbf{a}_1 = \mathbf{e}_1,$$

$$\mathbf{a}_2 = \mathbf{e}_2 - \frac{\mathbf{e}_2 \cdot \mathbf{a}_1}{\mathbf{a}_1 \cdot \mathbf{a}_1}\, \mathbf{a}_1,$$

$$\mathbf{a}_3 = \mathbf{e}_3 - \frac{\mathbf{e}_3 \cdot \mathbf{a}_1}{\mathbf{a}_1 \cdot \mathbf{a}_1}\, \mathbf{a}_1 - \frac{\mathbf{e}_3 \cdot \mathbf{a}_2}{\mathbf{a}_2 \cdot \mathbf{a}_2}\, \mathbf{a}_2, \quad \cdots \ ,$$

and, in general,

(1) $$\mathbf{a}_k = \mathbf{e}_k - \sum_{i=1}^{k-1} \frac{\mathbf{e}_k \cdot \mathbf{a}_i}{\mathbf{a}_i \cdot \mathbf{a}_i}\, \mathbf{a}_i.$$

If $\mathbf{a}_1, \mathbf{a}_2, \cdots, \mathbf{a}_{k-1}$ are not zero, these equations show that the subspace L_{k-1} they span is the same as that spanned by $\mathbf{e}_1, \mathbf{e}_2, \cdots, \mathbf{e}_{k-1}$. Now, if $\mathbf{a}_1, \mathbf{a}_2, \cdots, \mathbf{a}_{k-1}$ form an orthogonal set, the same is true when $\mathbf{a}_k$ is added, for from (1)

$$\mathbf{a}_k \cdot \mathbf{a}_j = \mathbf{e}_k \cdot \mathbf{a}_j - \mathbf{e}_k \cdot \mathbf{a}_j = 0 \qquad (j < k).$$

Moreover $\mathbf{a}_k \neq \mathbf{0}$; for, if $\mathbf{a}_k = \mathbf{0}$, (1) implies that $\mathbf{e}_k$ is a vector of the subspace L_{k-1} spanned by $\mathbf{a}_1, \mathbf{a}_2, \cdots, \mathbf{a}_{k-1}$ (or by $\mathbf{e}_1, \mathbf{e}_2, \cdots, \mathbf{e}_{k-1}$) and $\mathbf{e}_k$ could not be a base vector. Thus, if the construction succeeds for $\mathbf{a}_1, \mathbf{a}_2, \cdots, \mathbf{a}_{k-1}$, it will succeed for $\mathbf{a}_1, \mathbf{a}_2, \cdots, \mathbf{a}_k$; and, since $\mathbf{a}_2 \neq \mathbf{0}$ and $\mathbf{a}_2 \cdot \mathbf{a}_1 = 0$, we have an induction proof for its general validity.

From the orthogonal basis $\mathbf{a}_i$ we may now form the *orthonormal* basis $\mathbf{b}_i = \mathbf{a}_i / |\mathbf{a}_i|$; for the $\mathbf{b}_i$ are orthogonal and of length 1.

In view of (12.3) we may interpret the term

$$\frac{\mathbf{e}_k \cdot \mathbf{a}_i}{\mathbf{a}_i \cdot \mathbf{a}_i}\, \mathbf{a}_i = (\mathbf{e}_k \cdot \mathbf{b}_i)\, \mathbf{b}_i$$

as the projection of $\mathbf{e}_k$ on $\mathbf{a}_i$; thus (1) states that

(1) $$\mathbf{a}_k = \mathbf{e}_k - \sum_{i=1}^{k-1} \mathrm{proj}_{\mathbf{a}_i}\, \mathbf{e}_k.$$

Thus the Gram–Schmidt construction simply amounts to this: Take $\mathbf{a}_1 = \mathbf{e}_1$; take $\mathbf{a}_2$ as $\mathbf{e}_2$ minus its projection on $\mathbf{a}_1$; take $\mathbf{a}_3$ as $\mathbf{e}_3$ minus its projections on $\mathbf{a}_1$ and $\mathbf{a}_2$; and so on until the $\mathbf{e}$'s are exhausted.

96. Reciprocal Bases. We can now generalize to abstract vector spaces the concept of *reciprocal bases* (§15).

Two bases $\mathbf{e}_1, \mathbf{e}_2, \cdots, \mathbf{e}_n$ and $\mathbf{e}^1, \mathbf{e}^2, \cdots, \mathbf{e}^n$ of the same vector space are said to be *reciprocal* when they satisfy the n^2 equations:

(1) $$\mathbf{e}_i \cdot \mathbf{e}^j = \delta_i^j.$$

Since the $\mathbf{e}^i$ are vectors of the space spanned by $\mathbf{e}_i$, we have (using the summation convention)

(2) $\mathbf{e}^i = \lambda^{ik}\mathbf{e}_k$ $(i = 1, 2, \cdots, n)$.

Hence from (93.6)

$$\mathbf{e}^i \cdot \mathbf{e}_j = \lambda^{ik}\mathbf{e}_k \cdot \mathbf{e}_j = \lambda^{ik}g_{jk},$$

or, from (1),

(3) $\lambda^{ik}g_{jk} = \delta^i_j$ $(i, j = 1, 2, \cdots, n)$.

In order to solve these equations for the n^2 lambdas, we introduce the reduced cofactor g^{ij} of g_{ij} in the determinant

$$g = \begin{vmatrix} g_{11} & g_{12} & \cdots & g_{1n} \\ g_{21} & g_{22} & \cdots & g_{2n} \\ \cdot & \cdot & \cdots & \cdot \\ \cdot & \cdot & \cdots & \cdot \\ g_{n1} & g_{n2} & \cdots & g_{nn} \end{vmatrix}$$

The *cofactor* G^{ij} of g_{ij} is obtained by striking out row i and column j in the determinant and giving the resulting minor the sign $(-1)^{i+j}$; then the *reduced* cofactor is

(4) $g^{ij} = G^{ij}/g$.

Note that $g_{ij} = g_{ji}$ implies $g^{ij} = g^{ji}$.

A fundamental theorem now states that, if the elements of a row (column) are multiplied by their corresponding cofactors we get g; but, if the elements of a row (column) are multiplied by the corresponding cofactors of *another* row (column), we get zero. With the aid of the summation convention all this is expressed by

$$g_{ir}G^{jr} = g_{ri}G^{rj} = \delta^j_i g,$$

or, in terms of reduced cofactors,

(5) $g_{ir}g^{jr} = g_{ri}g^{rj} = \delta^j_i$.

In these equations r is a summation index.

Return now to the n^2 equations (3). Multiply (3) by g^{jh}; then

$$\lambda^{ik}g_{jk}g^{jh} = \delta^i_j g^{jh}.$$

Summing on j and k as required by convention, we have

$$\lambda^{ik} g_{jk} g^{jh} = \lambda^{ik} \delta^h_k = \lambda^{ih}, \qquad \delta^i_j g^{jh} = g^{ih};$$

hence $\lambda^{ih} = g^{ih}$, and, from (2),

$$(6) \qquad\qquad \mathbf{e}^i = g^{ik} \mathbf{e}_k.$$

It is easy to verify (6); for

$$\mathbf{e}^i \cdot \mathbf{e}_j = g^{ik} \mathbf{e}_k \cdot \mathbf{e}_j = g^{ik} g_{jk} = \delta^i_j.$$

If we dot-multiply (6) by $\mathbf{e}^j$, we have

$$(7) \qquad\qquad \mathbf{e}^i \cdot \mathbf{e}^j = g^{ik} \mathbf{e}_k \cdot \mathbf{e}^j = g^{ik} \delta^j_k = g^{ij}$$

as a companion piece to $\mathbf{e}_i \cdot \mathbf{e}_j = g_{ij}$. If we regard $\mathbf{e}^i$ as the original base vectors with the metric g^{ij}, the reciprocal basis is $\mathbf{e}_i$ and equations (6) become

$$(8) \qquad\qquad \mathbf{e}_i = g_{ik} \mathbf{e}^k.$$

This result is also easily verified by solving equations (6) for $\mathbf{e}_j$ by multiplying both members by g_{ij}:

$$\mathbf{e}^i g_{ij} = g_{ij} g^{ik} \mathbf{e}_k = \delta^k_j \mathbf{e}_k = \mathbf{e}_j.$$

A vector $\mathbf{u}$, referred to reciprocal bases, now has two forms:

$$(9) \qquad\qquad \mathbf{u} = \begin{cases} u^1 \mathbf{e}_1 + u^2 \mathbf{e}_2 + \cdots + u^n \mathbf{e}_n \\ u_1 \mathbf{e}^1 + u_2 \mathbf{e}^2 + \cdots + u_n \mathbf{e}^n. \end{cases}$$

These equations show that the components of $\mathbf{u}$ are

$$(10) \qquad\qquad u^i = \mathbf{u} \cdot \mathbf{e}^i, \qquad u_i = \mathbf{u} \cdot \mathbf{e}_i.$$

If we now put $\mathbf{e}^i = g^{ik} \mathbf{e}_k$, $\mathbf{e}_i = g_{ik} \mathbf{e}^k$ in (10), we also obtain the equations

$$(11) \qquad\qquad u^i = g^{ik} u_k, \qquad u_i = g_{ik} u^k,$$

which enable us to pass from one type of component to the other without intervention of base vectors.

The simplicity of formula (94.9') for the inner product $\mathbf{u} \cdot \mathbf{v}$ referred to an orthonormal basis may now be regained; for, if we refer $\mathbf{u}$ to one basis and $\mathbf{v}$ to the reciprocal basis, we find

$$\mathbf{u} \cdot \mathbf{v} = (u_i \mathbf{e}^i) \cdot (v^j \mathbf{e}_j) = u_i v^j \delta^i_j = u_i v^i,$$

or

$$\mathbf{u} \cdot \mathbf{v} = (u^i \mathbf{e}_i) \cdot (v_j \mathbf{e}^j) = u^i v_j \delta^j_i = u^i v_i;$$

hence

$$(12) \qquad\qquad \mathbf{u} \cdot \mathbf{v} = \begin{cases} u_1 v^1 + u_2 v^2 + \ldots + u_n v^n \\ u^1 v_1 + u^2 v_2 + \cdots + u^n v_n. \end{cases}$$

Finally we note that, for an orthonormal basis $\mathbf{a}_i$,

$$g_{ij} = \delta_i^j = g^{ij} \qquad (93.8),$$

and hence $\mathbf{e}^i = \mathbf{e}_i$ from (6). Conversely, if

$$\mathbf{e}_i = \mathbf{e}^i, \qquad g_{ij} = \mathbf{e}_i \cdot \mathbf{e}_j = \mathbf{e}^i \cdot \mathbf{e}_j = \delta_j^i.$$

Therefore: *A basis is self-reciprocal when and only when it is orthonormal.*

PROBLEMS

1. If the metric is given by

$$g_{ij} = \begin{pmatrix} 1 & 1 & 3/2 \\ 1 & 4 & 3 \\ 3/2 & 3 & 9 \end{pmatrix},$$

find the lengths and angles between the base vectors $\mathbf{e}_i$.

2. (*a*) Find g^{ij} corresponding to g_{ij} in Prob. 1.

(*b*) Express $\mathbf{e}^1$, $\mathbf{e}^2$, $\mathbf{e}^3$ linearly in terms of $\mathbf{e}_1$, $\mathbf{e}_2$, $\mathbf{e}_3$.

3. If $u^i = [0, 1, 2]$, $v^i = [-1, 0, 1]$ and g_{ij} has the values in Prob. 1, compute

(*a*) u_i and v_i;

(*b*) $|\mathbf{u}|$ and $|\mathbf{v}|$ in two ways;

(*c*) $\mathbf{u} \cdot \mathbf{v}$ in four ways;

(*d*) the angle $(\mathbf{u}, \mathbf{v})$.

4. If $\mathbf{e}_1 = \mathbf{i} + \mathbf{j}$, $\mathbf{e}_2 = \mathbf{i} - \mathbf{j}$, $\mathbf{e}_3 = \mathbf{i} + \mathbf{j} - \mathbf{k}$, compute

(*a*) g_{ij} and g^{ij};

(*b*) $\mathbf{e}^1, \mathbf{e}^2, \mathbf{e}^3$;

(*c*) the components u^i and u_i of $\mathbf{u} = \mathbf{i} + 2\mathbf{j} + \mathbf{k}$.   Check by finding $|\mathbf{u}|$ in two ways.

5. If the basis $\mathbf{e}_i$ is changed to $\bar{\mathbf{e}}_i$ by the nonsingular linear transformation

$$(13) \qquad\qquad \bar{\mathbf{e}}_i = c_i^j \mathbf{e}_j, \qquad c = \det c_i^j \neq 0,$$

prove that the components u^i of any vector $\mathbf{u}$ transform according to

$$(14) \qquad\qquad u^i = c_j^i \bar{u}^j$$

owing to the invariance of the vector $\mathbf{u} = u^i \mathbf{e}_i = \bar{u}^j \bar{\mathbf{e}}_j$.

Show also that

$$(15)(16) \qquad\qquad \bar{u}_i = c_i^j u_j, \qquad \mathbf{e}^i = c_j^i \bar{\mathbf{e}}^j.$$

6. In Prob. 5 show that the vectors $\bar{\mathbf{e}}_i$ actually form a new basis: i.e. that they are *linearly independent.*

7. If γ_j^i is the reduced cofactor of c_i^j in det c_i^j, show that (14) and (16) may be written

$$(14)'(16)' \qquad\qquad \bar{u}^i = \gamma_j^i u^j, \qquad \bar{\mathbf{e}}^i = \gamma_j^i \mathbf{e}^j.$$

8. If the basis $\mathbf{a}_i$ is orthonormal, and the transformation,

$$(15) \qquad\qquad \bar{\mathbf{a}}_i = c_i^j \mathbf{a}_j, \qquad c = \det c_i^j \neq 0,$$

leads to a new orthonormal basis $\bar{\mathbf{a}}_i$, prove that $c_i^j = \gamma_j^i$: i.e. *each element c_i^j in the determinant $\det c_i^j$ is its own cofactor.*

$[\mathbf{a}_i = \mathbf{a}^i, \bar{\mathbf{a}}_i = \bar{\mathbf{a}}^i.]$

9. A linear transformation between orthonormal bases is said to be *orthogonal*. If C is the matrix (c_i^j) of an orthogonal transformation and C' is the transpose of C (rows and columns interchanged), prove that

$$(a) \quad CC' = I(\text{unit matrix}); \qquad (b) \quad c^2 = 1.$$

10. Prove that in three dimensions the determinant c of an orthogonal transformation is 1 when the transformation *revolves* the trihedral $\mathbf{a}_1, \mathbf{a}_2, \mathbf{a}_3$ into $\bar{\mathbf{a}}_1, \bar{\mathbf{a}}_2, \bar{\mathbf{a}}_3$.

97. Hilbert Space. A sequence $u_1, u_2, \cdots$ of real or complex scalars, for which the infinite series $\sum |u_i|^2$ converges, is called a *vector*

$$\mathbf{U} = [u_1, u_2, \cdots]$$

having $u_1, u_2, \cdots$ as components. The product of $\mathbf{U}$ by a scalar and the sum $\mathbf{U} + \mathbf{V}$ are defined by

$$(1) \qquad\qquad a\mathbf{U} = [au_1, au_2, \cdots],$$

$$(2) \qquad\qquad \mathbf{U} + \mathbf{V} = [u_1 + v_1, u_2 + v_2, \cdots].$$

Since

$$\sum_{i=1}^{\infty} |au_i|^2 = a^2 \sum_{i=1}^{\infty} |u_i|^2,$$

$a\mathbf{U}$ is a vector. Moreover the sum $\mathbf{U} + \mathbf{V}$ of two vectors is a vector, for we shall prove that $\sum |u_i + v_i|^2$ converges. The null vector is

$$(3) \qquad\qquad \mathbf{0} = [0, 0, \cdots],$$

and the negative of $\mathbf{U}$,

$$(4) \qquad\qquad -\mathbf{U} = [-u_1, -u_2, \cdots].$$

With these definitions all the postulates of §88 are satisfied; and the totality of such vectors constitutes the *Hilbert vector space*.

We now define the inner product $\mathbf{U} \cdot \mathbf{V}$ and the length $|\mathbf{U}|$ of $\mathbf{U}$ by a direct extension of the definitions of §94:

$$(5) \qquad\qquad \mathbf{U} \cdot \mathbf{V} = u_1 \bar{v}_1 + u_2 \bar{v}_2 + \cdots,$$

$$(6) \qquad\qquad |\mathbf{U}|^2 = \mathbf{U} \cdot \mathbf{U} = u_1 \bar{u}_1 + u_2 \bar{u}_2 + \cdots.$$

Since $u_i \bar{u}_i = |u_i|^2$, the existence of $|\mathbf{U}|$ is implied by the convergence of $\sum |u_i|^2$. To deal with the series in (5), apply the Schwarz inequality (94.14) to the finite vectors:

$$\mathbf{U}_n = [|u_1|, |u_2|, \cdots, |u_n|],$$
$$\mathbf{V}_n = [|v_1|, |v_2|, \cdots, |v_n|];$$

then $|\mathbf{U}_n \cdot \mathbf{V}_n| \leq |\mathbf{U}_n| \, |\mathbf{V}_n|$ becomes

$$\sum_{i=1}^{n} |u_i v_i| \leq \left(\sum_{i=1}^{n} |u_i|^2 \right)^{1/2} \left(\sum_{i=1}^{n} |v_i|^2 \right)^{1/2}.$$

Since this holds for every n, it holds as $n \to \infty$; and since $|u_i \bar{v}_i| = |u_i v_i|$, we have

(7)
$$\sum_{i=1}^{\infty} |u_i \bar{v}_i| \leq |\mathbf{U}| \, |\mathbf{V}|.$$

Thus the series in (5) converges absolutely and hence also converges in the usual sense† to a sum defined as $\mathbf{U} \cdot \mathbf{V}$. Moreover

$$|\mathbf{U} \cdot \mathbf{V}| = \left| \sum_{i=1}^{\infty} u_i \bar{v}_i \right| \leq \sum_{i=1}^{\infty} |u_i \bar{v}_i|,$$

and hence, from (7),

(8)
$$|\mathbf{U} \cdot \mathbf{V}| \leq |\mathbf{U}| \, |\mathbf{V}|;$$

this is the Schwarz inequality in Hilbert space.

The distributive law

$$\mathbf{U} \cdot (\mathbf{V} + \mathbf{W}) = \mathbf{U} \cdot \mathbf{V} + \mathbf{U} \cdot \mathbf{W}$$

obviously holds for three vectors; for we have just seen that the series for $\mathbf{U} \cdot \mathbf{V}$ and $\mathbf{U} \cdot \mathbf{W}$ converge. In particular

$$(\mathbf{U} + \mathbf{V}) \cdot (\mathbf{U} + \mathbf{V}) = \mathbf{U} \cdot \mathbf{U} + \mathbf{U} \cdot \mathbf{V} + \mathbf{V} \cdot \mathbf{U} + \mathbf{V} \cdot \mathbf{V},$$

shows that the series for $(\mathbf{U} + \mathbf{V}) \cdot (\mathbf{U} + \mathbf{V})$ converges; hence the sum of two vectors is a vector (as stated above). The triangle inequality

(9)
$$|\mathbf{U} + \mathbf{V}| \leq |\mathbf{U}| + |\mathbf{V}|$$

now follows from (8) as in §94.

The vectors $\mathbf{U}$ and $\mathbf{V}$ are said to be *orthogonal* when $\mathbf{U} \cdot \mathbf{V} = 0$. The set of vectors $\mathbf{A}_1, \mathbf{A}_2, \cdots, \mathbf{A}_n$ are said to be *orthonormal* when

(10)
$$\mathbf{A}_i \cdot \mathbf{A}_j = \delta_{ij}.$$

† *Advanced Calculus*, p. 63.

A vector $\mathbf{U}$ then is said to have the components $\mathbf{U} \cdot \mathbf{A}_1, \cdots, \mathbf{U} \cdot \mathbf{A}_n$ relative to this set.

Now let $\lambda_1, \lambda_2, \cdots, \lambda_n$ be n arbitrary scalars, and consider the vector

$$(11) \qquad \mathbf{T}_n = \lambda_1 \mathbf{A}_1 + \lambda_2 \mathbf{A}_2 + \cdots + \lambda_n \mathbf{A}_n.$$

We propose to find the values λ_i that make $\mathbf{T}_n$ the best approximation to $\mathbf{U}$ in the sense of the method of least squares; that is, those values that give the squared length

$$D_n = |\mathbf{U} - \mathbf{T}_n|^2 = (\mathbf{U} - \mathbf{T}_n) \cdot (\mathbf{U} - \mathbf{T}_n) \geqq 0$$

its minimum value.   Making use of (10) and (94.13) we then find

$$D_n = \mathbf{U} \cdot \mathbf{U} - \mathbf{U} \cdot \mathbf{T}_n - \mathbf{T}_n \cdot \mathbf{U} + \mathbf{T}_n \cdot \mathbf{T}_n$$

$$= |\mathbf{U}|^2 - \sum_{i=1}^{n} (\bar{\lambda}_i \mathbf{U} \cdot \mathbf{A}_i + \lambda_i \mathbf{A}_i \cdot \mathbf{U}) + \sum_{i=1}^{n} \lambda_i \bar{\lambda}_i.$$

Since $\mathbf{A}_i \cdot \mathbf{U} = \overline{\mathbf{U} \cdot \mathbf{A}_i}$, this may be written

$$D_n = |\mathbf{U}|^2 + \sum_{i=1}^{n} (\lambda_i - \mathbf{U} \cdot \mathbf{A}_i)(\bar{\lambda}_i - \overline{\mathbf{U} \cdot \mathbf{A}_i}) - \sum_{i=1}^{n} (\mathbf{U} \cdot \mathbf{A}_i)(\overline{\mathbf{U} \cdot \mathbf{A}_i})$$

$$= |\mathbf{U}|^2 + \sum_{i=1}^{n} |\lambda_i - \mathbf{U} \cdot \mathbf{A}_i|^2 - \sum_{i=1}^{n} |\mathbf{U} \cdot \mathbf{A}_i|^2.$$

Thus D_n will assume its least value when $\lambda_i = \mathbf{U} \cdot \mathbf{A}_i$; then $\mathbf{T}_n$ becomes

$$(12) \qquad \mathbf{S}_n = \sum_{i=1}^{n} (\mathbf{U} \cdot \mathbf{A}_i)\mathbf{A}_i,$$

and this least value is

$$(13) \qquad \min D_n = |\mathbf{U} - \mathbf{S}_n|^2 = |\mathbf{U}|^2 - \sum_{i=1}^{n} |\mathbf{U} \cdot \mathbf{A}_i|^2.$$

We have thus proved

THEOREM 1. *For any given n, the sum $\mathbf{T}_n = \sum_{i=1}^{n} \lambda_j \mathbf{A}_i$ is the best approximation to $\mathbf{U}$ when the scalars $\lambda_i = \mathbf{U} \cdot \mathbf{A}_i$, the components of $\mathbf{U}$ on the orthonormal basis $\mathbf{A}_i$.*

If the orthonormal basis $\mathbf{A}_i$ contains an infinite number of vectors, the terms for the best approximation for a given set $\mathbf{A}_1, \cdots, \mathbf{A}_n$ are retained when this set is augmented by others.   Since $D_n \geq 0$, and n can be taken arbitrarily large, (13) also proves *Bessel's inequality*:

$$(14) \qquad \sum_{i=1}^{\infty} |\mathbf{U} \cdot \mathbf{A}_i|^2 \leq |\mathbf{U}|^2,$$

and at the same time shows that the components $\mathbf{U} \cdot \mathbf{A}_i$ form a null sequence.

The orthonormal basis $\mathbf{A}_1$, $\mathbf{A}_2$, $\cdots$ is said to be *closed* if

$$(15) \qquad \lim_{n \to \infty} |\mathbf{U} - \mathbf{S}_n| = 0$$

for all vectors $\mathbf{U}$.   From (13) we now have

THEOREM 2.   *A necessary and sufficient condition that the orthonormal basis $\mathbf{A}_i$ be closed is that*

$$(16) \qquad \sum_{i=1}^{\infty} |\mathbf{U} \cdot \mathbf{A}_i|^2 = |\mathbf{U}|^2.$$

This equation is called *Parseval's equation*; it corresponds to the equal sign in Bessel's inequality and is a generalization of the Pythagorean theorem to space of a countable infinity of dimensions.

An orthonormal basis is said to be *complete* when there is no nonzero vector which is orthogonal to all base vectors.

THEOREM 3.   *Every closed basis is complete.*

Proof.   If a vector $\mathbf{U}$ were orthogonal to each base vector $\mathbf{A}_i$ of an orthonormal set, $\mathbf{U} \cdot \mathbf{A}_i = 0$ and $\mathbf{U} = 0$ from Parseval's equation (16). Hence no nonzero vector is orthogonal to all base vectors.

DEFINITION.   A sequence of vectors $\{\mathbf{U}_n\}$ is said to *converge strongly* to a vector $\mathbf{U}$ when

$$(17) \qquad \lim_{n \to \infty} |\mathbf{U} - \mathbf{U}_n| = 0;$$

and we write $\operatorname*{Lim}_{n \to \infty} \mathbf{U}_n = \mathbf{U}.$†

Thus the condition (15) for closure of an orthonormal basis A_i may be written

$$\operatorname*{Lim}_{n \to \infty} \sum_{i=1}^{n} (\mathbf{U} \cdot \mathbf{A}_i)\mathbf{A}_i = \mathbf{U}$$

for all vectors $\mathbf{U}$.

† Note capital L in Lim.

LEMMA 1. *A necessary and sufficient condition that* $\operatorname{Lim} \mathbf{U}_n$ *exist is that to every* $\varepsilon > 0$ *there corresponds an integer N such that*

$$(18) \qquad |\mathbf{U}_n - \mathbf{U}_m| < \varepsilon \quad for \quad m, n > N.$$

Proof. The condition is *necessary*; for, if $\operatorname{Lim} \mathbf{U}_n = \mathbf{U}$,

$$|\mathbf{U} - \mathbf{U}_n| < \tfrac{1}{2}\varepsilon \qquad \text{when} \quad n > N.$$

Hence when $m, n > N$,

$$|\mathbf{U}_n - \mathbf{U}_m| = |(\mathbf{U}_n - \mathbf{U}) + (\mathbf{U} - \mathbf{U}_m)| \leqq |\mathbf{U}_n - \mathbf{U}| + |\mathbf{U} - \mathbf{U}_m| < \varepsilon.$$

To show that the condition is *sufficient*, we first observe that, if $\mathbf{U}_n = [u_{n1}, u_{n2}, \cdots]$, (18) shows that

$$\sum_{i=1}^{\infty} |u_{ni} - u_{mi}|^2 < \varepsilon^2, \qquad m, n > N;$$

hence

$$|u_{ni} - u_{mi}| < \varepsilon, \qquad m, n > N, \qquad i = 1, 2, 3, \cdots,$$

and $\lim\limits_{n \to \infty} u_{ni}$ exists by Cauchy's criterion:† denote it by u_i. Then, if we let $n \to \infty$ in the sum of p terms

$$\sum_{i=1}^{p} |u_{ni} - u_{mi}|^2 < \varepsilon^2, \qquad m, n > N,$$

we obtain

$$\sum_{i=1}^{p} |u_i - u_{mi}|^2 \leqq \varepsilon^2, \qquad m > N.$$

As this holds for every p, we also have

$$\sum_{i=1}^{\infty} |u_i - u_{mi}|^2 \leqq \varepsilon^2, \qquad m > N,$$

or upon writing $\mathbf{U} = (u_1, u_2, \cdots)$,

$$\lim_{m \to \infty} |\mathbf{U} - \mathbf{U}_m| = 0.$$

Moreover $\mathbf{U}$ is a vector; for $\mathbf{U} - \mathbf{U}_m \ (m > N)$ and $\mathbf{U}_m$ are vectors, and hence their sum is a vector.

† Advanced Calculus, §17.

LEMMA 2.   If $\operatorname{Lim}_{n\to\infty} \mathbf{U}_n = \mathbf{U}$, $\operatorname{Lim}_{n\to\infty} \mathbf{V}_n = \mathbf{V}$, then

(19) $$\operatorname{Lim}_{n\to\infty} (\mathbf{U}_n + \mathbf{V}_n) = \mathbf{U} + \mathbf{V},$$

(20) $$\lim_{n\to\infty} (\mathbf{U}_n \cdot \mathbf{V}_n) = \mathbf{U} \cdot \mathbf{V}.$$

Proof of (19).   Choose N so that

$$|\mathbf{U} - \mathbf{U}_n| < \tfrac{1}{2}\varepsilon, \qquad |\mathbf{V} - \mathbf{V}_n| < \tfrac{1}{2}\varepsilon, \qquad n > N.$$

Then by the triangle inequality (9),

$$|\mathbf{U} + \mathbf{V} - \mathbf{U}_n - \mathbf{V}_n| \leqq |\mathbf{U} - \mathbf{U}_n| + |\mathbf{V} - \mathbf{V}_n| < \varepsilon, \qquad n > N.$$

Proof of (20).   Since

$$\mathbf{U} \cdot \mathbf{V} - \mathbf{U}_n \cdot \mathbf{V}_n = (\mathbf{U} - \mathbf{U}_n) \cdot \mathbf{V} + \mathbf{U} \cdot (\mathbf{V} - \mathbf{V}_n) - (\mathbf{U} - \mathbf{U}_n) \cdot (\mathbf{V} - \mathbf{V}_n),$$

$$\begin{aligned}
|\mathbf{U} \cdot \mathbf{V} - \mathbf{U}_n \cdot \mathbf{V}_n| &\leqq |(\mathbf{U} - \mathbf{U}_n) \cdot \mathbf{V}| + |\mathbf{U} \cdot (\mathbf{V} - \mathbf{V}_n)| \\
&\qquad + |(\mathbf{U} - \mathbf{U}_n) \cdot (\mathbf{V} - \mathbf{V}_n)| \\
&\leqq |\mathbf{U} - \mathbf{U}_n| |\mathbf{V}| + |\mathbf{U}| |\mathbf{V} - \mathbf{V}_n| + |\mathbf{U} - \mathbf{U}_n| |\mathbf{V} - \mathbf{V}_n|,
\end{aligned}$$

on making use of the Schwarz inequality (8).   Now choose N so that

$$|\mathbf{U} - \mathbf{U}_n| \text{ and } |\mathbf{V} - \mathbf{V}_n| < \frac{\tfrac{1}{2}\varepsilon}{|\mathbf{U}| + |\mathbf{V}|}, \qquad n > N;$$

then

$$|\mathbf{U} \cdot \mathbf{V} - \mathbf{U}_n \cdot \mathbf{V}_n| \leqq \varepsilon \left[\frac{1}{2} + \frac{\varepsilon}{4(|\mathbf{U}| + |\mathbf{V}|)^2} \right] < \varepsilon, \qquad n > N,$$

provided $\varepsilon < 2(|\mathbf{U}| + |\mathbf{V}|)^2$.

We are now in position to prove

THEOREM 4.   *Every complete basis is closed.*

Proof.   If $\mathbf{U}$ is any vector and $\mathbf{A}_1$, $\mathbf{A}_2$, $\cdots$ a complete orthonormal basis, consider the vector $\mathbf{S}_n$ in (12).   As $n \to \infty$, $\mathbf{S}_n$ converges strongly to a limiting vector $\mathbf{S}$.   For, if $m < n$,

$$\begin{aligned}
|\mathbf{S}_n - \mathbf{S}_m|^2 &= \left(\sum_{i=m}^{n} (\mathbf{U} \cdot \mathbf{A}_i)\mathbf{A}_i \right) \cdot \left(\sum_{i=m}^{n} (\mathbf{U} \cdot \mathbf{A}_i)\mathbf{A}_i \right) \\
&= \sum_{i=m}^{n} (\mathbf{U} \cdot \mathbf{A}_i)\overline{(\mathbf{U} \cdot \mathbf{A}_i)} = \sum_{i=m}^{n} |\mathbf{U} \cdot \mathbf{A}_i|^2;
\end{aligned}$$

and, since $\displaystyle\sum_{i=1}^{\infty} |\mathbf{U} \cdot \mathbf{A}_i|^2$ converges by (14), we can choose an integer N so that the last sum $< \varepsilon^2$ when $m, n > N$.   Hence,

$$|\mathbf{S}_n - \mathbf{S}_m| < \varepsilon, \qquad m, n > N;$$

and, by Lemma 1, $\displaystyle\lim_{n \to \infty} \mathbf{S}_n = \mathbf{S}$.   Now from (19),

$$\lim_{n \to \infty} (\mathbf{U} - \mathbf{S}_n) = \mathbf{U} - \mathbf{S};$$

and, since

$$(\mathbf{U} - \mathbf{S}_n) \cdot \mathbf{A}_i = \mathbf{U} \cdot \mathbf{A}_i - \mathbf{U} \cdot \mathbf{A}_i = 0 \qquad \text{when} \quad n \geq i,$$

we have, on letting $n \to \infty$,

$$(\mathbf{U} - \mathbf{S}) \cdot \mathbf{A}_i = 0, \qquad i = 1, 2, 3, \cdots,$$

from (20).   Thus $\mathbf{U} - \mathbf{S}$ is orthogonal to all base vectors $\mathbf{A}_i$; and, since the basis is complete, $\mathbf{U} - \mathbf{S} = \mathbf{0}$.   Again from (20) we have

$$\lim_{n \to \infty} (\mathbf{U} - \mathbf{S}_n) \cdot (\mathbf{U} - \mathbf{S}_n) = (\mathbf{U} - \mathbf{S}) \cdot (\mathbf{U} - \mathbf{S}) = 0.$$

Since this implies (15), the basis is closed.

Relative to the orthonormal basis

(21) $\mathbf{E}_1 = [1, 0, 0, \cdots], \qquad \mathbf{E}_2 = [0, 1, 0, \cdots], \qquad \cdots,$

the components of $\mathbf{U} = [u_1, u_2, \cdots]$ are obviously $\mathbf{U} \cdot \mathbf{E}_i = u_i$; and, since

$$\sum_{i=1}^{\infty} |\mathbf{U} \cdot \mathbf{E}_i|^2 = \sum_{i=1}^{\infty} u_i \bar{u}_i = |\mathbf{U}|^2$$

from (6), Parseval's equation (16) is satisfied.   The basis (21) is therefore closed and complete.

98. Linear Equations.   Consider the set of n homogeneous equations

(1) $\mathbf{X} \cdot \mathbf{A}_1 = 0, \qquad \mathbf{X} \cdot \mathbf{A}_2 = 0, \qquad \cdots, \qquad \mathbf{X} \cdot \mathbf{A}_n = 0,$

where $\mathbf{A}_1, \mathbf{A}_2, \cdots, \mathbf{A}_n$ are n given vectors of Hilbert space and $\mathbf{X}$ is a vector to be determined.

THEOREM 1.   *If* $\mathbf{X}$ *satisfies equations* (1) *and is linearly dependent upon* $\mathbf{A}_1, \mathbf{A}_2, \cdots, \mathbf{A}_n$, *then* $\mathbf{X} = \mathbf{0}$.

Proof. If $\mathbf{X} = c_1\mathbf{A}_1 + \cdots + c_n\mathbf{A}_n$, is a solution of (1),

$$\mathbf{X} \cdot \mathbf{X} = \bar{c}_1\mathbf{X} \cdot \mathbf{A}_1 + \cdots + \bar{c}_n\mathbf{X} \cdot \mathbf{A}_n = 0,\dagger$$

and hence $\mathbf{X} = \mathbf{0}$.

THEOREM 2. *If the n vectors $\mathbf{A}_1$ are linearly independent, the general solution of equations* (1) *is*

$$
(2) \quad \mathbf{X} = \frac{
\begin{vmatrix}
\mathbf{A}_1 \cdot \mathbf{A}_1 & \mathbf{A}_2 \cdot \mathbf{A}_1 & \cdots & \mathbf{A}_n \cdot \mathbf{A}_1 & \mathbf{U} \cdot \mathbf{A}_1 \\
\cdot & \cdot & \cdots & \cdot & \cdot \\
\cdot & \cdot & \cdots & \cdot & \cdot \\
\mathbf{A}_1 \cdot \mathbf{A}_n & \mathbf{A}_2 \cdot \mathbf{A}_2 & \cdots & \mathbf{A}_n \cdot \mathbf{A}_n & \mathbf{U} \cdot \mathbf{A}_n \\
\mathbf{A}_1 & \mathbf{A}_2 & \cdots & \mathbf{A}_n & \mathbf{U}
\end{vmatrix}
}{G(\mathbf{A}_1, \mathbf{A}_2, \cdots, \mathbf{A}_n)}
$$

where $\mathbf{U}$ is an arbitrary vector and $G(\mathbf{A}_1, \mathbf{A}_2, \cdots, \mathbf{A}_n)$ is the Gramian of $\mathbf{A}_1, \cdots, \mathbf{A}_n$ (the cofactor of $\mathbf{U}$ in the numerator).

Proof. The proof of Theorem 94 applies without change to Hilbert space; hence $G(\mathbf{A}_1, \mathbf{A}_2, \cdots, \mathbf{A}_n) \neq 0$. If we expand the numerator determinant of (2) by elements in the last row, we have

$$(3) \quad \mathbf{X} = c_1\mathbf{A}_1 + c_2\mathbf{A}_2 + \cdots + c_n\mathbf{A}_n + \mathbf{U}.$$

Since $\mathbf{U}$ is arbitrary, any vector, and consequently any solution of equations (1), can be put in this form. Now, if we form $\mathbf{X} \cdot \mathbf{A}_i$ from (2), the numerator determinant will have the same elements in the ith and last rows and $\mathbf{X} \cdot \mathbf{A}_i = 0$, $i = 1, 2, \cdots, n$.

Let us indicate the dependence of the solution $\mathbf{X}$ in (2) on $\mathbf{U}$ by writing $\mathbf{X}(\mathbf{U})$. Now from (3) and Theorem 1 we see that $\mathbf{X}(\mathbf{U}) = \mathbf{0}$ when and only when $\mathbf{U}$ is linearly dependent upon $\mathbf{A}_1, \mathbf{A}_2, \cdots, \mathbf{A}_n$. Moreover (3) shows that

$$(4) \quad \mathbf{X}(\mathbf{U}_1) - \mathbf{X}(\mathbf{U}_2) = \mathbf{X}(\mathbf{U}_1 - \mathbf{U}_2);$$

hence $\mathbf{X}(\mathbf{U}_1) = \mathbf{X}(\mathbf{U}_2)$ when and only when $\mathbf{U}_1 - \mathbf{U}_2$ is linearly dependent upon $\mathbf{A}_1, \mathbf{A}_2, \cdots, \mathbf{A}_n$.

From (3) we have

$$\mathbf{X} \cdot \mathbf{X} = \bar{c}_1\mathbf{X} \cdot \mathbf{A}_1 + \bar{c}_2\mathbf{X} \cdot \mathbf{A}_2 + \cdots + \bar{c}_n\mathbf{X} \cdot \mathbf{A}_n + \mathbf{X} \cdot \mathbf{U} = \mathbf{X} \cdot \mathbf{U},$$

in view of equations (1). But, if we compute $\mathbf{X} \cdot \mathbf{U}$ from (2), we have

$$(5) \quad \mathbf{X} \cdot \mathbf{X} = \frac{G(\mathbf{A}_1, \mathbf{A}_2, \cdots, \mathbf{A}_n, \mathbf{U})}{G(\mathbf{A}_1, \mathbf{A}_2, \cdots, \mathbf{A}_n)}.$$

---

† Throughout this article equations (94.13) must be kept in mind.

Now this equation applies to any $n + 1$ vectors which are linearly independent, say $A_1, A_2, \cdots, A_n, A_{n+1}$. Then both Gramians $\neq 0$, and we have, with an obvious notation,

$$(6) \qquad\qquad X \cdot X = G_{n+1}/G_n > 0,$$

for $X \neq 0$ since A_{n+1}, by hypothesis, is not linearly dependent on A_1, $A_2, \cdots, A_n$. Consequently, if $G_n > 0$, also $G_{n+1} > 0$. But $A_1 \neq 0$, since the A's are linearly independent; hence $G_1 = A_1 \cdot A_1 > 0$. With this starting point, we can now prove by induction

THEOREM 3. *The Gramian of any number of linearly independent vectors is positive.*

Finally let us consider the nonhomogeneous equations

$$(7) \qquad Y \cdot A_1 = b_1, \qquad Y \cdot A_2 = b_2, \qquad \cdots, \qquad Y \cdot A_n = b_n.$$

THEOREM 4. *If $A_1, A_2, \cdots, A_n$ are linearly independent, the only solution of equations (7) of the form*

$$(8) \qquad\qquad Y_0 = c_1 A_1 + c_2 A_2 + \cdots + c_n A_n$$

is given by

$$(9) \qquad Y_0 = \frac{\begin{vmatrix} A_1 \cdot A_1 & A_2 \cdot A_1 & \cdots & A_n \cdot A_1 & -b_1 \\ \cdot & \cdot & \cdots & \cdot & \cdot \\ \cdot & \cdot & \cdots & \cdot & \cdot \\ A_1 \cdot A_n & A_2 \cdot A_n & \cdots & A_n \cdot A_n & -b_n \\ A_1 & A_2 & \cdots & A_n & 0 \end{vmatrix}}{G(A_1, A_2, \cdots, A_n)}$$

Proof. If we compute $Y_0 \cdot A_i$ from (9), the last row of the upper determinant becomes

$$A_1 \cdot A_i, \quad A_2 \cdot A_i, \quad \cdots, \quad A_n \cdot A_i, \quad 0;$$

and, when the ith row is subtracted from this, it becomes

$$0, \qquad 0, \qquad \cdots, \qquad 0, \qquad b_i;$$

hence

$$Y_0 \cdot A_i = \frac{b_i G_n}{G_n} = b_i, \qquad i = 1, 2, \cdots, n,$$

and equations (7) are satisfied. If there were a second solution Y_1 of the form (8), $Y_0 - Y_1$ would be a solution of equations (1), linearly dependent on $\mathbf{A}_1, \mathbf{A}_2, \cdots, \mathbf{A}_n$, and $\mathbf{Y}_0 - \mathbf{Y}_1$ would vanish. Thus $\mathbf{Y}_0$ is the only solution having the form (8).

The general solution $\mathbf{Y}$ of equations (7) is obtained by adding the particular solution $\mathbf{Y}_0$ to the general solution $\mathbf{X}$ of the homogeneous equations (1):

$$(10) \qquad\qquad \mathbf{Y} = \mathbf{X} + \mathbf{Y}_0.$$

We shall call $\mathbf{Y}_0$ the *principal solution* of equations (7). It is characterized by the following property.

THEOREM 5. *Of all the vectors which satisfy equations* (7), *the principal solution has the smallest length.*

Proof. From (10),

$$|\mathbf{Y}|^2 = (\mathbf{X} + \mathbf{Y}_0) \cdot (\mathbf{X} + \mathbf{Y}_0) = |\mathbf{X}|^2 + |\mathbf{Y}_0|^2;$$

for, from (8),

$$\mathbf{X} \cdot \mathbf{Y}_0 = \bar{c}_1 \mathbf{X} \cdot \mathbf{A}_1 + \cdots + \bar{c}_n \mathbf{X} \cdot \mathbf{A}_n = 0,$$

and $\mathbf{Y}_0 \cdot \mathbf{X} = \overline{\mathbf{X} \cdot \mathbf{Y}_0} = 0$. Hence

$$(11) \qquad\qquad |\mathbf{Y}|^2 \geqq |\mathbf{Y}_0|^2,$$

the equal sign holding only when $\mathbf{X} = \mathbf{0}$, in which case $\mathbf{Y} = \mathbf{Y}_0$.

The above results may be extended to a system of an infinite number of linear equations.†

PROBLEMS

1. Show that, if equations (1) have a solution of the form (3), it must be given by (2). [Use Cramer's rule.]

2. Show that, if equations (7) have a solution of the form (8), it must be given by (9).

3. If the vectors $\mathbf{A}_i = [a_{i1}, a_{i2}, \cdots, a_{in}, 0, 0, \cdots]$, prove that

$$G(\mathbf{A}_1, \mathbf{A}_2, \cdots, \mathbf{A}_n) = |\det a_{ij}|^2, \qquad i, j = 1, 2, \cdots, n.$$

† Cf. Bôcher and Brand, "On Linear Equations with an Infinite Number of Variables", *Ann. Math.*, vol. 13, 1912, pp. 167–186.

Appendix

Quantity	Symbol	M	L	T	Q	Unit
Mass	m	1				kilogram (kg)
Length	l		1			meter (m)
Time	t			1		second (sec)
Frequency	f			-1		
Velocity	$\mathbf{v}$		1	-1		meter/sec.
Acceleration	$\mathbf{a}$		1	-2		meter/sec.^{2}
Force	$\mathbf{f}, \mathbf{F}$	1	1	-2		newton
Momentum	$m\mathbf{v}$	1	1	-1		kg. m./sec.
Work	W	1	2	-2		joule
Energy	E	1	2	-2		joule
Torque	$\mathbf{r} \times \mathbf{F}$	1	2	-2		newton-meter
Power	P	1	2	-3		watt
Charge	q				1	coulomb
Charge density	ρ		-3		1	coulomb/meter^3
Current	I			-1	1	ampere
Current density	$\mathbf{J}$		-2	-1	1	ampere/meter^2
Electric intensity	$\mathbf{E}$	1	1	-2	-1	volt/meter
Magnetic intensity	$\mathbf{H}$		-1	-1	1	ampere/meter
Permittivity	ε	-1	-3	2	2	farad/meter
Permeability	μ	1	1		-2	henry/meter
Electric flux density	$\mathbf{D} = \varepsilon\mathbf{E}$		-2		1	coulomb/meter^2
Magnetic flux density	$\mathbf{B} = \mu\mathbf{H}$	1		-1	-1	weber/meter^2
Magnetic flux	$\Phi = \int \mathbf{n} \cdot \mathbf{B} \, dS$	1	2	-1	-1	weber
Emf	V	1	2	-2	-1	volt
Potential	φ	1	2	-2	-1	volt
Vector potential	$\mathbf{A}$	1	1	-1	-1	weber/meter
Resistance	R	1	2	-1	-2	ohm
Conductance	$1/R$	-1	-2	1	2	mho
Capacitance	C	-1	-2	2	2	farad
Inductance	$\mathscr{L}$	1	2		-2	henry
Conductivity	σ	-1	-3	1	2	mho/meter

Supplementary Problems_____

Verify the following statements:

1. If $P_1, P_2, \cdots, P_6$ are six points in space and $Q_1, Q_2, \cdots, Q_6$ are the mean centers of the triangles $P_1P_2P_3, P_2P_3P_4, \cdots, P_6P_1P_2$, show that $Q_1Q_2 \cdots Q_6$ is a hexagon whose opposite sides are equal and parallel.

2. The six planes passing through the mid-points of the edges of a tetrahedron $OABC$ meet in a point P if they are perpendicular to these edges or to the opposite edges. If $\mathbf{a}', \mathbf{b}', \mathbf{c}'$ is the set reciprocal to the position vectors $\mathbf{a}, \mathbf{b}, \mathbf{c}$,

$$\mathbf{p} = \tfrac{1}{2}(\mathbf{a}\cdot\mathbf{a}\,\mathbf{a}' + \mathbf{b}\cdot\mathbf{b}\,\mathbf{b}' + \mathbf{c}\cdot\mathbf{c}\,\mathbf{c}'),$$

or

$$\mathbf{p} = \tfrac{1}{2}(\mathbf{a}\cdot(\mathbf{b} + \mathbf{c})\mathbf{a}' + \mathbf{b}\cdot(\mathbf{c} + \mathbf{a})\mathbf{b}' + \mathbf{c}\cdot(\mathbf{a} + \mathbf{b})\mathbf{c}').$$

3. If P is a point in the plane of the triangle ABC and

$$\mathbf{p} = \alpha\mathbf{a} + \beta\mathbf{b} + \gamma\mathbf{c}, \qquad \alpha + \beta + 1 = 1 \qquad \text{(Theorem 5.2)},$$

the numbers α, β, γ are the *areal coordinates* of P, namely the ratios of the signed areas PBC, PCA, PAB, to ABC. The signed areas are positive or negative according as the given circuit has the same sense as ABC or the opposite.

4. The point $A(\alpha, \mathbf{a}_O)$ and the line $(\mathbf{b}, \mathbf{b}_O)$ determine the plane $(\alpha\mathbf{b}_O - \mathbf{a}_O \times \mathbf{b}, \mathbf{a}_O\cdot\mathbf{b}_O)$.

5. If $(\mathbf{a}, \mathbf{a}_O)$ and $(\mathbf{b}, \mathbf{b}_O)$ are nonintersecting line vectors, all tetrahedrons whose opposite edges are $\mathbf{a}, \mathbf{b}$ have the same volume

$$V = \tfrac{1}{6}(\mathbf{a}\cdot\mathbf{b}_O + \mathbf{b}\cdot\mathbf{a}_O),$$

irrespective of the position of $\mathbf{a}$ and $\mathbf{b}$ on their lines.

6. The line through the point P and cutting two skew lines $(\mathbf{a}, \mathbf{a}_O)$, $(\mathbf{b}, \mathbf{b}_O)$ has the coordinates (§ 17)

$$(\mathbf{a}_P \times \mathbf{b}_P, \mathbf{p} \times (\mathbf{a}_P \times \mathbf{b}_P)), \qquad \mathbf{p} = \overrightarrow{OP}.$$

7. If $(\mathbf{a}, \mathbf{a}_O)$ and $(\mathbf{b}, \mathbf{b}_O)$ are nonparallel lines and $\mathbf{n}$ is a unit vector along $\mathbf{a} \times \mathbf{b}$, their common normal has the coordinates

$$[\mathbf{a} \times \mathbf{b}, \mathbf{n}\cdot(\mathbf{b}_O\mathbf{a} - \mathbf{a}_O\mathbf{b}) \times \mathbf{n}].$$

8. The only curves of constant curvature that lie on a plane or sphere are circles.

268

9. In order that a twisted curve lie on a sphere it is necessary and sufficient that

$$\rho\tau + \frac{d}{ds}\left(\frac{1}{\tau}\frac{d\rho}{ds}\right) = 0.$$

[If $(\mathbf{r} - \mathbf{c})\cdot(\mathbf{r} - \mathbf{c}) = a^2$ is the sphere,

$$(\mathbf{r} - \mathbf{c})\cdot\mathbf{T} = 0, \qquad (\mathbf{r} - \mathbf{c})\cdot\mathbf{N} = -\rho, \qquad (\mathbf{r} - \mathbf{c})\cdot\tau\mathbf{B} = -d\rho/ds.]$$

10. The closed spherical curve

$$x = \sin^2 t, \qquad y = \sin t \cos t, \qquad z = \cos t \qquad (0 \leq t \leq 2\pi),$$

consists of two loops that cut at right angles at the double point $A(1, 0, 0)$; and $\kappa = 1$, $\tau = \pm\frac{3}{4}$ at A.

11. Two curves whose curvature and torsion are the same functions of the arc are *congruent*.

[If $\mathbf{T}_1\mathbf{N}_1\mathbf{B}_1$ and $\mathbf{T}_2\mathbf{N}_2\mathbf{B}_2$ coincide at the common origin of arcs and $f(s) = \mathbf{T}_1\cdot\mathbf{T}_2 + \mathbf{N}_1\cdot\mathbf{N}_2 + \mathbf{B}_1\cdot\mathbf{B}_2$, show that $f'(s) = 0$, $f(s) = 3$; $\mathbf{T}_1 = \mathbf{T}_2$, $\mathbf{N}_1 = \mathbf{N}_2$, $\mathbf{B}_1 = \mathbf{B}_2$ at corresponding points, and $\mathbf{r}_1(s) = \mathbf{r}_2(s)$.]

12. If $\mathbf{r} = \mathbf{r}(s)$ is a twisted curve of constant curvature κ, the locus $\mathbf{r}_1 = \mathbf{r} + \rho\mathbf{N}$ of its centers of curvature has $\kappa_1 = \kappa$, $\tau_1 = \kappa^2/\tau$.

$$\left[\mathbf{T}_1\frac{ds_1}{ds} = \frac{\tau}{\kappa}\mathbf{B}; \qquad \therefore \frac{ds_1}{ds} = \frac{\tau}{\kappa}, \quad \mathbf{T}_1 = \mathbf{B};\right.$$

$$\kappa_1\mathbf{N}_1\frac{\tau}{\kappa} = -\tau\mathbf{N}; \qquad \therefore \kappa_1 = \kappa, \quad \mathbf{N}_1 = -\mathbf{N}, \quad \mathbf{B}_1 = \mathbf{T};$$

$$\left. -\tau_1\mathbf{N}_1\frac{\tau}{\kappa} = \kappa\mathbf{N}; \qquad \therefore \tau_1 = \kappa^2/\tau.\right]$$

13. The triangle ABC is on the positive side of the lines which form its sides. If x, y, z are the signed perpendicular distances from a point P to the lines BC, CA, AB, the locus of $\alpha x + \beta y + \gamma z = 0$ is a straight line perpendicular to $\alpha\mathbf{N}_1 + \beta\mathbf{N}_2 + \gamma\mathbf{N}_3$, where $\mathbf{N}_1$, $\mathbf{N}_2$, $\mathbf{N}_3$ are unit vectors normal to BC, CA, AB in the positive sense. Discuss the case when $\alpha/a = \beta/b = \gamma/c$ (a, b, c are sides of ABC).

As P ranges over the triangle ABC, show by a construction just where $x + y + z$ attains its least and greatest values.

$$[\nabla(x + y + z) = \mathbf{N}_1 + \mathbf{N}_2 + \mathbf{N}_3.]$$

14. A point P in the plane of the triangle ABC is at distances r_1, r_2, r_3 from A, B, C. Then $r_1 + r_2 + r_3$ attains its minimum value at a point Q for which the angles $BQC = CQA = AQB = 120°$. Construct Q.

$$[\nabla(r_1 + r_2 + r_3) = \mathbf{R}_1 + \mathbf{R}_2 + \mathbf{R}_3, \quad \text{unit radial vectors.}]$$

15. On the surface $\mathbf{r} = \mathbf{r}(u, v)$ the unit normal $\mathbf{n} = (\mathbf{r}_u \times \mathbf{r}_v)/H$ has the gradient

$$\text{Grad } \mathbf{n} = \mathbf{a}\mathbf{n}_u + \mathbf{b}\mathbf{n}_v \qquad (H = \mathbf{r}_u \times \mathbf{r}_v)$$

where $\mathbf{a}$, $\mathbf{b}$, $\mathbf{n}$ denotes the set reciprocal to $\mathbf{r}_u$, $\mathbf{r}_v$, $\mathbf{n}$ (Prob. 42.7–8). The *mean curvature* J and *total curvature* K of the surface are defined as the invariants of Grad $\mathbf{n}$:

$$J = -\text{ Div } \mathbf{n}, \qquad K = (\mathbf{a} \times \mathbf{b})\cdot(\mathbf{n}_u \times \mathbf{n}_v).$$

Prove that J and K are determined by the equations

$$-J\,\mathbf{r}_u \times \mathbf{r}_v = \mathbf{r}_u \times \mathbf{n}_v - \mathbf{r}_v \times \mathbf{n}_u, \qquad K\,\mathbf{r}_u \times \mathbf{r}_v = \mathbf{n}_u \times \mathbf{n}_v,$$

and are independent of the choice of parameters u, v.

Show that the total curvature of the surface of revolution of Prob. 36.1 is

$$K = \frac{f'f''}{u(1 + f'^2)^2};$$

and, for a sphere of radius a, $K = 1/a^2$.

16. The points P, Q, R divide the sides BC, CA, AB of the triangle ABC in the ratios $x/(1 - x)$, $y/(1 - y)$, $z/(1 - z)$. Then the signed areas PQR and ABC (sign determined by the sense of circuit) have the ratio

$$PQR/ABC = 1 - x - y - z + yz + zx + xy.$$

17. If $\mathbf{f} = \mathbf{i}P(x, y, z) + \mathbf{j}Q(x, y, z) + \mathbf{k}R(x, y, z)$, the differential equation

$$P\,dx + Q\,dy + R\,dz = 0 \qquad \text{or} \qquad \mathbf{f}\cdot d\mathbf{r} = 0$$

is said to be *exact* when $\mathbf{f} = \nabla\varphi$, the gradient of a scalar.

The equation $\mathbf{f}\cdot d\mathbf{r} = 0$ is exact when and only when rot $\mathbf{f} = \mathbf{0}$; and then its solution is

$$\int_{\mathbf{r}_0}^{\mathbf{r}} \mathbf{f}\cdot d\mathbf{r} = \text{const} \qquad \text{for an arbitrary path of integration.}$$

18. The function $\lambda(x, y, z)$ is called a *multiplier* of the differential equation $\mathbf{f}\cdot d\mathbf{r} = 0$ when $\lambda\mathbf{f}\cdot d\mathbf{r} = 0$ is an exact equation (Prob. 17).

If the equation $\mathbf{f}\cdot d\mathbf{r} = 0$ admits a multiplier, then $\mathbf{f}\cdot$rot $\mathbf{f} = 0$.

When $\mathbf{f} = \mathbf{i}P(x, y) + \mathbf{j}Q(x, y)$ this condition is always fulfilled.

19. If an exact equation $\mathbf{f}\cdot d\mathbf{r} = 0$ admits a non-constant multiplier $\lambda(x, y, z)$, its general solution is given by $\lambda(x, y, z) = \text{const}$.

$$[\text{rot}\,(\lambda\mathbf{f}) = \nabla\lambda \times \mathbf{f} = \mathbf{0}.]$$

20. If the differential equation $\mathbf{f}\cdot d\mathbf{r} = 0$ admits two multipliers λ, μ whose ratio is not constant, its general solution is $\lambda/\mu = \text{const}$.

[Use Prob. 19.]

Answers to Problems ─────────────────────────────

CHAPTER 1

5.4 $-4/3$ (AB); $-2/1$ ($A'B'$).

5.7 $-7/5$ (AB); $-7/10$ (CD).

11.1 (a) $60°$; (b) $90°$; (c) $180°$; (d) $70°33'$; (e) all $= \cos^{-1} \dfrac{ab + bc + ca}{a^2 + b^2 + c^2}$.

11.2 $\mathbf{a} \times \mathbf{b} = \mathbf{c}$.

11.3 $14/13$.

11.4 3.

13.1 (a) $[-2, 3, -1]$, $[0, 3, 3]$, $[4, 0, 2]$;
   (b) 6, 6, 6;
   (c) $[-4, -5, -7]$, $[6, -3, 3]$, $[-2, 8, 4]$, $[0, 0, 0]$;

13.2 (a) $\sqrt{30}$; (b) $p = \frac{1}{2}\sqrt{30}$; (c) 5; (d) 30.

14.7 (i) $A = 60°$, $B = 120°$, $C = 60°$;
   (ii) $A = 45°$, $B = 90°$, $C = 60°$.

15.1 $\mathbf{e}^1 = [1, -1, 0]$, $\mathbf{e}^2 = [0, 1, -1]$, $\mathbf{e}^3 = [0, 0, 1]$.

15.5 $\dfrac{\mathbf{b} \times (\mathbf{a} \times \mathbf{b})}{\lambda^2}, \dfrac{(\mathbf{a} \times \mathbf{b}) \times \mathbf{a}}{\lambda^2}, \dfrac{\mathbf{a} \times \mathbf{b}}{\lambda^2}$ where $\lambda = |\mathbf{a} \times \mathbf{b}|$.

15.6 $\mathbf{r} = \alpha\mathbf{a}' + \beta\mathbf{b}' + \gamma\mathbf{c}'$, where $\mathbf{a}'$, $\mathbf{b}'$, $\mathbf{c}'$ is the set reciprocal to $\mathbf{a}$, $\mathbf{b}$, $\mathbf{c}$.

17.4 $(8, -11, -11)$.

17.8 $\mathbf{r} = \alpha_0\mathbf{a}' + \beta_0\mathbf{b}' + \gamma_0\mathbf{c}'$ (Prob. 15.6).

17.10 Yes.

CHAPTER 2

19.1 (i) $[4, 5, 6]$; (ii) 4, 5, 6; (iii) $40/3$.

19.2 $23/3$.

21.9 $\mathbf{f} = [1, 2, -1]$; axis: $y + 2z = z + x = 2x - y = 2$.

271

23.1 (a) $\mathbf{f}_A = [7, -1, -4]$; (b) $2\frac{1}{3}$; (c) $\mathbf{f}_O = [7, -5, -6]$.

23.3 20**j** at $(0, 0)$.

23.5 $Z_a = Z_b = 5500$ lb, $Z_c = Z_d = -4500$ lb.

CHAPTER 3

28.2 $[a, b, c]$; a straight line; $\sqrt{a^2 + b^2 + c^2}$.

31.1 (a) $\mathbf{T} = \mathbf{i}$, $\mathbf{N} = \mathbf{j}$, $\mathbf{B} = \mathbf{k}$;

     $\mathbf{T} = \frac{1}{3}[1, 2, 2]$, $\mathbf{N} = \frac{1}{3}[-2, -1, 2]$, $\mathbf{B} = \frac{1}{3}[2, -2, 1]$.

     (b) $\kappa = \tau = \frac{2}{3}$; $\kappa = \tau = \frac{2}{27}$.

     (c) $x = 0$, $z = 0$; $x + 2y + 2z = 13$, $2x - 2y + z = 2$.

31.2 (a) $\kappa = \tau = 2/3(1 + 2t^2)^2$;

     (b) $\kappa = \tau = 1/3a(1 + t^2)^2$.

32.4 $\mathbf{v} = 3[2, 2, 1]$, $\mathbf{a} = 6[1, 2, 0]$;

     $\mathbf{T} = \frac{1}{3}[2, 2, 1]$, $\mathbf{N} = \frac{1}{3}[-1, 2. -2]$, $\mathbf{B} = \frac{1}{3}[-2, 1, 2]$;

     $\kappa = \tau = 2/27$; $\mathbf{a} \cdot \mathbf{T} = 12$, $\mathbf{a} \cdot \mathbf{N} = 6$.

32.5 $\mathbf{v} = [0, -1, 2]$, $\mathbf{a} = [-1, 0, 0]$;

     $\mathbf{T} = \dfrac{1}{\sqrt{5}}[0, -1, 2]$, $\mathbf{N} = [-1, 0, 0]$, $\mathbf{B} = \dfrac{1}{\sqrt{5}}[0, -2, -1]$;

     $\kappa = \frac{1}{5}$, $\tau = -\frac{2}{5}$; $\mathbf{a} \cdot \mathbf{T} = 0$, $\mathbf{a} \cdot \mathbf{N} = 1$.

32.6 $\mathbf{v} = [1, -1, \sqrt{2}]$, $\mathbf{a} = [1, 1, 0]$;

     $\mathbf{T} = \frac{1}{2}[1, -1, \sqrt{2}]$, $\mathbf{N} = \dfrac{\sqrt{2}}{2}[1, 1, 0]$, $\mathbf{B} = \frac{1}{2}[-1, 1, \sqrt{2}]$;

     $\kappa = -\tau = \sqrt{2}/4$; $\mathbf{a} \cdot \mathbf{T} = 0$, $\mathbf{a} \cdot \mathbf{N} = \sqrt{2}$.

35.1 10 mi/hr.

CHAPTER 4

36.1 Parallel circles $u = a$; meridians $v = b$.

     $\mathbf{n} = [f'(u) \cos v, f'(u) \sin v, 1]/\sqrt{f'^2 + 1}$.

36.2 Circular helices $u = a$; lines $\perp$ z-axis.

36.3 (i) Ruled surface with rulings through Γ and parallel to $[\cos \alpha, \cos \beta, \cos \gamma]$.

     (ii) Cone with vertex at O and rulings through Γ. Parametric curves $u = a$ are rulings.

36.4 $x = a \sin u \cos v$, $y = b \sin u \sin v$, $z = c \cos u$.

36.5 Rulings.

36.6 Rulings.

36.8 $[1, -1, 0]$.

37.1 (a) $[-2, 2]$; (b) 0; (c) $135°$, $2\sqrt{2}$.

37.2 (a) $[4, 4, 2]$; (b) $10/\sqrt{3}$; (c) 6;

     (d) $2x + 2y + z = 7$, $x - 1 = y - 1 = 2z - 6$.

37.3 $R - 2ar^{-1} \cos \varphi \, P$; $(1 + 4a^2r^{-2} \cos^2 \varphi)^{\frac{1}{2}}$.

39.5 Scalar 0; vector $- 2a$.

41.1 $\nabla f = \begin{pmatrix} 1 & 0 & -1 \\ -1 & 1 & 0 \\ 0 & -1 & 1 \end{pmatrix}$; div $f = 3$, rot $f = [1, 1, 1]$;

$\nabla g = \begin{pmatrix} 2x & z & y \\ z & 2y & x \\ y & x & 2z \end{pmatrix}$; div $g = 2(x + y + z)$, rot $g = 0$.

$\nabla h = \begin{pmatrix} 0 & 2zx & y^2 \\ z^2 & 0 & 2xy \\ 2yz & x^2 & 0 \end{pmatrix}$; div $h = 0$, rot $h = [2xy - x^2, 2yz - y^2, 2zx - z^2]$.

41.2 (a) $2r$, 6; (b) $-r/r^3$, 0.

CHAPTER 5

43.1 $7/3$; $17/6$; $11/6$; $5/2$; $(22 + 3\pi)/12$.

43.2 (a) $-2\pi r^2 (x_0 + y_0)$; (b) 0; (c) -2.

43.3 $3.75 - 2 \log 4$.

43.4 (a) $-1/4$; (b) $-1/4$; (c) $-1/4$.

43.5 (a) $77\frac{1}{3}$; (b) $94\frac{2}{3}$; (c) $88\frac{2}{3}$.

43.6 -2π.

46.1 $F = \frac{2}{3}x^3 + 3x^2y - \frac{1}{3}y^3$; $32\frac{2}{3}$.

46.2 $F = (x^2/y) - 3x + 4y - 4$.

46.3 $F = x^2yz^3$; 14.

46.4 $\log \left(\dfrac{x^2 + y^2}{a^2 + b^2} \right)^{1/2}$; 0; yes.

46.5 $33/2$.

46.6 $3a^2/2$.

47.3 $\frac{1}{2}ab \, \varphi$.

47.4 $\frac{1}{2}ab \, \varphi$.

47.5 $3a^2/2$.

47.8 $\frac{1}{4}\pi ab^3$, $\frac{1}{4}\pi a^3b$, $\frac{1}{4}\pi ab(a^2 + b^2)$.

47.9 $\frac{4}{3}ab(a^2 + b^2)$.

47.10 $2\pi ab$.

47.11 $80\frac{2}{3}$.

47.12 14.

47.13 $\frac{16}{3}$.

47.14 $-\frac{1}{12}$.

50.3 2π.

52.2 $8\pi/3$.

52.3 $g = r^m \mathbf{r}/(m + 3)$.

52.7 (a) 3; (b) 40π.

52.10 $\frac{4}{3}\pi(a + b + c)$.

52.11 $4\pi/\sqrt{abc}$; $4\pi(a + b + c)/3\sqrt{abc}$.

54.2 $\mathbf{g} = \mathbf{r} \times \{\frac{1}{3}(\mathbf{a} - \mathbf{b}) \times \mathbf{r} - \frac{1}{2}\mathbf{a} \times \mathbf{b}\}$.

54.3 (a) $\mathbf{G} = xz[1, -1, 0]$, $\mathbf{g} = \frac{1}{3}[xz + yz, -2xz, xy - x^2]$.

    (b) $\mathbf{G} = [x(y + z) - \frac{1}{2}(y^2 + z^2), yz - \frac{1}{2}z^2, 0]$, $\mathbf{g} = \frac{1}{3}\mathbf{f} \times \mathbf{r}$.

    (c) $\mathbf{G} = [-y^2z, -xyz, 0]$, $\mathbf{g} = \frac{1}{4}\mathbf{f} \times \mathbf{r}$; $\mathbf{G} - \mathbf{g} = \nabla(-\frac{1}{2}x,y^2z)$.

    (d) $\mathbf{G} = [xz - \frac{1}{2}y^2, -\frac{1}{2}z^2, 0]$, $\mathbf{g} = \frac{1}{3}\mathbf{f} \times \mathbf{r}$.

54.4 (a) $\mathbf{g} = \dfrac{r^3(\mathbf{c} \times \mathbf{r}) \times \mathbf{r}}{6}$;

    (b) $\mathbf{g} = [\frac{1}{3}yz + \frac{1}{2}z, -\frac{2}{3}xz, \frac{1}{3}xy - \frac{1}{2}\bar{x}]$.

55.2 $\nabla^2\varphi = \dfrac{6}{a}\left(\dfrac{1}{a} - \dfrac{1}{r}\right), r < a$; $\nabla^2\varphi = 0, r \geqq a$. No; yes.

CHAPTER 6

60.1 (a) $\varphi = -\mathbf{c} \cdot \mathbf{r}$; (b) none; (c) none;

    (d) $\varphi = \dfrac{r^{n+1}}{n + 1} + C\ (n \neq -1)$, $\varphi = \log r + C, (n = -1)$.

60.3 $\varphi = y + 2z - xyz^2$; $W = 2$.

60.5 $v_2{}^2 = v_1{}^2 - 2\gamma M\left(\dfrac{1}{r_1} - \dfrac{1}{r_2}\right)$.

60.6 $\varphi = \frac{1}{2}mkr^2$.

60.7 (a) $h = v_0{}^2/2g$; (b) $h = Rv_0{}^2/(2gR - v_0)$.

61.1 $h = \sqrt{\gamma Mp}$.

61.3 35.30 ast. units; $\varepsilon = 0.97$.

61.4 36,000,000 miles.

63.4 271 slug-ft².

CHAPTER 7

72.3 $v_r = -a\dfrac{\pi}{\alpha}r^{(\pi/\alpha)-1}\cos\dfrac{\pi}{\alpha}\theta$, $v_\theta = a\dfrac{\pi}{\alpha}r^{(\pi/\alpha)-1}\sin\dfrac{\pi}{\alpha}\theta$.

CHAPTER 8

77.2 $[\gamma] = M^{-1}L^3T^{-2}$.

77.5 $[a] = [b] = [\gamma] = T^{-1}$, $[C] = L^2T^{-1}$, $[A] = L$, $[B] = L(a \neq b)$, $[B] = LT^{-1}\ (a = b)$.

84.1 φ.

CHAPTER 9

96.1 $|e_1| = 1, |e_2| = 2, |e_3| = 3;$ all angles $60°$.

96.2 $g^{ij} = \begin{pmatrix} \frac{3}{2} & -\frac{1}{4} & -\frac{1}{6} \\ -\frac{1}{4} & \frac{3}{8} & -\frac{1}{12} \\ -\frac{1}{6} & -\frac{1}{12} & \frac{1}{6} \end{pmatrix};$

$e^1 = \frac{3}{2}e_1 - \frac{1}{4}e_2 - \frac{1}{6}e_3, e^2 = -\frac{1}{4}e_1 + \frac{3}{8}e_2 - \frac{1}{12}e_3, e^3 = -\frac{1}{6}e_1 - \frac{1}{12}e_2 + \frac{1}{6}e_3.$

96.3 $u_i = (4, 10, 21), v_i = (\frac{1}{2}, 2, \frac{15}{2});$

$|u| = 2\sqrt{13}, |v| = \sqrt{7}; \ u \cdot v = 17; \ (u,v) = 27°.$

96.4 $g_{ij} = \begin{pmatrix} 2 & 0 & 2 \\ 0 & 2 & 0 \\ 2 & 0 & 3 \end{pmatrix}, g^{ij} = \begin{pmatrix} \frac{3}{2} & 0 & -1 \\ 0 & \frac{1}{2} & 0 \\ -1 & 0 & 1 \end{pmatrix};$

$e^1 = \frac{1}{2}i + \frac{1}{2}j + k, \quad e^2 = \frac{1}{2}i - \frac{1}{2}j, \quad e^3 = -k.$

$u^i = (\frac{5}{2}, -\frac{1}{2}, -1), u_i = (3, -1, 2).$

Index

Page numbers with asterisks locate definitions.

3-13   § 32-35   P 77   , 2, 4
P 85   , 3 7

20   36 -39   P 80   2, 3, 8;   P 93   2,3,5

27   40 42   P 98 # 3 c